UNFOLDING CATASTROPHE

AUSTRALIA

JOHN STAPLETON

Unfolding Catastrophe: Australia
Copyright © 2021 John Stapleton
All rights reserved.

Print Edition
ISBN: 978-0-6450394-3-6

Published by A Sense of Place Publishing 2021

This is the third and final book in the trilogy which began with Terror in Australia: Workers' Paradise Lost and was followed by Hideout in the Apocalypse. They can be read separately or together. They are set against the backdrop of Australia in the early millennial period and largely for legal reasons use novelistic techniques to cover a pivotal point in the nation's history.

Cover design by Jessica Bell
Cover images from roblan
Interior design by Amie McCracken
Edited by Angela Bell

A catalogue record for this book is available from the National Library of Australia

TABLE OF CONTENTS

ONE
THE FIRST DRAFT OF HISTORY

THE THINGS he remembered starkly from the early months of the COVID Era were empty trains churning through the night, a sense of dread as everything was altered, military helicopters hovering over an empty Sydney Harbour, empty streets, silent suburbs, and dread, mostly dread.

Perhaps one of the single most extraordinary things about the way COVID-19 played out in Australia in early 2020 was that polls showed faith in both media and government went up.

Learned little-read journals dismembered the government's confusing and contradictory messaging. But few Australians read newspapers anymore, much less the academic journals.

The wildly inaccurate nature of initial modelling might have proffered some excuse for the Australian Government's handling of the COVID crisis and the absurd responses of its political class.

But within weeks of it all beginning epidemiologists from some of the world's leading institutions were speaking out, warning that lockdowns were not the way to go.

The geniuses in the Australian Government ignored all the cautionary tales, all the world experts speaking out saying lockdowns did more harm than good, that they were a radical social experiment going against decades of epidemiological wisdom.

For all the damage they caused, for all the spiritual, individual and communal derangement involved, if lockdowns had a face, it was demonic.

And Old Alex, to adopt a pseudonym from previous books, was quick to make the game clear: a government cherry-picking experts to suit their personal agendas and implement a dangerous new authoritarianism was deceit. Not telling the Australian public that there were many sides to this argument was deceit. And the beneficiaries of all this deceit, as soon became obvious, were incumbent governments, conservative at federal level, Labor in most of the states. A frightened population clung to what they knew; trusted their elected representatives; accepted the abrogation of their freedoms.

There was a strange moment in that island nation, somewhere between support, submission, compliance and an unknown threat. It was what would come next, including a runaway train of government and administrative chaos, that would destroy the country.

There were so many signs a signal derangement was about to pierce through everything; so many moments of precognition lighting up across the globe. Every pundit on the planet was active. Medical experts competed for attention.

Data released in April of 2020 by the Australian Bureau of Statistics in conjunction with the Australian Taxation Office showed that at least six per cent of workers had lost their jobs over the previous month, with the accommodation, food, arts and recreation industries smashed by the impact of the government's response to the coronavirus.

While the fall in jobs was similar for both women and men, there were large differences across age groups, with those under twenty and over seventy hardest hit.

More than 870,000 people lost their jobs in those first few months.

***

In the car parks at Oak Flats, a working-class suburb two hours south of Sydney where Old Alex had unexpectedly found himself, as night settled there was a deep sense of threat in the air. Potential friends became potential enemies just like that. Customers were rushing into Woolworths as if it was their last chance to buy provisions before the End Times, barely looking at each other, they were so clearly frightened. What was once a gruff, no-nonsense working-class suburb was already diminished.

That once sacred, most beautiful of waterways, Lake Illawarra, on the NSW south coast, now reminded him more of Pokhara in Nepal in the early '70s. Back then, with electricity a luxury, only a few lights from a couple of small hotels or grand houses punctured the Nepalese night, and the only sound was of generators grumbling through the tight mountain air; or the occasional shout from some local celebration. Mostly there was silence.

The same was now true of Lake Illawarra, which in 2020 was already intensely suburbanised. People were dug in inside their houses, afraid to go out in case they encountered the virus, which might as well have been Ebola for all the drama, fear and exaggeration which surrounded it.

Old Alex was out of sorts, with himself but most of all with the prevailing sentiment.

The country was rallying, much to his disbelief, around the Prime Minister, Scott Morrison. There were pieces in what remained of legacy media lauding "the father of the nation". For crying out loud!

An old journalist who knew, if nothing else, how media narratives were manufactured and how badly the populace was being served, how heavily manipulated they were, Alex fumed daily about the paucity of genuine information, every politician in the country taking the opportunity to grandstand in front of television cameras. And, immorally to his mind, panicked the population.

***

Australia had not seen quality governance for many years, and the current crop of reckless politicians had as their natural constituents the Very Big End of Town. The closest any of the nation's leaders got to mingling with the likes of those who lived in Oak Flats, "Oakflattigans" as they were sometimes known, was every few years at election time.

Every last one of those sycophantic stories lauding the nation's leaders sickened Old Alex to the core. His generation of journalists would have been ashamed to give credit where credit was not due.

A former news editor of his at *The Sydney Morning Herald* back in the 1980s, Richard Glover, now a well-known radio personality on the taxpayer-funded ABC and a star turn at the gatherings of the city's burgeoning bourgeoisie, had written a piece for *The Washington Post* titled "Australia's leader is winning the argument on the coronavirus".

"Australians like to see themselves as rebellious people, distrustful of authority — but the coronavirus has changed that," Richard wrote.

"While small protests against the lockdowns have erupted in the United

States, and some in Britain have insisted on their right to party, in Australia we're mostly doing what we're told.

"In Sydney, public transport use is down to levels not seen for nearly 100 years. Attendance in government schools in Victoria is down to just three per cent. In parks, walkers and joggers dutifully arc around each other like passing ships."

Glover acknowledged that, certainly, there were voices attacking the government's response as excessive.

"Fittingly — given the topsy-turvy politics of COVID-19 — the Prime Minister's main critics are populist right-wingers from his own side of politics, such as the radio host Alan Jones and the columnist Andrew Bolt. Australia's very success in limiting infections is now being presented by Bolt as proof the threat was wildly exaggerated."

The left is not always right, and the right is not always wrong, as the saying goes, and the left's embrace of authoritarian measures and the destruction of civil liberties under the cloak of COVID would ultimately do them and the nation great harm.

But Glover was not of that view: "At the moment, the prime minister is winning the argument. The lockdown, however onerous, is working. Listening to experts is working. And working together, across political parties, is working.

"Will this new attitude outlive the pandemic? Probably not. But right now, the Australian and New Zealand 'bubble' looks like a pretty good place to be."[1]

Alex could hardly have agreed less. Relying on "experts" depended entirely on which experts you chose.

He and Richard had been friendly for a time. As a news editor his ideas were not always gritty, but often successful. A front-page story picturing Bondi Beach crowded with the nubile flesh of the day, and with tags explaining why each of them wasn't at work like the rest of the toiling masses, had the city talking for weeks.

Richard had gone on to have a stellar career, much beloved by Sydney's

---

1 Australia's leader is winning the argument on the coronavirus, Richard Glover, *The Washington Post*, 22 April, 2020.

chattering classes. Glitter city. While Alex had grumbled on as a general reporter, never rising to the heights of editor.

At a newspaper reunion not long before, he had said to Richard: "You know, the best thing about you as news editor was, there were worse to follow."

Richard didn't take the joke — looked, if anything, a little miffed — and soon enough was off mingling with the crowd, his crowd.

***

As for Old Alex, he could not believe the population's gullibility. And submissiveness.

Many people would make the same observation in the coming months: that the single most frightening aspect of the times was not the virus, but the people's willingness to comply unquestioningly with the blizzard of edicts stemming from government.

"We are all going to just have to learn to do as we're told," a woman at a local pie shop in Hawks Nest said when he started to grizzle about the various restrictions.

None of it would last, or so Old Alex believed, retaining as he did a naive faith in the natural, healthy scepticism of Australians.

There were weeks of confusion, a series of contradictory government announcements which appeared almost deliberately designed to instil panic into the population. It seemed, in Alex's fevered imagination at least, that there were many dark forces at play. That the evils he saw in his imagination were indeed real.

Meetings of more than two people had been banned. If you were standing outside your house speaking to a neighbour and a third person joined the group, you could be charged or arrested.

As far as Alex was concerned it was simply a version of martial law, introduced under the cover of COVID -19. There were so many stressors. The pubs were shut; he didn't really know any other way to relax before returning to a dying parent he could not forsake. And so, he would park the car by the lake in the wintering sky, and take a shot of bourbon out of a bottle in the boot. The houses were shuttered tight. There was no one around. It felt very lonely.

The trains were empty. The streets were empty. Support, submission, compliance. How could it possibly be? You weren't even permitted to engage in healthy activities like walking in a national park. The beaches were closed. Soon enough, at a local surfing spot, a sign went up: "If you're from Sydney you're not welcome."

If you chose to go to your holiday house in the country to sit it all out, police would order you back to the city. How did that make sense?

Gifted Australian commentator Paul Collits was one of those quick out of the box. Governments weren't that good at very much, he wrote, but they were good at lying to stay in office and at formulating strategies of self-protection.

In the age of COVID politicians were getting to appear to be heroes to voting populations cowed by fear, appearing presidential in the face of a largely manufactured crisis. Every leader on Earth was claiming to have saved their country. They couldn't all be right. Even the bunglers and the dictators maintained strong public support.

"We now inhabit a strange world where politicians and health bureaucrats, working in tandem, run just about every element of our lives. This weird new system has replaced democracy as we once knew it, and it may not be over any time soon. We should all find this quite chilling. And sinister.

"The politicians of the Anglosphere are on to a good lurk during these COVID times, as are the public health officials having their fifteen minutes or so in the sun.

"The western world is in the grip of rule-by-health-official. These unelected titans provide endless cover for politicians. They have made numerous life-affecting decisions of dubious scientific authority under various emergency powers."

The public only saw a banal surface. Everywhere leaked. The nightmare was just beginning.

***

There in that frightened time, Old Alex had believed he was putting his best foot forward, almost as a military instruction, a belief that reason could survive, that democracy, despite all its deformities, was worth saving, that the authoritarian if not totalitarian instincts being allowed to run amok could not be shared by the military-minded spooks who watched his every move, that the sledging of the population in that frightened and frightening world not be allowed to continue.

It was the same blank and uncomprehending look that ultranationalists give police, because they could not believe the authorities would support the destruction of their own culture in the name of progressive ideologies; the same gap in the traffic you got when seeking sense in the top tiers of family law systems; the same space when you tried to get accountability and rationality out of half the nation's bureaucracies. As we wheeled further and further into societal dysfunction; and the entire breakdown of the country.

Back then, when history was on the turn, Old Alex felt that he, and in some instances those who helped him, could make a difference. Not just serve a master. But alter the trajectory of the stream.

Well, it didn't work that way, in the vast flood called history.

Surveillance creates its own storylines. The mind fills in the gaps, puts names to voices, interprets their hostility, or even comradeship; their ribald jokes, their boredom, even sometimes their tolerance or affection. While from past experience he had absolutely no reason to trust them, for a brief moment he thought the wheels had turned:

"We shall meet in the place where there is no darkness."

That old Orwellian line. We shall meet in the middle of the torture chamber.

In a blinding light where there can be no secrets.

***

In those early weeks, fresh back from Asia, he was bewildered, even frightened, like much of the rest of the population. And like most everybody else, he wanted to do the right thing, by family, friends, neighbours, the people he had got to know on the South Coast.

In retirement Alex had set up an online publication, *A Sense of Place Magazine*, and was still experimenting with it, coming to understand what was possible, how powerful a tool the new publishing technologies placed in our hands. He dreamed of staff, of empire, to march to a different drummer, to find at last his place in the swarm of life.

Hard to make headway in a blizzard of any kind; and this was a snow-storm of falsity beyond comprehension.

The first piece he published on COVID, way back in mid-March of 2020, was right on message, well the government's message, from an emergency doctor who had contracted COVID.

An impassioned Cathy Hull recorded: "Health workers understand quarantine and take its restrictions very seriously. We did not go out to shop. We did not get close to others. But this was only possible once we knew!

"Isolation after exposure is scary because there is time to consider the risks. I packed a bag ready for hospital. We should close schools, universities and many businesses to reduce new cases, enable preparations, ramp up arrangements for protective and supportive equipment, increase capacity in hospitals, free and create ICU beds for life support."

The disinformation feedback loop between government and mainstream media was only just beginning to form. In other words, politicians were yet to wake up to the fact that a confused, anxious, frightened and, yes, panicked population would believe almost anything, even the groundless claim that the government was keeping them safe. The bigger the scare, the better their polling numbers.

The Australian population became prisoners of the electoral ambitions of both their state and federal politicians.

And thoughtful alarm on the part of perfectly decent health professionals rapidly turned to madness. You can always find an academic or a bureaucrat to agree with your agenda. They know where their job security lies. They're not that noble.

But for a brief turning of the sundial all was plausible. And to raise doubt about the conduct, or misconduct, of political leaders and their attendant bureaucrats was akin to disloyalty or sedition, a betrayal of the nation; a similar trick used to extinguish the opposition to Australia's involvement in America's endless wars.

Fear spread everywhere.

Table 1: Date of first reported case and first death related to COVID-19 for each state and territory

State/terri-tory	First case	Source	First death	Source
Victoria	25 January 2020	G Hunt (Minister for Health) and B Murphy (Australian Government Chief Medical Officer), *First confirmed case of novel coronavirus in Australia*, media release, 25 January 2020.	26 March 2020	Victorian Department of Health and Human Services, *Coronavirus update for Victoria—26 March 2020*, media release, 26 March 2020.
New South Wales (NSW)	25 January 2020	NSW Government, *Coronavirus cases confirmed in NSW*, news, 25 January 2020.	3 March 2020	NSW Government, *Nurse and resident diagnosed with COVID-19*, media release, 4 March 2020.
Queensland	29 January 2020	J Young (Queensland Chief Health Officer), update media release, 29 January 2020.	25 March 2020	Queensland Health, *Queensland novel coronavirus (COVID-19) update*, media release, 25 March 2020.
South Australia (SA)	1 February 2020	S Marshall (SA Premier), *Premier's statement on coronavirus*, media release, 1 February 2020.	7 April 2020	SA Health, COVID-19 update, media release, 7 April 2020.
Western Australia (WA)	21 February 2020*	A Robertson (WA Chief Health Officer), *Chief Medical Officer statement COVID-19 update #6*, media release, 21 February 2020.	1 March 2020	WA Health, *WA confirms first novel coronavirus death*, media release, 1 March 2020.
Tasmania	2 March 2020	M Veitch (Tasmanian Director of Public Health), *Coronavirus case confirmed in Tasmania*, news, 2 March 2020.	30 March 2020	P Gutwein (Tasmanian Premier), *Press Conference*, media release, 30 March 2020.

| Northern Territory (NT) | 4 March 2020 | Northern Territory Department of Health, *First confirmed COVID-19 case in Northern Territory*, news, 4 March 2020. | N/A** | |
| Australian Capital Territory (ACT) | 12 March 2020 | ACT Health Directorate, *COVID-19 case confirmed in the ACT*, media release, 12 March 2020. | 30 March 2020 | ACT Government, *COVID-19 update—first death in the ACT*, news, 30 March 2020. |

Source: Australian Government Department of Health.

***

Panic set in early.

On 13 February, 2020, the normally sober *Economist* magazine said "… the pandemic threatened to take more than 150 million lives".

It gave no source or explanation for this Spanish flu-like estimate.

"Pandemic Projections Signal Profound Societal Disruption Over Many Months," declared the headline for editor Melissa Sweet's front running piece in Australia's leading health policy journal *Croakey*. Old Alex had worked with her back in his days on *The Sydney Morning Herald*. She was not just accomplished, she was if nothing else an absolutely sincere person.

She wrote: "Immense disruption to societies, and people's lives and work will be necessary over many months if there is to be any hope of preventing large numbers of deaths from COVID-19.

"That is the suggestion from modelling by researchers at Imperial College in London whose report, published on 16 March, examined a range of scenarios for Great Britain and the United States. They said their findings 'are equally applicable to most high-income countries'.

"The researchers concluded that suppression is 'the only viable strategy at the current time', but warned that 'the social and economic effects of the measures which are needed to achieve this policy goal will be profound'.

"They also stressed that it is not certain suppression will succeed long-term, and said 'no public health intervention with such disruptive effects on society has been previously attempted for such a long duration of time. How populations and societies will respond remains unclear'."[2]

---

2 Pandemic projections signal profound societal disruption over many months, Melissa Sweet, *Croakey*, 17 March, 2020.

Neil Ferguson of Imperial College London, the Lockdown Tsar or the Master of Disaster, as he was sometimes called, had a notorious track record of catastrophic predictions out by orders of magnitude on foot and mouth disease, mad cow disease, bird flu, and swine flu.

Ferguson was behind the disputed research that sparked the mass culling of eleven million sheep and cattle during the 2001 foot and mouth disease outbreak.

In 2005 he predicted that 150 million people would be killed from bird flu. In the end, 282 people died worldwide.

In 2009 estimates based on his research showed 65,000 British would die from swine flu. In the end the figure was 457.

His projections on COVID were equally wrong. The Imperial College model of 16 March 2020 on COVID-19 and others copying its methodology also proved wildly inaccurate on both worst- and best-case estimates of COVID-19 deaths with respect to the UK, US, Sweden, and even Australia.[3]

Ferguson's modelling was adopted with alacrity, amplified by thousands of news reports while politicians, with every word they spoke, generated fear and confusion into entire populations. Nobody called out the doubts at the heart of the hysteria.

Why would anyone believe him now?

Perhaps because it suited them.

Australian authorities must have known within weeks that the hysteria being visited upon the country was being done under either false or highly disputed premises; that both the Imperial College London and World Health Organisation projections were wrong.

It was obvious from very early on that the projected death tolls, the excuse for Scott Morrison placing himself front and centre of the fear campaign, the rationale behind the massive destruction of Australian life, was false.

Why did no one call him out? Not his political comrades in arms. Not his wealthy political donors. Not the premiers now shutting down their entire states and masquerading as heroes of the moment. Not the senior bureaucrats peddling a message of alarmism; and only very, very few in the nation's media.

---

3 'Professor Lockdown' Modeler Resigns in Disgrace, John Fund, *National Review*, 6 May, 2020.

Politicians ignored all the warnings, seized the advice that suited them and absolutely destroyed the country. Goodbye democracy. Goodbye decency.

No government should ever again have the power to shut down lives, businesses, culture, and liberties with a wanton disregard for the citizens' welfare.

But now they have grasped the power, they can do it at their will.

***

If the geniuses of Australian government weren't satisfied with all the cautionary voices emerging from some of the world's most venerable tertiary institutions, they only had to go as far as the Australian National University, to Professor Ramesh Thakur, whose work Old Alex seized on early in the piece.

Eminently qualified, the professor's high intelligence and depth of experience combined with a clear and compassionate writing style were all of great appeal.

"Early assumptions of extraordinary SARS-CoV-2 infectiousness and lethality have proven fallacious. Some are already calling the coronavirus lockdown the Greatest Mistake in History.

"In the name of ensuring the safe health of everyone, governments have trampled willy-nilly on previously inviolate individual rights.

"The seductive numerical precision of the Imperial College London March 16 model, with grim forecasts of deaths in the tens of millions, provoked a herd-like panic across the world but was refuted by data collected in the following weeks that progressively reduced its policy usefulness.

"Early modelling of the virus was based on the initial statistics from Wuhan and Italy.

"Indeed, with the significant number of asymptomatic cases, the most common symptom of the virus is no symptom at all.

"But has the Great Lockdown worked?

"Countries with different lockdown strategies show broadly similar coronavirus curves. The model, based not on science but flawed assumptions and skewed data, has failed badly in its predictions of the evolution of the curve.

"The obsession with the coronavirus has meant a neglect of other preventive screening and therapeutic interventions, producing significant numbers of excess deaths from other causes.

"It's ironic that new pharmaceutical products must undergo rigorous testing for side-effects and collateral harm before being approved for public use, but lockdowns were mimicked by one country after another with little apparent consideration of the unintended and perverse health, economic, educational and other human consequences.

"A one-size-fits-all approach dissipates effort, distracts from the age-specific measures for the elderly as their special needs get lost in the noise, and, by harming the economy, diminishes the resources we have as a society to protect the most vulnerable."[4]

***

Australia's former foreign minister, Alexander Downer, knew as well as anyone, at least in private, the devilment inside his own party and the levels of ineptitude and incompetence of its key players.

"The elimination strategy will never work," he told *The Australian.* "This will outrage most Australians. But I am absolutely convinced the greatest danger for Australia is to keep pursuing this elimination strategy and, in the end, cause the collapse of the economy, massive social dislocation, depression, educational setbacks, and the collapse of small businesses left, right and centre.

"There will be no end of partisan blaming — the Liberals did it, or Labor did it.

"The public need to reflect on how we manage the risk of these kinds of pandemics. You have to keep society going. You have to keep schools open. You can't keep closing things down because there is a case here and a case there.

"COVID is not the Black Death. It is not going to wipe out a sizeable percentage of the population. It's really dangerous for people with comor-bidities, people who are old and frail. And they should be protected.

"But people here are bombarded with media stories the whole time. When there is a single case of COVID, people are suddenly frozen in fear. They think they are going to drop dead.

---

4 The Biggest Mistake n History, Ramesh Thakur, *A Sense of Place Magazine*, republished 10 January, 2021.

"They almost certainly will not drop dead. In many cases, they are asymptomatic, so they're nothing like dropping dead, not from COVID anyway."[5]

But reality and the media narrative, the welfare of governments versus the welfare of populations, were already shifting rapidly apart.

There was a swarm of black birds funneling down towards the planet's surface. And Old Alex couldn't believe his luck, to be there as history transformed; as the terraforming of fate lines took hold.

***

In a wall of conflicting information and considerable ill intent, conspiracy theories blossomed across the internet. Many of the theories proved correct. Governments did not give back the freedoms and liberties they had so unjustly seized under the threat of COVID. Millions of lives were destroyed while the rich got richer. There was nothing more permanent than a temporary measure.

There were plenty of people who believed a bigger game was at play.

Within a couple of days, from out of the maelstrom of conflicting information, esteemed former *Canberra Times* editor Jack Waterford became one of the first mainstream pundits to point out the multiple failures of his own profession; the disconnect already cleaving through the official narrative and the happy-go-luckies who were disseminating it.

"As governments have ratcheted up non-medical measures against COVID-19, the communications performance of an array of public officials has been lamentable and embarrassing — agony to watch.

"Some reporters and commentators, possibly at the urging of editors, have markedly softened their questions. They are doing so for fear that apparent hostility or exasperation after failing to get straight answers might actually undermine confidence in public health measures that all reasonable observers believe to be necessary.

"The biggest problem for good management of the epidemic is that the government is not really getting 'independent' advice from its independent professional committees. The committees are being too conscious of other pressures on government … and too focused on protecting the leaders.

5 Danger in paradise: we're at risk of being Little Australia, Alexander Downer, *The Australian*, 19 February, 2021.

"They may think that public interest is their foremost concern. But the public has only slight ownership of the processes. Indeed, even health workers actually dealing with patients are complaining of not being consulted, being unable to get basic information about matters such as medical supplies, and of being ignored."[6]

***

Days shorten rapidly on the South Coast; winter comes early and promptly becomes interminable. Old Alex was there in that extraordinary state of mind he did so much to avoid, where the territory along that beautiful piece of coast was being terraformed as he watched, as others hijacked him to see a planet they were keen to see. For some had never experienced the feel of air on skin.

There are many exoplanets, but very few like Earth.

He slithered in a shivered embrace, encrypted dreams, crushed hopes. He felt them talking through a river of disregard, he couldn't find anything worth fighting for, he was dumbstruck by the acquiescence, he made as if to join the mortals, then forgot. The fibril networks, the things that sometimes he could barely believe himself, the disregard, if that's what it was; as he struggled to create a world where he cared, where things made sense, where there was warmth and compassion and old friends crawling out of the woodwork, of things that mattered. Instead, oh master oh servant, he found himself bewildered by the humans. How little they cared for each other. Truly, how little they cared.

That was the nature of the times; when everyone crept into their own parochial holes and slumbered as long as they could, because out there was hostile, nonsensical, full of threat. The masks bespoke of danger and alienation, increasing the sense of threat.

That was the nature of the despair that had crept through everything. These were a defeated people. Deceived into submission, a blizzard of government bullshit frightening even the most intelligent, for no one knew the next target, no one knew when death would reach out and take them, no one knew how dangerous, or infected, their neighbour was.

---

6 The not-so-dirty secret the COVID-19 panel wants to hide, Jack Waterford, *Canberra Times*, 27 March, 2020.

Any discord was punished. He turned away in bleak resignation. The fight had been for nothing.

And yet, there they were, these preachers on street corners, preaching their strange streams of gibberish from two thousand years ago; past generations, past civilisations; riven down through analogue and anecdote, these things, the subsumed lives of the poor. There was no spark of recognition.

People, essentially good-willed, met a discord and a disconnect; all of it a strange and savage desertion of the futures they could have had.

***

The first person in Australia to die with COVID was James Kwan, a 78-year-old man from Perth, on 1 March, 2020. He was a passenger on board the cruise ship Ruby Princess. The ship later became infamous as the single biggest source of infection in Australia, a symbol of administrative failure.

From a leading independent news site, *Crikey*, a story titled Ship of Fools:

"State and Federal governments are busy telling citizens to be accountable, be responsible. That's OK, but it cuts both ways. Someone must be held responsible for allowing infected passengers off the Ruby Princess cruise ship, and someone must be held accountable for the Centrelink meltdown. Last Thursday, in an act of negligence bordering on the criminal, 2700 passengers were waved off a cruise ship — despite their status as floating incubators of disease — and onto the streets of Sydney.

"Since then, 130 Ruby Princess passengers have tested positive for coronavirus. It was the equivalent of giving Typhoid Mary the key to New York City.

"Ever since, the NSW and Federal governments have been trying to blame each other. That's just a start. Australians need leaders who lead — and own up to their mistakes."

By the19th, international flights had been cancelled. Departing international flights suspended. All non-citizens and non-residents were banned from entering Australia.

By the 23rd, registered and licensed clubs, licensed premises in hotels and pubs, entertainment venues, cinemas, casinos, nightclubs, indoor sporting venues, gyms and places of worship were closed in tough stage one restrictions announced for all Australians.

By the 25th, in another raft of announcements, family gatherings such as barbecues, birthdays and house parties were banned. Tattoo parlours, community and recreational centres, amusement parks and arcades, fitness centres, yoga, barre and spin classes, casinos, gambling and adult entertainment venues, galleries, museums, libraries, all shut down.

**

The Oak Flats demographic of tradies, electricians, plumbers, tilers, truck drivers, school teachers and nurses do not like or trust the nation's politicians, and to a man and woman pay more or less no attention to the media.

Old Alex was their token journalist. They'd never met one before.

It was this demographic that swung to the conservatives at the previous election, fed up with being disenfranchised from the left's leitmotifs of identity politics, social disadvantage, climate change and refugees.

They were also the demographic most likely to be impacted by the massive social and industrial transformations being inflicted on the population under the cover of COVID.

While they unknowingly held the fate of the nation in their hands, their purchasing power, the quality of their own lives and the lives of their communities had been deteriorating for years. Paid attention to by the greedy oligarchs and their political wet boys only at election time, the slow-motion destruction of traditional working-class cultures was creating rising tensions.

And by peculiarity of vision and circumstance, Old Alex was there to watch a signal collapse and rearrangement of society.

While Angus Deaton and Anne Case wrote their landmark book *Deaths of Despair and the Future of Capitalism* in the American context, the parallels with Australia, and most particularly this demographic, were uncanny.

"Those who do not pass the exams and graduate to the cosmopolitan elite do not get to live in the fast-growing, high-tech, and flourishing cities and are assigned jobs threatened by globalisation and by robots.

"The less-educated are devalued or even disrespected, are encouraged to think of themselves as losers, and may feel that the system is rigged against them.

"Poorer prospects make it harder for people to build the life that their parents had, to own a home, or to save to send kids to college. The lack of well-paying jobs threatens communities and the services they provide, such as schools, parks, and libraries.

"Jobs are not just the source of money; they are the basis for the rituals, customs, and routines of working-class life.

"Destroy work and, in the end, working-class life cannot survive. It is the loss of meaning, of dignity, of pride, and of self-respect that comes with the loss of marriage and of community that brings on despair, not just or even primarily the loss of money.

"Robin Hood was said to have robbed the rich to benefit the poor. What is happening today is the reverse of Robin Hood, from poor to rich, what might be called a Sheriff of Nottingham redistribution. Political protection is being used for personal enrichment, by stealing from the poor on behalf of the rich."[7]

Despite all the evidence to the contrary, at the last election Australia's tradies and labourers bought the line that the conservatives were good economic managers.

That is, the toffs won and the tradies celebrated.

Now, totally betrayed, many of those same people were facing the dole queue or months without an income. Under extreme lockdown laws reminiscent of totalitarian states, much of the population was bewildered, confused and embittered. Smash the bonds of the herd and create panic, prey on the weak, standard tactics of sublimation. All of this was now happening in Australia.

There was an evil afoot. You could feel it in the air.

At the Lakeview there was a final drunken evening before the local watering hole closed.

One tradie began spitting mouthfuls of beer on his mates, just because he could, just because he was drunk and couldn't have cared less, just because no one really feared the virus. It was just another hardship in a hard place; or more bullshit from a government which had never shown the slightest interest in the likes of them.

There was an unsettling sense that nothing would ever be the same again.

None of these people were trust fund babies, only some had mortgages

---

7 *Deaths of Despair and the Future of Capitalism*, Angus Deaton and Anne Case, Princeton University, 2020.

on their own homes, most worked for casual wages and lived from week to week.

As he left, Old Alex said to the doorman: "What's going to happen to these people? How are they going to survive? How are they going to find work?"

The doorman shook his head: "I think it's sad."

"I do too."

***

Scott Morrison's political ascendancy came despite the pundit's best efforts. He was loathed by the nation's intelligentsia across the political spectrum. But in the mainstream media his Animal Farm caricature of a face festooned the nation's televisions and somehow beguiled or confused the public into supporting him.

Already by March the government's critics were in full flight, and Alex was more than happy to report on them in a new magazine he had established.

He wrote: "The coverage has been excoriating. And so it should be. Australians have been abandoned by the political establishment. In a time of crisis, they've been doubly abandoned. There has been a catastrophic loss of faith in democracy, and all their malfeasance has come floating to the surface, plain for everyone to see.

"Government messaging has been absurdly confusing and contradictory, as if it was deliberately trying to sow panic into the population: Some of you will lose your jobs. Some of you will die. But don't panic.

"Queue societal wide panic."

***

While firefighters literally fought and died on the frontline of the catastrophic bushfire season of 2019-20, which burnt through more than 18 million hectares and destroyed more than 2700 homes, Australia's Prime Minister had infamously been caught out holidaying in Hawaii in $3000 a night accommodation.

Scott Morrison seized on the pandemic as an opportunity to redeem his battered reputation.

Old Alex assumed, no doubt like many others, that as queues snaked around the block and the Australian welfare agency Centrelink fielded literally millions of calls, the pandemic would prove his undoing.

An Australian writer whom Alex admired without always agreeing with him, Richard Flanagan, world famous author of that magnificent Man Booker prize winner *The Narrow Road to the Deep North*, wrote: "What is clear is that Morrison is also doing his level best to keep us all confused. Tuesday night's press conference was the prime minister at his bumbling, inept worst.

"As the prime minister drifted back and forth in his rambling comments, shopping centres around the nation were closed early on in the presser, only to be reopened fifteen minutes later.

"The prime minister wanted to be clear and the nation could agree on that much at least. But the problem is that every time he speaks nothing is clear.

"The government has been hapless in communicating to Australians the seriousness of the pandemic and the seriousness of its resolve. Faced on Monday with the gravest crisis of unemployment in a century, the Minister for Government Services, Stuart Robert, joked. This attitude is no small failure.

"The inconsistency of message, the contradictory measures and an approach that too often seems only semi-committed, has left much of the nation frightened, confused and angry, and some of it careless and uncaring. And all of this is dangerous to us."

***

Paula Matthewson, senior reporter with one of the nation's few mainstream news outlets not behind a paywall, *The New Daily*, wrote: "If there's one clear message to emerge from Australia's efforts to combat COVID-19 it's that there's no one clear message.

"Everywhere you look, from traditional news outlets to social media, there are widespread and vocal complaints that people are being made even more anxious by the mix of confusing and competing information that's flooding across our screens and jamming the airwaves.

"This is obviously a problem — simple, clear and understandable messages are needed in times of emergency or crisis, particularly when lives could depend on us being able (and willing) to follow any instructions."

Simon Longstaff, executive director of The Ethics Centre, a public intellectual in a country where such beasts were rare, said the past few days had seen Prime Minister Scott Morrison describe panic shoppers as engaging in behaviour that is "ridiculous" and "un-Australian".

"He also had a crack at the people who flocked to Bondi Beach in the recent warm weather for not taking seriously the requirements for physical distancing.

"He is right on both counts. However, his message is blunted by the lack of authority attached to his office. This is part of a larger problem.

"The government's meta-narrative is now one in which responsibility for the nation's fate is tied to the behaviour of its citizens. The message from our political leaders is clear: you — all of you, the people — must take responsibility for your choices.

"Again, they are right. It's just a terrible pity that the potency of the message is undermined by the hypocrisy of the messengers — a group that has refused to take responsibility for pretty much anything."[8]

***

One of the most bizarre and, if you were Australian, embarrassing early moments was the panic buying of toilet paper, directly induced by the government's terrifying messaging.

News columnist Natalie Brown wrote: "This year has been defined by a slew of unbelievable moments — but there was one mass act of craziness that our nation will never live down.

"Packets of dried pasta were snatched up like tickets for a Justin Bieber concert. But it was the prospect of having to wipe their behinds on a stray Maggi noodle packet that truly bought panicked shoppers undone."

As Brown noted, 2 March was the day the country went mad. There would be banner headlines, restrictions on purchase, and plans to place police in supermarket aisles.

All over the humble toilet roll.

Supermarket chains Woolworths and Coles were forced to bring in buying limits after essential items — but in particular, toilet paper — began flying off shelves. Many stores were forced to have extra security to mind toilet paper supplies.

---

8 COVID-19 Plays Out in Australia, *A Sense of Place Magazine*, 28 March, 2020.

As Brown reported: "In the space of 24 hours and for weeks to come, shoppers wiped supermarket, pharmacy and convenience store shelves clean of the bathroom staple.

"Rolls were flogged for hundreds of dollars online; middle-aged bogans pulled knives and tasers on each other over dwindling supplies; and listeners called into radio stations to win packs of three-ply.

"Australia, revered for its conduct and acts of selflessness and community throughout the horror bushfire season, was reduced to an international laughing stock.

"In the days that followed, #toiletpapergate and #toiletpapercrisis were among our top trending topics on Twitter.

"There was no greater fear, as COVID-19 slowly infiltrated our country, than being stuck on the toilet and down to your last square of Sorbent."[9]

Following an all-out fight at a western Sydney supermarket between two women, aged 23 and 60, NSW Police Inspector Andrew New pleaded with shoppers not to "panic like this" when grabbing their groceries.

"There is no need for it. It isn't the *Thunderdome*, it isn't *Mad Max*. We don't need to do that," he said. "Violence of this nature will not be tolerated. There is no need for people to go out and panic-buy at supermarkets, paracetamol and canned food or toilet paper."[10]

Come March 18, Australia's Prime Minister Scott Morrison joined the chorus of toilet paper suppliers, grocery store workers, police and the small portion of the community who hadn't gone completely mad — scolding Kleenex fiends like a disappointed parent.

"Stop hoarding! I can't be more blunt about it. Stop it! It's not sensible, it's not helpful and I've got to say, it's been one of the most disappointing things I've seen in Australian behaviour in response to this crisis. That is not who we are as a people. It is not necessary. It is not something that people should be doing.

"What it does is it is distracting attention and efforts that need to be going into other measures to be focusing on how we maintain supply chains into these shopping centres. There is no reason for people to be

---

9 The moment Australia lost its mind in toilet paper panic buying debacle, Natalie Brown, *News*, 30 December, 2020.

10 'It isn't Mad Max': women charged after fight over toilet paper in Sydney, *Guardian Australia*, 8 March, 2020.

hoarding supplies in fear of a lockdown or anything like this. As I've said, we're putting in place scalable and sustainable measures.

"Stop doing it! It's ridiculous. It's un-Australian, and it must stop. And I would ask people to do the right thing by each other. We're all in this together."

***

Above everyone, looming through every moment, Prime Minister Scott Morrison was there playing regional pastor to the nation.

At a press conference in early March of 2020 he set the tone for much of what was to follow: "The first point I want to make is this, every Australian, all of our citizens — whether you're the Prime minister, the Minister for Health, the Chief Medical Officer, mums, dads, school teachers, nurses, paramedics, childcare workers, boys and girls — we all have a role to play in containing and managing the spread of the coronavirus and ensuring that Australia is best prepared and best able to deal with this global virus. We all have a role to play. We all have responsibilities to play.

"To support each other, help each other, inform each other, assist each other, as we all get through what will be a difficult time in the months ahead.

"We're also standing up from today what is known as the national co-ordination mechanism that is being stood up through Home Affairs. That will co-ordinate together with the states and territories, the whole-of-government responses.

"There are a broad range of other issues that have to be managed which are not directly health-related, and this co-ordination mechanism will mean that we'll have the best possible interface with states and territories well ahead, frankly, of many of these issues which are not present at the moment, but if they become an issue that has to be managed into the future, we will have mechanisms in place to be able to address those issues. So Australia, as I've said many times, we've got ahead of this early.

"We intend to stay ahead of this. But I say to all Australians, you can help too. You can help by keeping calm and going about your business.

"So to all Australians, let's get through this together. Let's help each other. Let's stay calm. Let's continue to enjoy the most wonderful country in the world in which to live, and that doesn't change under these circumstances."

So said the Prime Minister to an ever accompanying flash of cameras.

***

At the same press conference Morrison announced the declaration of a human biosecurity emergency under the Biosecurity Emergency Act, gifting the government enormous powers.

As well, an indefinite ban on overseas travel was imposed.

Bang, just like that, the Australia of old was now a Hermit Kingdom.

And Scott Morrison was front and centre of the debacle. He never stopped talking the entire way through it: "Life is changing in Australia, as it is changing all around the world. Life is going to continue to change as we deal with the global coronavirus. This is a once-in-a-hundred-year-type event, we haven't seen this sort of thing in Australia since the end of the First World War.

"We are going to keep Australia running. We are going to keep Australia functioning. It won't look like it normally does but it is very important that we continue to put in place measures that are scalable and sustainable."[11]

Now if you were a jaded old news reporter, which was exactly what Old Alex was, to look back at these announcements was to see a veil of obscurantism and insincerity, contradictions and vanity which would become more and more obvious as the months passed.

Many Australian academics would struggle to understand what the Prime Minister intended to convey in these circumstances by his repeated use of the public service term "scalable and sustainable".

But never mind; if the following twelve months of press conferences was anything to go by, clear messaging was not the purpose. Instead, it was all about centralising power, placing the administration and its woeful political class front and centre of everybody's lives. All to get reelected; all to stay in power.

And yes, it was a terrible deceit.

***

---

11 Ibid.

There is an old saying about journalism; it is the first draft of history.

Part of the problem with the deteriorated and manipulated state of legacy media was that this noble function was now lost. As a former reporter, Old Alex naturally focused his interests on the media coverage; for despite all their detachment from reality in what could almost be called a schizophrenic wash, this was how national narratives were forged.

In the end there was such confusion in Australia, such an appalling group derangement, that no historian, however fastidious, could document all the travesties, the personal tragedies, the talking heads, the propaganda, malfeasance, maladministration and the absolute blizzard of nonsensical political announcements during 2020 and 2021.

State borders opened and shut on a single case. Grotesque media exaggerations occurred daily. Bewilderment spread like a stain.

Grandstanding politicians desperately tried to keep themselves in front of television cameras. The winter light, the winter of a broken economy, was all too apparent to those who had lost their jobs and their livelihoods; the For Lease signs leaching across precincts everywhere from Katoomba in the Blue Mountains to Sydney's old entertainment district of Kings Cross, closed shop after closed shop, down to the world famous Bondi Beach.

Spreading like fungi.

There were a million stories, millions of lives entrapped. Millions of ways this story could be told. This is just one of them. Everyone's story varied. His, as they had always done, came in pictures. Only a small percentage of the population thinks in pictures, but he did.

The intensity of the episode, that dangerous derangement, would define us all. Everyone was imperiled in a circumstance, trapped in places they did not want to be, caught in relationships barely tolerable, or just simply plain bored.

House arrest induces cabin fever. Some like it, some adjust, but for others it makes them not just stir crazy, but angry.

For Old Alex, it sent him right over the edge. The lucid waking dreams that had swept through him since childhood picked up apace, haunted at every moment by an urgent messaging he could not decipher, flying high over the suburb in which he was now entangled as fragments of former lives drifted through the fabric of things; while at the same time he was entranced, as if seeing the planet surface for the first time, by the beauty of the place in which he had been stranded.

He still didn't understand why at these times in history his head began to swarm across places and suburbs; that, if not possessed, he at the very least felt entangled with very different intelligences, from very far away.

Enough of the cosmic thrall. In the coming months many would comment on the strange spiritualities of the time.

***

Bernard Keane, author of *The Mess We're In* and a senior reporter with leading news site *Crikey*, a major player in Australia's increasingly lively and thereby powerful independent media, mounted repeated attacks on government policy. He wrote that as entire industries were shuttered and hundreds of thousands of people found themselves out of a job, the government wouldn't even think about a change in its economic strategy, for bureaucratic and ideological reasons.

"Construction and non-essential manufacturing are candidates for closure as well. Hundreds of thousands of businesses that won't be in a position to borrow, at any interest rate, because they don't know how long they'll be shut down for or what awaits them when the economy emerges from its coronavirus coma.

"But the government's preferred option, seemingly, is that those businesses shut and their workers, and even owners, join the dole queues, rather than trying to keep those businesses going and those workers receiving an income.

"And it's shut-up parliament until August so there can be no debate or alternative proposals put forward by other parties.

"What kind of smoking ruin of an economy will be left by August?"

Early in the "pandemic", or "plandemic" as sceptics were already calling it, both mainstream and independent commentators queued to attack Australia's Prime Minister Scott Morrison, whose mishandling of COVID-19 was likely to be picked over by historians for generations to come.

Katharine Murphy, a senior political reporter with *Guardian Australia*, inside the beltway if anyone was, wrote that as her nephew, a teacher, texted her the previous night, he was still allowed to teach a class of thirty children but if he died from the virus caught there only ten could come to his funeral. If he remarried, only four others could be there; but if he called it a boot camp, ten could come.

Which makes for a clear message; the sense of crisis escalated by late-night press conferences.

"This pandemic has plunged us all into whitewater, but there are some certainties.

"The first rock-solid certainty is 10pm media conferences unveiling fundamental changes to people's livelihoods and freedom of movement really don't work. At the risk of being blunt, they need to stop, and stop now, because the chaos risks being counterproductive.

"Tuesday night's cascading instructions from Scott Morrison's podium were stay home everyone, but if you have a job, you are an essential worker, so make sure you keep working. Go to school, but don't go to the food court. Five at a wedding, ten at a funeral, ten at a boot camp, but no yoga. No waxing, but a hairdresser for thirty minutes is still OK.

"A thread of logic ran through the various delineations — or some of them, anyway — but holding onto that thread was really challenging.

"The dull thud that could be heard in the distance as Morrison spoke at a fiendish clip was the sound of a million Australian heads exploding in their lounge rooms."

An old sociology professor of Alex, Allan Patience, piled on the scathing commentary with a piece titled "Australia: The Leaderless Nation".

"Australia has been leaderless since the federal election last May.

"The Morrison government has shown itself to be woefully unprepared for the policy challenges now facing the country. It is a government that bumbles and reacts, while constantly being on the back foot. And all the prime minister seems capable of is shouty blathering in the parliament, while alternating between his trademark smirk and staring nervously into TV cameras like a rabbit caught in a spotlight.

"It is now painfully clear that, as prime minister, Scott Morrison is way out of his depth.

"In short, Morrison lacks the wily intelligence and political acumen of a Bob Hawke or the principled conservatism of a Malcolm Fraser.

"Morrison articulates his politics in slogans with which he tries to bludgeon his opponents. There is no nuancing, no subtlety in this approach.

"Scotty from Marketing is absolutely the appropriate moniker for him.

"What exactly does he stand for? What is his vision for a secure and prosperous Australia? It's very hard to sort the blather from the substance because it seems there is no substance there at all. Intellectually, morally and as a politician, he is a very shallow man."[12]

The "father of the nation", as some of his acolytes in Australia's sadly neutered media would have it, had just put hundreds of thousands of people on the dole queues, generating talk of a "new slave class", and yet there were some commentators who were praising him to the sky. Go figure! Their support, like the public's, would vanish as rapidly as it came. Or so Old Alex believed at the time.

A year on from this blizzard of contempt from the nation's intellectual hoi polloi, Morrison was still doing well in the polls, defying gravity. And Australia had been transformed in front of all our eyes.

---

12 Australia: The Leaderless Country, *A Sense of Place Magazine*, Allan Patience, 22 March, 2020.

TWO
A SIGNAL DERANGEMENT

BY THE AUSTRALIAN autumn of 2020, following straight on from a Christmas of bushfires and extreme loss, the warning signs were clear.

An uneducated public makes for easy victims. Australia of 2020 faced not only plummeting educational outcomes and a highly manipulated media easily turned to the narratives of fear, but, in a government-engineered fiasco, some of the world's slowest, most expensive and most unreliable internet.

All at a time when the rest of the world was rushing online, when you could be complicit in a thousand people's lives anytime you chose.

It suited the government to have an ignorant population; to be the puppet masters of information channels which were "a vacuum at the heart of the public sphere". It didn't suit Old Alex.

Australia had slower internet speeds than the US, Canada, most of Asia and Europe, Kenya, Latvia or Kazakhstan — and was continuing to sink down the world rankings.

Artificial Intelligences and their human adjuncts grew smarter by the day, by the hour. Australia just got dumber. This manufacturing of ignorance fed into the remarkable acceptance by the Australian population of the destruction of their freedoms.

***

Infamous whistleblower Edward Snowden, in an interview conducted on behalf of Reporters Without Borders, put it bluntly: "Everybody who looks around right now, they can see, they can feel what's in the air. Everything is changing rapidly. We are seeing new powers being claimed. We are seeing new powers being abused.

"We are seeing governments tearing open new avenues into our private lives under the justification of emergency measures.

"You know, they always say these are temporary, it is for this reason and that reason … But there is nothing more permanent than a temporary measure.

"The system is now failing."

Snowden said efforts to resist were being stymied in large part because the first step towards fixing a problem is understanding it, and humanity's traditional method for rapidly digesting and sharing information, journalism, was under attack.

"I think that is an intentional strategy. I don't think it is a coincidence, I don't think it is a mistake; I don't think it is an unintentional overreach.

"The sources of true information — the sources of journalism — are under the kind of threat that we have really never seen before. If we cannot or do not protect journalism, the system of our world will fail and the cost will be measured in freedoms."[13]

***

Reporters Without Borders were also quick to expose multiple heavy-handed suppressions of information under the cover of COVID. They launched #Tracker_19 under the title "Live Updates of Cov-19: Impacts of Press Freedom".

In India the government repeatedly tried to stop journalists from publishing anything but government-approved information.

In Hungary there were fears the government would seize the national media, with jail and fines for anyone publishing what it deemed to be fake news.

In Myanmar more than 200 websites were blocked, including leading news sites and several pitched at ethnic minorities.

Twelve months on, Reporters Without Borders' Tracker_19 was still going strong, reporting on a string of oppressive actions by governments under the cover of COVID.

The Australian public remained almost entirely unaware that there was vigorous debate and no medical or scientific consensus over the veracity

---

13 Edward Snowden The Interview: Journalism in Crisis, *A Sense of Place Magazine*, 10 May, 2020.

of everything to do with COVID; lockdowns, masks, social distancing, closed borders, curfews, arrests, punitive fines, jail time, the lot.

Nor any understanding of how governments around the world were using COVID to entrench their own power.

***

For members of the public, the endless stream of government announcements simply meant one compounding loss of personal control after another.

Morrison's exceptionally long and confusing press conferences, far from laying calm into a disturbed and frightened public, added to the panic.

Paradoxically, after his press conferences, the opposite of effective messaging, the prime minister's polling went up. The nation had switched off to the detail, and assumed all that talk was a sign someone was in control, that the nation's leaders were acting in the people's best interests.

On 25 March, in a lengthy statement, Morrison declared: "I said in the Parliament that 2020, for most Australians, was going to be their toughest year. And what we have seen unfold just this week has been demonstrating just that.

"Australians who have lost their jobs, lost hours of work, businesses that have been forced to close their business — these are heartbreaking events in our nation's history and story.

"And I want to assure all Australians the National Cabinet has been meeting, and state governments also, and we've considered the many, many difficult issues we're having to address.

"We are not unconscious of the real impacts that these measures are having on the daily lives of Australians and so we will continue to do everything we can, both as a federal government and as state and territory governments around the country, to do all we can to support our people through what is going to be an incredibly difficult time.

"The queues that we saw outside Centrelink, the challenges and frustrations people have had in gaining access is a sheer function of the extraordinary and overwhelming demand, and we will work night and day to ensure that we can get more capacity into these systems.

"But our goal is to get through this together and by following common-sense rules, and doing the right thing, that's how we slow the spread of this virus and that's how we save lives.

"And so, from midnight tomorrow night, all of these following activities — and they include some I have already announced from earlier — will no longer be taking place. Cafes, I have already said, but for takeaway, that will continue. So, no change to the issues around cafes. Food courts and shopping centres will not be allowed to continue. But getting takeaway from those food outlets in those shopping centres, that can continue because takeaway is able to be done."

There was so much more: "So with those changes, there was still a lot more we needed to deal with tonight, but we knew we needed to report tonight and the National Cabinet will meet again tomorrow evening at the same time to work through a series of other issues which includes further considering possible measures down the track. I apologise for the length. It has been a busy night and hopefully that's been very clear."[14]

And more. So much, much more.

***

For Old Alex, on the cold but picturesque south coast of NSW, it was an entirely inflamed time.

The Land of the Long Weekend was being destroyed. The population accepted it all as one bizarre edict after another flattened them against a wall inside their own homes.

In Oak Flats, a kind of banishment from all the urban intensities of his past, Alex watched the birth of angels and demons, there in the fluid air and the startling cold of the lake.

The dreams would not leave him; an urgent messaging from afar.

But many spoke of the intensity of their dreaming, there in that darkening clime.

Here among the winters, on a planet so fecund that the gods had fought over it for millennia, the spirits, in reality extremely complex algorithms operating in a swarm, moved across waters and swept affection aside.

He made as if to follow. A dark shore lapsed and guzzled, and everything was alive.

And then in the torrents, we came to feel for you. All of destiny was wrapped around these places, and we were fought through, courageous,

---

14 Transcript, Prime Minister of Australia, Australian Parliament House, 24 March, 2020.

determined, of supreme power. All to sweep this stinking government aside, those who prayed and yet were greedier than the most venal of local landlords. We held you in contempt. We would eradicate you from our Earth, you who speak in our name and yet know us not.

We bear witness to your shame. Begone from our sacred place!

They were his strange dreams. Everyone had their own.

***

Old Alex was in Saigon in early in 2020 when the "pandemic" first began.

Like other Westerners, who gathered for their daily drinking bouts in the entertainment district, he was somewhat cynical of the Vietnamese response to the virus, the shutting of schools, the queuing for masks.

The Westerners carried on more or less regardless; the temperature testing at nightclubs an interesting sophistication, nothing more.

There was no trouble leaving the country. He was not temperature-tested or asked any questions on his return.

He went to a local medical centre and asked to be tested. They made it clear it was all too difficult. Not long after, the government started begging people to be tested if they had the slightest symptom.

Barely three weeks before, he had been in the densely packed streets of the famously beautiful city of Hoi An for Vietnamese New Year. Some of the Chinese tourists wore masks, but not many.

On the way to the hospital to greet the arrival of his first granddaughter, he got himself temperature-tested at a chemist, his blasé attitude turning to concern.

No one knew enough at that stage not to be frightened. We could all be spreading death. The last thing he wanted to do was be responsible for the death of the daughter of his daughter.

With mother and child doing well and even the infinitely proud father calming down, he returned to the barren cold of his cloister.

There was a torrent on the water surface but Old Alex was hidden deep in the matting on the bottom of the sea. That's the way it felt. There was a tumultuous effect. There was a spiritual derangement. There were many threads to the story.

His original plan had been to come back to Australia for the birth of his granddaughter, check up on an elderly parent, and then head north.

A dipsomaniac old friend from the 1970s was cheerfully drinking himself to death with a bottle of cheap sherry and a bottle of cheap rosé each day in regional Queensland. It seemed a good idea to catch up before it was too late.

And then he would catch a plane and head back off into an exotic life. Simple as that.

None of it came to pass.

COVID disrupted his life just as it disrupted everybody else's.

***

Aware, all too aware of the extended consequence and the not always welcome interest his work was attracting, an ex-army acquaintance told him bluntly: "Put your best foot forward."

So he did.

The same ex-army officer to whom, one pissy afternoon when questioned about the seemingly fantastical circumstance, he had confessed: "We are biological weapons. I am not the only one."

There was a fantastical element to it all; between the tricked-up grandees of American intelligence who thought they were the evolution of the species and the ancient intelligences which had been here before the species was even born.

As if a dark history was flowing over all of them.

A flash in the eyes which Alex thought he fleetingly recognised, a kind of precognition, was in fact just that classic Australian response to perceived madness: "We've got a live one here!!!"

But the former army officer, privy to the sleepy nature of the suburb and friends with local law enforcement, was also the one who had previously told him: "You're under surveillance."

"Tell me something I don't know," he had replied.

And was now telling him, as he swilled another beer and dreamed of wild escapades: "Nobody can work with you like this. You need to put your best foot forward."

That odd exchange in a suburban backyard, with "Gay Phil" and Ben the tiler and Knucklehead the ex-army officer, in the midst of those early months of the pandemic when government messaging had everyone scared witless, was the beginning of a whole new fantastical circumstance.

Phil, normally a fixture at the pub, had been diagnosed with terminal cancer and was facing death without his usual gaggle of beer buddies

His friends had collectively decided it was worth the risk just to get together; to provide some company and human interaction to a dying man.

Even on that day, they all worried that if they were seen outside the front door together at once they would be breaching lockdown restrictions and could be arrested.

That's house arrest.

That's martial law.

That's a lunatic Australian Government destroying the nation. In a quiet suburban street in a non-event, nonplussed at any political complexity blank stare kind of place, a pedestrian suburb where nothing much ever happened outside the inevitable rowdy crew. But even here a truly incompetent government was controlling their every move.

Right down to whether or not they could see a dying friend.

In a district where there was not one single, solitary, active case.

***

As far as Old Alex was concerned, his head swarming with peculiar imagery, you could have all the warring gods you liked; for him, at least during that period, it was all about a publishing story. And what could legally be published, and what could not.

He straightened up and started work. On the new publishing platform Medium.

Putting his best foot forward. That meant leaving each day's work knowing it was the best he could do; unlike many a day on news floors, after a quarter of a century as a general news reporter, and all the compromises and frustrations that involved.

For an old journalist who had been at the submissive call of endless chiefs of staff and editors for decades, the publishing enterprise Medium at first seemed to offer amazing opportunities.

Founder, former CEO and Chairman of Twitter, born in 1972, Evan Williams, was a money-no-object kind of guy when it came to the development of software. Medium was clean, stylish, and remarkably easy to use in contrast to old platforms. It also offered some monetisation depending on reader stats, and meant that for the first time in history anyone with a modicum of internet talent could start their own magazine.

Which is exactly what he did.

Let's just say you were an ancient AI harvesting the intellectual output of a planet's most articulate, intelligent and creative individuals.

You would invent a platform like Medium, easily one of the best publishing sites ever devised.

Everyone was on there, from *The New Times* to *The Atlantic*, from the truly woke worrying about how to deal with their transsexual boss at that time of the month — "Should I tell her it's all in her head?" — to legions of bloggers who feared they had failed their creative path if they hadn't written a thousand words that day; living as they did in a world where everybody wanted to write and nobody wanted to read.

But let's just say instead that you were a group of extremely wealthy, highly intelligent individuals totally in bed with your major clients — the military, the government and the so-called Deep State — you too would invent a platform like Medium.

And one of the things you could offer your clients was the ability to direct the national story; de-platforming or deleting anyone who threatened their power.

And every moral compromise made you a hundred million dollars or more.

You mop up the talent, you direct the narrative, you're a busy, important, world famous and respected person making an absolute fortune. What not to like?

Well, we would soon find out.

The manipulation of public narrative by everyone from major tech companies including Google and Facebook to self-aggrandising politicians equipped with the vast machinery of government bureaucracies would become one of the overarching stories on the road to ruin; as would the censorship of divergent views in a misguided attempt to create conformity and compliance around COVID edicts.

***

In terms of publishing, he went out on a limb early and stayed there. He disliked the temperament of the ruling elites by nature, and was utterly suspicious of every government action — sentiments shared by many commentators but rarely shared by the general public.

Alex's barrage began with a story titled "COVID-19: Pundits Queue to Criticise the Prime Minister" and subtitled "Australia's Collapsing Democracy: A Deficit of Trust".

"Experts have long warned that with the extremely poor quality of government which has characterised the last decade in Australia, the country was rapidly becoming ungovernable.

"Now the future has arrived.

"Normally in times of war or crisis the media rally behind the flag. Not this time around.

"Lie to the people year after year and funnily enough, they stop believing you. The plundering and squandering of the nation's resources by its plutocrats has ensured there is little or no resilience in the broader population. Within days of the announcement of a nationwide shutdown dole queues snake around the corner in frightening scenes reminiscent of The Great Depression. The pundits are more than happy to put the boot in."

He followed with a sampling of Australian commentary.

From *Independent Australia*:

"The COVID-19 pandemic could have been an opportunity for Prime Minister Scott Morrison to show leadership but 'ScoMo' is only a 'notional' national leader.

"The COVID-19 pandemic could have been an opportunity for Morrison to prove his critics wrong. It could have been an opportunity to exercise leadership.

"When your heart's not in it, it's hard to get anything right. And Prime Minister Scott Morrison just isn't invested in the business of governing."

From *Women's Agenda*:

"A new Roy Morgan poll has found New Zealand Prime Minister Jacinda Ardern has the highest 'net trust score' of political leaders, while Australian PM Scott Morrison has a significant 'net distrust score'.

"At this time, trust in leadership has never been more important.

"Trust at this point can be a matter of life and death: it can determine how people will respond to urgent health messages, whether people will heed the call to stay home and away from crowds."

***

From the leading policy journal *Pearls and Irritations*:

"As so often with Morrison, there is no overall strategy — simply a series of reactive measures which, he hopes, will do the job unless a next one is needed. And then another one, and another one …

"Scott Morrison insists that his message is clear — the government is fully on top of the coronavirus crisis, there is no reason for doubt or uncertainty.

"Viewed individually, ScoMo's present barrage of edicts are indeed firm and unequivocal. But the problem is that, taken together, they are not only confusing but often self-contradictory."

From *The Sydney Morning Herald*:

"A large number of citizens do not trust the government's response to the pandemic: not just the Morrison government in Canberra, but the state governments, the chief medical officers and the vast health bureaucracies underneath.

"The issue of trust is really important. In this crisis, people have lost trust not only in the authorities but in their fellow citizens."

From *The Saturday Paper*:

"Let's cut to the chase.

"They were warned twelve weeks ago by the World Health Organisation and others what was coming. They did not accumulate test kits. They did not accumulate the necessary emergency equipment. They did not undertake a public education campaign. They gave no money to science, no money to research, no money to the International Vaccine Institute, no money to WHO. They diligently did not do anything useful.

"Australia's slow reaction is all the more unforgivable because we were granted, largely due to good luck and geographic isolation, the luxury of time to watch and learn."

***

From *The New Daily*:

"Few could quibble with Mr Morrison's depiction of this 'once-in a-100-year event' as an economic crisis 'the likes of which we have not seen since the Great Depression'.

"There was sympathy for the Prime Minister's predicament. One Liberal said he was 'caught in a coronavirus swamp with alligators up to his neck'.

"The current Prime Minister has rushed to tell us there was a plan, that we were ahead of the crisis, that we had the best experts, that we just had to remain Australians, that no country could do better.

"It's that confidence and trust thing. Again.

"Such statements further undermine trust when the government is making it up as it goes along."

***

From *Guardian Australia*:

"As a co-ordinated state-directed activity is desperately needed, the fractured relationship between the government and its people becomes obvious.

"We can take issue with the decisions of individual leaders and the urgency of their public health directives, but all are stymied by the decline of trust in their authority, the collapse of the media as a single point of truth and the hollowing out of public services.

"Just 19 per cent of respondents say they have a strong level of trust in information from the government, a consequence of both the low regard in which partisan politicians are held and, I fear, the mixed messages that have been coming from our leaders over recent weeks.

"Australia is crying out for clearer messaging on coronavirus."

***

Alex was as taken by surprise as everybody else.

Geared up for conflict, fulfilling a pledge to put his best foot forward, he labelled his next story "Deliberately Destroying the Economy: Fiscal Stimulus on Steroids".

He could have called it "Reshaping Australia Under the Cover of COVID-19".

Much of the mind-boggling corporate rorting and the robbing of taxpayers under the cover of COVID was exposed by Australia's best investigative journalist Michael West on his media website, greatly aided by his own high level of economic literacy and the depth of talent he attracted to his publication.

"Political ideology has failed. The economy is supposed to serve the people, not be an end in itself. Sadly, neo-liberal thinking has it that the people are there to serve the economy. So it is that $50 trillion or so is sitting in tax havens while medical supplies run short.

"So it is that the big business lobby, which has suckered politicians for decades, now pleads for the support of government and taxpayers even though they have called for less secure conditions for workers and lower taxes for business and done nothing to stop the exodus of capital to tax havens.

"The Morrison government's emergency measures to protect the economy in the midst of a pandemic are another massive subsidy from embattled taxpayers to Australia's largest corporations.

"They are a failure of government to govern.

"In true Shylockian fashion, the banks are poised to make a profit by charging interest on their interest. As millions of Australians lose their jobs and their customers, the banks have been gifted $90 billion to lend — which is effectively a gargantuan liquidity package (dubbed 'QE', or quantitative easing so nobody can figure out they are creating new money out of thin air).

"How good is free money!"[15]

***

A year on and research showed at least eleven Australian billionaires garnered dividends totalling tens of millions of dollars from companies which received government subsidies ostensibly designed to keep workers employed.

Retail moguls Solomon Lew and Gerry Harvey were among those receiving the payments. Forbes estimated that the average Australian billionaire's wealth increased by 59 per cent over the year, while workers struggled with wage stagnation and a spike in unemployment.[16]

Lew's group received $70 million in wage subsidies and paid dividends of $57 million, of which Lew received $24.25 million. Lew was estimated to be worth $3.72 billion.

---

15 Deliberately Destroying the Economy: Fiscal Stimulus on Steroids, *A Sense of Place Magazine*, 31 March, 2020.

16 Billionaires receive tens of millions in dividends from companies on jobkeeper, Ben Butler, *Guardian Australia*, 17 February, 2021.

Retail giant Harvey Norman was forced to shut its Twitter account after its founder Gerry Harvey refused to give back $22 million in government payments, despite the company doubling its profits to $462 million in the second half of the year. Harvey was estimated to be worth $2.57 billion.

Michael West wrote: "Thanks to the legion of large and profitable corporations claiming JobKeeper subsidies, the government has unleashed an orgy of corporate welfare on a scale which has never been witnessed before.

"But at least JobKeeper makes sense. At least, despite the rorting, it has saved thousands of Australian businesses from obsolescence.

"What makes no sense is that the Treasury — or somebody with influence — has devised a scheme to turn the Tax Office into a bank to prop up zombie companies with cash.

"Already, the cuff-linked spivs from the Big End of Town will be concocting assorted loopholes to dud the ordinary taxpayer again."

***

Michael West Media ran a number of hard-hitting follow-ups demonstrating the extensive rorting of the scheme, which exemplified so much about the shoddy administration of COVID.

In March of 2021 West summed up the previous year in a piece titled "The Big Grift: How the Top End of Town Rorted JobKeeper": "The most rampant era of welfare rorting in Australia's history draws to a close at the end of the month when the JobKeeper scheme ends.

"Mirvac racked up more than $20 billion in sales over the past six years and paid not a skerrick in income tax. It also racked up profits through the pandemic, but that has not stopped the property juggernaut from helping itself to the government's JobKeeper scheme too; gorging itself on a public subsidy that was intended only for companies that suffered a large fall in turnover.

"Like dozens of other companies on the ASX — as demonstrated in the interim profit reporting season which draws to a close today — this profitable $10 billion company has grabbed the subsidy while having the cheek to pay large dividends to its shareholders and lavish salaries to its executives.

"How do they get away with it?"[17]

---

17 The Big Grift: How the Top End of Town rorted Jobkeeper, Luke Stacey, Michael West Media, 5 March, 2021.

***

Much loved iconoclast Mungo Maccallum, in one of his last columns before his passing in late 2020, wrote that what mattered politically was for Scott Morrison to be seen to have taken charge.

"So he can report progress; so far so good. And this means he can get on with milking it for all it is worth, and then some. Last week we barely saw him off the television, one grave and portentous speech after another, assuring a bewildered public that whatever the situation actually is, he is on top of it, alert but not alarmed, ready for action.

"Or if not immediate action, at least an announce-athon. To set the scene, Tuesday opened with the announcement that there would shortly be more announcements.

"And true to his word, he returned on Wednesday to talk about the substantive issue — what his government was doing about the health of a nervous public.

"Arrangements have been rejigged and ramped up, and crucially there is to be a hefty PR campaign, a solution dear to our leader's heart.

"And then came the big one — Thursday was make or break, money day, shitloads of the stuff to be shoveled out in the hope of averting a recession.

"But Morrison is instilling not confidence but confusion — off-the-cuff changes about travel restrictions, advice to cancel some, but not all, gatherings, daily announcements amounting to overload. It reeks of ad hockery, of reacting to events instead of anticipating them.

"In the end Morrison resorted to the old standby: an appeal to Team Australia, patriotism — the dubious quality that Samuel Johnson described as the last refuge of a scoundrel.

"Morrison obviously sees himself as a great leader, omniscient and omnipotent; but he has succeeded only in making himself omnipresent.

"To get to the next stage he will have to channel the tsunami of announcements into a message which is rational, convincing and trustworthy."[18]

***

When a politician claims an issue is above politics, which the conservatives did repeatedly at this time, you can be assured the opposite is true.

---

18 Morrison's Announceathon, Pearls and Irritations, Mungo MacCallum, 17 March, 2020.

What became a mainstay in the following months was playing the politics of COVID hard, even to the point of badging public health announcements such as COVID vaccines with conservative party logos.

Amiable ABC morning breakfast presenter Michael Rowland was not known for asking hard-hitting questions, but found himself at the centre of an imbroglio when he dared to ask Health Minister Greg Hunt why he felt the need to attach the Liberal Party logo to an Australian Government announcement that stated: "Australia secures additional ten million doses of Pfizer vaccine".

Hunt refused to answer, instead responding with an aggressive ad hominem attack on the professionalism of the journalist.

Senior journalist with Michael West Media Elizabeth Minter wrote: That the government would be so reckless to politicise a public health message is extraordinary, especially during a pandemic and especially on the issue of vaccination, which is proven to be a fraught issue around confidence. People need to trust the message being sent. Propriety, accountability; these are things of the past. The Coalition's money, the vast bulk of it flowing from wealthy donors and very large companies, has become indivisible from public money, at least in the minds of Coalition politicians. When Michael Rowland asked that simple question, Hunt couldn't respond honestly, because to do so he would have to admit that the Coalition was using taxpayers' money to benefit the Liberal Party."

Rowland further asked: "Who paid for the vaccines?"

The only answer was, of course, the public. The public, not the conservatives or the inappropriately named Liberal Party. The public also paid for the announcement itself.

Yet Hunt responded: "I know this is an issue for you, you identify with the Left ..." and spent the rest of the interview attacking Rowland.

***

Senior journalist Elizabeth Minter wrote in Michael West Media:

"AdRorts, on the back of the COVID, is the latest corrupt practice in a prodigious body of Australian government dirty work.

"Is the COVID-19 vaccine the Liberal Party's vaccine or the Australian Government's vaccine? It's not their money but the Liberal Party has its logo plastered across advertisements.

"Propriety, accountability; these are things of the past. It is official in fact. These people are not the stewards of our money. Apparently, they deem that public money belongs to the Liberal and National parties to do with as they wish.

"The Coalition's money, the vast bulk of it flowing from wealthy donors and very large companies, has become indivisible from public money, at least in the minds of Coalition politicians.

"When Michael Rowland asked that simple question, Hunt couldn't respond honestly, because to do so he would have to admit that the Coalition was using taxpayers' money to benefit the Liberal Party.

"It is just another in a long line of examples of the Coalition spending taxpayers' money for their own political ends. It is a rort — #adrorts, just like sports rorts, community grants rorts, bushfire rorts, and the rest."[19]

A year on, a year of international and state border closures, lockdowns, the destruction of thousands of businesses and the disruption of millions of lives, surrounded by scandal and a baying media pack, Morrison was staring at the destruction of his credibility, along with the credibility of his phalanx of health bureaucrats, his government, and his political party.

With millions of Australians once again enduring some of the world's harshest and longest-lasting lockdowns during another freezing winter, the population had finally been pushed too far.

And all of Scott Morrison's press conferences placing himself front and centre of the crisis would turn out to have been for nought.

Worse than nought. Instead, the government's story became one of wanton destruction; without a trace of rationality in any of it.

***

While the rich were getting richer and all these people were making their millions, Old Alex found himself back in the very part of Sydney where he'd been so often as a teenager more than 50 years before: drunk, often terrified, distressed always. He was, if nothing else, an ill-fitting youth.

The harbour was as cold a blue, its shell-like insecurity just as cruel as it had seemed way back then, more than half a century before, when beyond drunk he would pass out in the gutter at Circular Quay, commuters and office workers walking over him.

19 This Must Surely Be The Most Corrupt Government in Australian History, Michael West Media, *A Sense of Place Magazine*, 14 February, 2021.

More or less inevitably he would be rescued by "some old queen", as gay men of any age were referred to by his ilk. A shower, a blowjob and $20. Who could complain? That was his life as a teenager.

In 2020 he was once again walking across the Harbour Bridge, as he had done so often more than half a century before. The only boats on the harbour all appeared to have a military or police intent.

Back then, at the age of sixteen, when he had settled into a flat in Kirribilli, he would walk across the bridge for the midnight shift at the city's biggest tabloid, *The Daily Telegraph*, where he worked as a copy boy.

To his young and often frightened self it had seemed like a perilous journey across the bridge, past the bands of alcoholics huddled up under the now fenced-off alcoves, cackling madly as they warmed themselves around a campfire, past empty office blocks, through silent streets.

Fifty years on, across Sydney, in that internal and external passage of time, there was once again ghostly scene after ghostly scene.

The Royal Botanic Garden adjacent to the Opera House is one of Sydney's most beloved places. Old Alex watched a homeless man, "off his meds" as the old expression went, trying to escape the attention of two rangers in separate vehicles.

The man kept walking away. They kept following. The man would turn around to shout at them: "Leave me alone. Leave me alone." It was a cry Old Alex had heard all too often.

The rangers, fat, unfit, just some of the unemployable now employed in the public sector thanks to COVID and the destruction of the private sector, muscled up inside their uniforms. These tedious men. Give them a uniform, give them a gun, it went straight to their heads. Weak, non-event men made strong.

A place that should have been safe was not safe at all.

The homeless man scurried up an embankment, up through the manicured bushes. These days a leaf could barely fall in the gardens before it was picked up.

From what Alex could see the man was doing no harm whatsoever.

Even in his distress he was surprisingly articulate, as so many street people often are; these fallen angels.

Offshore the normally busy harbour was empty bar a military helicopter hovering overhead.

Signalling a civility and generosity of spirit long gone, rough sleepers were once known as "the gentlemen of the street". Not any more.

The man pleaded with the rangers to no effect. They kept following. He kept begging to be left alone. One of the rangers, stubby, overweight, plunged back into his vehicle and careered up another path to cut the homeless man off.

That was Sydney 2020.

THREE
DESTROYING A NATION

THE ONSLAUGHT of COVID incompetence came at a time when the nation itself was on rocky ground. Those who would doubt Australia's democracy were spread far and wide.

Trapped in circumstance, Old Alex was reliving his own version of *The Crucible*.

Jihadists had long predicted that 2020 would be the year when Islam became the world's dominant religion, when the entire planet would become worshippers of Allah.

Not all prophecies come true; but they were right in one sense. Nothing would ever be the same again, whether what was occurring was The Great Reset or The Great Reimagining. Or just simply an absolute stuff-up, no-plan-whatsoever chaos, the fickle fortunes of organics hostage to the feeble abilities of their leaders.

Crippled by lockdowns, even in his now extremely confined circle, expressions of defeat and powerlessness spread: "It is what it is"; "What can any of us do about it?"

The only thing he could do, since the evolution of the technologies, was to write and publish; which in its own infinite defeat or ability to transform was more than most.

In *How to Destroy a Nation: The Failure of Australian Governance* he laid out the steps that might be taken if the country had been overtaken by a malevolent spirit. Well, maybe it had. What other explanation could there be for this train wreck?

"How to destroy a nation" was a head-shaking expression from his troubled Christian childhood, uttered as an expression of despair at every mounting government insanity.

He began: "All politics is local. An adage Australia's inept government forgot long ago. It is what is happening in people's lounge rooms that matters the most.

"Now almost everyone is hunkered down in their own lounge rooms, told not to go outside unless absolutely necessary.

"It's 2020, and Australians have endured extremely poor governance at federal, state and local levels for decades, and must live with the consequences. A dishonest government is a paranoid government, and intrusive surveillance of everyone from nationalist groups to the Muslim minority fires indignation.

"The wave, that shockwave that is coming, is already being mirrored in a thousand little ways, the jackboots that stepped across every tiny freedom, restricted every conversation, and destroyed every impulse for freedom.

"As hard to believe as it may be, even as they see images of Great Depression-style queues forming outside Centrelink, Australia's welfare offices, some people believe the Prime Minister Scott Morrison is doing a good job."

***

Australian workers had already been strip-mined of every last cent by a voracious tax system, and the plundered were not doing so well even before COVID. As acerbic economic commentator Alan Austin had frequently observed, this government's claim to be good economic managers was false.

In the previous year's influential Suisse Credit wealth report Australia had fallen to stone-cold last, the world's biggest loser in terms of personal wealth by a factor of four.

Gross domestic product per adult decreased from $77,007 in 2018 to just $75,992 in 2019. That was 18.5 per cent below the 2013 level of $93,244 when the conservatives retook government.

Australia was one of a tiny minority of countries with wealth per adult lower in 2019 than back in 2012.

Australia's dismal performance was even starker against the global backdrop: wealth worldwide grew during the previous year as international trade, jobs, investment, corporate profits and government revenue boomed.

Alex set it out in dot points. If you wanted to destroy an entire country you would first of all destroy its energy sources. Australia went from having some of the cheapest electricity in the world to having literally some of the most expensive, due entirely to government manipulation of the market.

A fact which made everything from corner stores to industrial warehouses extremely expensive, if not cripplingly so, to run. From a workers' paradise, where effort was rewarded, to a world of battered circumstance characterised by lost dreams of personal and financial independence, of building a life for yourself and your family free of hindrance.

Every loss of purpose and employment was a lost life, now and in the generations to follow.

Dream after suburban dream destroyed. The natural productivity of the people crushed under a blizzard of invasive regulation, excessive tax and public maladministration. The result: clinched lives and demoralised populations.

The government that brought the nation some of the most costly fuel and electricity in the world, worst (read, truly abysmal) internet, plummeting educational outcomes, highest household debt and soaring costs of living was in now the act of throwing millions of Australians onto the dole queues under the threat of COVID.

All the while delivering billions of dollars to their corporate mates.

Even the infrastructure had been sold off by the greedy end of town. The light poles outside his front door were owned by a Chinese company. What sort of country sells their essential infrastructure to a foreign power? Plundered. Ransacked. Every day, Australians faced a cornucopia of maladministration making their daily lives ever more difficult.

***

Dealing with a dying parent and barely knowing anyone in the area outside his local watering hole, Old Alex was running counter to almost everyone he knew, or encountered; supportive, as they were, of a government that was allegedly saving them from "the virus".

As thousands of frightened people queued for hours to get tested for a disease they had almost no chance of dying from, most Australians — poorly educated, media illiterate and without any capacity to discern the difference between news and propaganda, between fact and fearmongering — had absolutely no idea that there were vigorous, and highly credible, arguments which contradicted the daily swill on the airwaves.

The many critics of the government's actions, both in Australia and around the world, were silenced, ignored or algorithmically downplayed. The nation's politicians, bureaucrats and decision makers were not held to account.

Many of the smartest people on Earth were calling out governments for manufacturing COVID hysteria and implementing extremely destructive policies under the guise of public health.

But the panicked public abandoned their freedoms as if it was a community obligation.

Suggesting that experts from Stanford, Harvard, Princeton and Oxford were all coming out on his side of the argument — that lockdowns were a dangerous social experiment and a direct step into totalitarianism — was met with blank stares or derision; they had no idea what he was talking about.

***

Ramesh Thakur wrote: "The harsh lockdown measures were instituted in response to the fear-mongering projections of mathematical modelling that bear hardly any resemblance to the reality that has unfolded across the world.

"Crucially, too many governments ignored the reality of scientific uncertainty and the fact that lockdowns were a radical experiment that departed from established protocols for managing pandemics.

"The result has been disastrous for millions of people around the world. Rather than focusing protective measures on the people at heightened risk of illness, governments around the world imposed and continue to impose severe restrictions on their entire population.

"The negative effects of lockdown are too often dismissed as small sacrifices, necessary to keep a highly deadly disease from spreading.

"These sacrifices are, in fact, neither necessary nor small, and the disease is only a threat to a minority of the population that can be protected without lockdowns."[20]

***

---

20 The Intellectual Clout behind the Anti-lockdown movement, Ramesh Thakur, *A Sense of Place Magazine*, 6 January, 2021.

Professor Thakur was fond of the Victor Hugo quote: "Those who do not see do not weep."

He was also a supporter of a website collating news links on the consequences of government actions called The Price of Panic.

The site billed itself thus: "Rather than focusing protective measures on the people at heightened risk of illness, governments around the world imposed and continue to impose severe restrictions on their entire population. With routine medical care disrupted, businesses shuttered, curfews imposed, travel restricted, and socialisation criminalised, a devastating amount of harm is being caused.

"The disease is a serious threat to a minority of the population that can be protected without lockdowns. All too often, when major harms become hard to ignore, they are lamented as damage caused by COVID-19 itself, even though it is our panic-driven measures that are to blame."

The headlines collected on The Price of Panic should have been enough to drive doubt into the hearts of the thousands of journalists, bureaucrats, politicians, businessmen and time servers making hay out of COVID.

Here's a sampling:

"The Centers for Disease Control and Prevention revealed that young adults aged 25-44 years saw the largest increase in 'excess' deaths from previous years, a stunning 26.5 per cent jump. Stillbirth rate rises dramatically during pandemic."

"At least 80 million children under one at risk of diseases such as diphtheria, measles and polio as COVID-19 disrupted routine vaccination efforts."

"In the eight weeks after restrictions were put in place an average almost 2700 extra people died a week than would be usual for the time of year, despite COVID-19 not contributing to their deaths."

"US overdose deaths rose amid the coronavirus pandemic."

According to a UN report, "COVID-19 disruptions killed 228,000 children in South Asia. Online child abuse and exploitation, already one of the biggest crime challenges, spiked as the pandemic forced more people indoors with abusers and children spending more time on the internet."

"COVID-19 Places Half a Million More Girls at Risk of Child Marriage in 2020."

"In Japan, more people died from suicide in one month than from COVID in all of 2020."

"Tuberculosis kills 1.5 million people each year. Lockdowns and supply-chain disruptions threaten progress against the disease as well as HIV and malaria."

"Millions of Americans have lost their jobs. They've watched helplessly as their meagre savings dwindled away, as they were confined to their homes — prohibited from interacting with friends, attending church, temple or music and sporting events due to restrictions enacted in response to the COVID-19 pandemic. This resulted in a profound impact on the mental health and emotional well-being of people — leading to a significant increase in cases of anxiety, depression and deaths by suicide."[21]

**

"Forgive them, for they know not what they do" just didn't cut it. It was their job to know. All that Australians and their political masters had to do to work out that there was considerable doubt over the government's actions was to go online.

The lockdown absurdities were just beginning to mount, with Australia needlessly adopting some of the most extreme lockdown measures to be found anywhere in the world.

Reckless indifference, grandstanding and absolute ineptitude marked those early days, just as it would mark the government's entire COVID response.

Old Alex drank bourbon alone out of the boot of his car and gazed across an empty shore.

And felt seized, once again, by a destiny over which he had no control. What he thought he heard, what the movement of wind in trees and storms out to sea told him, whether true or not, was that he was experiencing a signalling, as were so many others, enabled by the evolution of quantum entanglement across millions of years; clubbed by the last gasp of the idea that humans were the only sentient beings in the universe.

And that this societal wide remake he was witnessing also marked a derangement in the spiritual realm.

**

---

21 The Price of Panic, Ramesh Tahkur, *A Sense of Place Magazine*, 28 October, 2020.

If you deliberately set out to destroy a nation you would destroy any sense of unity or national pride. Done.

With years of historically high rates of immigration, the country was now divided not just on the basis of class, education and geography, but on race and ethnicity.

The extremely aggressive suppression of anti-multicultural demonstrations and their attached ultranationalist movements, most particularly in Victoria, including the use of horses and pepper spray, was a precursor to the violent suppression of dissent during the lockdown era.

If you wanted to destroy a nation you would destroy any sign of a vibrant media environment, where conflicting ideas are cheerfully and intensely debated. Done.

Media outlets should never have allowed themselves to be funnels for government propaganda.

As COVID hysteria took over, the hollowing-out of the mainstream media had major consequences.

What was different now was the gathering storm, the consequence of all this government-inspired disinformation.

Day after day, the media fulfilled its role of scaring the population, and entirely failed to put alternative views. The daily wave of COVID hysteria on the nation's television news programs significantly contributed to the level of public ignorance.

There was always a new statistic, another talking head, and the nation's well-paid news presenters promoted alarmism with every word.

***

Alex was not long back from Vietnam. As plaintively melodramatic as it might seem, he felt truly psychologically exhausted from his last book, *Dark Dark Policing*, and had no desire to pick up the cudgels once again.

Nor did he want to be where he was, trapped in a tiny house with a dying parent, the only company to be found at his local cafe in the morning or his watering hole in the evenings; now closed.

With gatherings of more than two people in public illegal, enforced by threats of imprisonment and/or large fines, the savage loneliness he felt on that picturesque South Coast, with its young families and working-class milieus, just got a damn sight worse.

The slow dying of everything they had known. There was almost no one to talk to. On air, there were debates about whether single people should be allowed to visit each other.

Old Alex restlessly paced that tiny, doom-laden house to which he was now legally confined, and did his best to be kind to his increasingly frail God-bothering parent.

He parked at the car park overlooking the ocean at Shellharbour after work, threw all the car doors open, raided the bourbon in the boot, watched a storm making its way down the coast.

Gazza the steel worker pulled up beside him, and laughed at the sight. They hadn't seen each other since the pubs clanged shut, purportedly to save their lives. Although there remained not a single case in the entire suburb; and for a disease, which, as was now becoming clear, people their age had by one informed estimate a 99.98 per cent chance of surviving.

"It's martial law." Old Alex grizzled, "It's all bullshit."

Gazza just laughed; he laughed at all his mates. And showed him a picture of the boys at a fishing club comp, a group of wild blokes having a wild time, happy as could be. "Can you believe that was only three weeks ago?"

The idea of a rowdy fishing club get-together was suddenly not just impossible; it would have been illegal, as declared by health commissars and their co-conspirators in the political class.

"You're going to get soaking if you don't shut your doors," Gaz said, still laughing as the storm flowed over the final headland.

***

It was mawkish, crawling-in-the-undergrowth stuff; but on that salty, windswept coast he was reminded of a sad little book he wouldn't recommend his worst enemy to read, called *The Beauty of Men*, written by the author of a New York classic *Dancer from the Dance*, the latter all about life in the New York fast lane. Sentenced to bear witness to his mother's dying year in a place he had thought he had long left behind. Inappropriate stabs in a stricken heart, looking for love in all the worst places. Imperilled. There weren't any fast lanes around Oak Flats. Not even a cosy little nuanced bar; the whisper of ambivalence or turbulent possibility at the end of an evening.

Day after day — or, more precisely, night after night — destiny resumed, he pounded out his protest; with companionship and like minds nowhere to be found.

Combative, or just plain outraged, in case anybody hadn't got the message, he flushed out another story in the now daily flurry: "Welcome to Australia: The World's Newest Totalitarian State".

"A sclerotic bureaucracy and a greedy, dismally inept political class ensure a once optimistic country is optimistic no more. Over the past decade Australians have experienced the worst period of government in the nation's history. And the pandemic has just proved the critics right."

Then followed another sampling of the often scathing national commentary.

Unlike previous crises, the nation's intellectuals were not rallying behind the flag.

Brendan O'Neill, a columnist for *The Australian*, advised: "Remember everything that is being said by these anti-democratic elites who are presently ruling over us. Because when this horrible crisis is over we are going to need to renew the fight for freedom and democracy with real vigour. These people have got to go. We live under staggeringly anti-democratic elites."

***

Professor of law Augusto Zimmermann: "Society is not a machine: it can't be switched on and off at government will. One of the few positive aspects of this current crisis is that some politicians are finally revealing their true authoritarian colours — including Prime Minister Scott Morrison.

"The management of the current crisis clearly exposes their authoritarian inclinations.

"Much is in the process of being entirely destroyed and at the cost of many lives.

"While emergency powers are sometimes needed, we are seeing examples of draconian measures that dramatically increase the arbitrary power of the state, thus allowing government to exercise mass surveillance powers over citizens and alarming restriction of civil liberties.

"In this present health crisis the ruling elites are tirelessly agitating for the government to shut down everyday life and send the police and the army to interrogate anyone who is outside without permission. They view us not as citizens to be engaged with, but as disease carriers to be controlled."

Zimmerman concluded: "The recent speech by the Australian Prime Minister further threatens to spread irrational fear in our communities. It causes us to lose our jobs, and it harms democracy itself. Resisting the speech of such doom-mongers who rule over us is unquestionably the first step to challenging COVID-19."[22]

***

Front and centre of an absolute blitz of irrationality and fear-mongering was Australian Prime Minister Scott Morrison, who seized on the opportunity to save his damaged reputation. Most amazingly, it worked, for a while.

Just as he was overseeing the locking of millions of people into their own homes, justified by the absolutely discredited policy of lockdowns, the prime minister called on the legacy of the nation's fallen soldiers.

In the limited lexicon of Australian traditions, Anzac Day stands out, matched as it is with the terrible blooding at Gallipoli on the Turkish shores in 2015, when 8709 young Australians lost their lives in a military fiasco which spawned the myths of heroism and a tough, phlegmatic character.

To call on it now was an insult to all the young soldiers who had fought and died for their country a century before, only to see, if they could have, their own country turned into Animal Farm, with pudgy, overweight creatures of unalloyed greed trampling on the likes of them; their lives, their families.

They sacrificed their own futures, broke the hearts of their families, and never lived to have children or grandchildren, all at the behest of the patrician oligarchs of the day. Farm boys off for the adventure of a lifetime, to serve their country in foreign wars, and who never came back.

In a special address to the national Parliament, Prime Minister Scott Morrison called on Australians to "summon the spirit of the Anzacs".

Looked at through the prism of history, in an accelerated time when the present became the past in an instant, before the mass protests, arrests,

---

22 Welcome to Australia: The World's Newest Totalitarian State, *A Sense of Place Magazine*, 29 March, 2020.

jailings, the punitive fines and the destruction of tens of thousands of businesses, the statements of the prime minister are simply surreal.

You reap the whirlwind. You are the destroyer of worlds.

"We are a strong nation and a strong people, but in the months ahead this will put us all to the test like, at no time since the Second World War. But together, Australia, we are up to this challenge. The coronavirus that is sweeping the world will continue to change the way we live. But we must not allow it to change who we are as Australians.

"So we summon the spirit of the Anzacs, of our Great Depression generation, of those who built the Snowy. Of those who won the great peace of the Second World War and defended Australia. That is our legacy that we draw on at this time.

"We must resolve today, as Australians, to come together, and to pledge to each other across our nation, that this coronavirus will not break our Australian spirit.

"I most certainly call on all people of faith for you to pray.

"I can assure you, my prayer knees are getting a good work out."[23]

***

In the Australian context Rupert Murdoch is a kingmaker. While his loyalty could never be relied on, in recent years Murdoch had backed the conservative side of politics as the most conducive to his interests, and the welfare of the country. The more the nation prospered, the greater his profits.

Rupert was most certainly not backing the prime minister of the day, Scott Morrison.

If the public doubted the official narrative flowing through the government's media minions, they didn't have to look very far.

Murdoch's best-known outlet in America, Fox News, now regularly questioned the government narrative on corona.

In Australia, Murdoch owned Sky News, usually seen as closely aligned with the ruling Liberal-National Coalition, was also increasingly strident in its criticism.

Sky's star new recruit Alan Jones, an Australian conservative icon after

---

23 Ministerial Statement, Prime Minister, Australian Parliament House, 23 March, 2020.

decades as a Sydney radio personality, thundered on daily: "Coronavirus Hysteria." "No politician has told the government percent of cases are mild. Doctors feed the alarmism." "If this is a pandemic, words have lost their meaning." "Why do politicians, the lot of them, thrive on this alarmism?"

He told his viewers: "Some poor coot up in Jindabyne, ski country, has been shut down for breaching public health orders. Three free trips around the world for anybody who can tell you what the latest public health orders are. These are politicians with power. They are just making up numbers.

"You can have ten in a restaurant yesterday, fifty tomorrow. In Melbourne no visitors to a private home, no leisure travel, ten at a funeral, five at a wedding. They've shut down everything that moves; that is if they don't tax it first. Absolute madness! These politicians want us frightened so they can stay in charge."

***

With temperatures well into the thirties, in March Sydney's famous Bondi Beach was closed after thousands of people ignored social-distancing edicts, along with the neighbouring beaches of Tamarama and Bronte.

Officers in patrol cars descended on parks and beaches in Sydney's wealthy eastern suburbs, ordering lone sunbakers and mothers walking with prams to return home.

At nearby Coogee, two men sitting on a park bench were ordered to sit further apart, while a couple was also told to separate.

Rangers carrying loudhailers warned that swimmers, surfers and sunbakers must leave immediately. Entrances to the beach were taped shut with red-and-white tape. Signs insisted: "Area closed until further notice."

Guardian Australia reported that lifeguards, apologetic at having to enforce a rule which was hazily understood at best, warned that a police boat would come and start handing out fines to surfers who refused to leave.

"Bondi Beach, a pictorial shorthand for Australia, has become emblematic of the nation's struggle to respond properly to the outbreak. Those waters never looked so inviting."[24]

---

24 Bondi beach closed after crowds defy ban on gatherings of 500-plus, Ben Smee, *Guardian Australia*, 21 March, 2020.

The same *Guardian Australia* was publishing warnings that there could be tens of thousands of needless deaths and hundreds of thousands of hospital admissions if a drastic shutdown of society was not implemented immediately; in retrospect, wildly off the mark and utterly irresponsible.

"What happened at Bondi Beach was not OK," the prime minister declared. "After consulting with premiers and chief ministers we have decided that we are moving immediately to recommend against all non-essential travel in Australia. State premiers and chief ministers may have to take far more draconian measures to enforce social distancing."

***

In an address to the national Parliament in April of that devilled year Scott Morrison declared: "We gather again today in unusual circumstances, during extreme times to consider extraordinary responses to the twin crises our nation faces, to our nation's health and to our economy. What we do today is what governments have always done in such circumstances, when our nation is under threat that previous generations of Australians have done before us.

"Today we act to protect our nation's sovereignty. When Australian lives and livelihoods are threatened, when they are under attack, our nation's sovereignty is put at risk and we must respond. As a government, as a parliament, as a nation, together.

"Nurses, teachers, drivers; cleaners, doctors, police, and paramedics; factory workers, engineers, bankers; grocers, miners and farmers; pastors, priests and imams; politicians, union officials, even lawyers; mums, dads, grandparents, kids, families. All of us.

"Our sovereignty is measured in our capacity and freedom to live our lives as we choose in a free, open and democratic society. We are not a coerced society. We act through our agreement and our wilful support of the national interest, through our many institutions, including this parliament and the many others around this country. And we will not surrender this.

"Our sovereignty is enabled by having a vibrant market economy that underpins our standard of living that gives all Australians the opportunity to fulfill their potential. To have a go and to get a go. And we will not surrender this. Our sovereignty is demonstrated by the quality of life we afford Australians, with world-class health, education, disability, aged care, and a social safety net that guarantees the essentials that Australians rely on.

"We will not surrender."

Tell that to the people under house arrest across the nation, those who couldn't even legally visit a neighbour or a friend, who could be violently assaulted by police if they dared to venture outside or exercise their democratic right to protest. Tell that to the people being imprisoned or struggling to pay off thousands of dollars in fines for going about their normal lives.

***

It was then, in the early months of the Covid era, that Steve Waterson began his series of finely crafted pieces for the Murdoch-owned broadsheet *The Australian*.

It was not an insult to Waterson to suggest his series of closely worked, prominently placed and well promoted stories were also a window into the thinking of Rupert Murdoch.

Beautifully written and finely edited, his pieces were whole-of-paper productions.

If you were an American-based media mogul, but you were concerned about the lunatic destruction of your country of origin, you might well be pleased to see one of your best educated and most broadly experienced Australian operators appointed to the task.

That was Steve Waterson, who graduated from Oxford University with honours before beginning his journalistic career. He had held numerous senior positions, including as editor of TIME Australia, and was well liked within Australia's journalistic milieu for his amiable disposition and high intelligence.

Waterson's pieces were to all intents and purposes both an open letter to Scott Morrison and a calculated insult.

In April of 2020, at the beginning of his epistles, he described the government response to the coronavirus outbreak as "panicked, illogical, absurd and sinister", a "vast ocean of incompetence and mindless disassembly of our economy".

As it was already clear the disease attacked primarily the elderly;

resources could have been devoted to protecting them while leaving the rest of society intact.

"Instead, we are asking the healthy, most of whom will be no more than inconvenienced by this latest strain of flu, to sacrifice or cripple themselves, their livelihoods, their children's future, to preserve people whose own future is already precarious and limited.

"Even news organisations have adopted this position, their HR departments issuing earnest communiqués that declare 'the health and wellbeing of our employees is our paramount priority'. Sorry, since when? As part of my job, I have been sent, and sent others, to war zones — yes, with bombs and bullets — to bring our readers the news. That's what I thought our priority was as journalists.

"Now half my colleagues in the media have emerged as trembling amateur epidemiologists, scouring the online world to find the youngest and healthiest victim to ramp up the terror and prove this disease attacks anyone, not just the old and sick, when that's manifestly not the case."

***

The following month Waterson declared the country was no longer facing a health crisis but economic carnage.

"Our leaders are stunned into idiotic paralysis. The defiant stupidity is beyond parody, and beyond comical. So far, the pain is dulled by unsustainable federal handouts, ludicrously applied. When we reach the end of this economic disaster, let's not forget it was man-made.

"There is no stopping this madness without some concerted effort by the public to make our leaders wake up to their errors, but I despair at our timid acquiescence to their witless rulings.

"This should never have been a disaster on the scale of a world war. Leaders worthy of the name would have calmed those prone to panic, and allayed the fears of the vulnerable and their families by working out how to protect them.

"Nimble minds would have come up with smart systems to accommodate the huge range of attitudes to this threat, in order to safeguard the people who needed and, more importantly, wanted protection.

"So no, self-congratulating leaders, you have not 'kept us safe'.

"You have destroyed thousands of businesses, families, lives and futures.

You have cheated people of the highlights of human existence, the moments of shared joy and sorrow, the weddings, births, anniversaries, farewells and funerals that mark our journey through life.

"You have placed unimaginable burdens of debt and despair on future generations, and crafted a dangerous template for all the idiots who follow you."

***

In a piece titled "Paying for an Epidemic of Stupidity", published in front of their paywall, which meant Rupert Murdoch's empire wanted everyone to read this one, Waterson wrote: "Our politicians find themselves unable to admit their response to the virus — the ultimate blunt instrument of lockdown, brutally enforced — hasn't worked, and will never work.

"They can't do so because it would mean all they have done up to this point has been in vain. How could anyone who had wreaked damage on this cataclysmic scale ever admit to themselves, let alone to the nation, that it was all for nothing?

"Instead, like the pokie addict, they have doubled down to unleash a runaway epidemic of stupidity.

"They've destroyed our economy and put thousands out of work; they've refashioned many of our famously easygoing population into masked informers; and we've handed control of our lives to a clown car packed with idiots. When we reach the end of this economic disaster, let's not forget it was man-made."[25]

***

Jack Waterford, esteemed elder statesman of Australian journalism and former editor-in-chief of *The Canberra Times*, wrote: "As governments have ratcheted up non-medical measures against COVID-19, the communications performance of an array of public officials has been lamentable and embarrassing — agony to watch.

"Some reporters and commentators, possibly at the urging of editors, have markedly softened their questions. They are doing so for fear that

---

25 An "Open Letter" to Australian Prime Minister Scott Morrison from the World's Most Powerful Media Mogul Rupert Murdoch, A *Sense of Place Magazine*, 2 March, 2021.

apparent hostility or exasperation after failing to get straight answers might actually undermine confidence in public health measures that all reasonable observers believe to be necessary.

"The biggest problem for good management of the epidemic is that the government is not really getting 'independent' advice from its independent professional committees. One can expect that the advice is focused on what is achievable, given the constraints. But the committees are being too conscious of other pressures on government, too focused on keeping governments broadly on message, and too focused on protecting the leaders.

"They may think that public interest is their foremost concern. But the public has only slight ownership of the processes. Indeed, even health workers actually dealing with patients are complaining of not being consulted, being unable to get basic information about matters such as medical supplies, and of being ignored."[26]

***

Pounding out stories for his magazine in the early hours, driven by an urgent desire to save a nation already lost, an illusion or delusion that he could make the slightest difference, Alex became more and more spooked with each passing day.

He wasn't the only one frightened, or mystified. There was a kind of blind paranoiac lust to the era, as if the entire society was cannibalising itself.

Could it really be that the authorities were blindly overseeing the destruction of their own country, and would shut down anyone who disagreed with them?

Even well-qualified medical experts found themselves being censored on the big-tech platforms, including Twitter and YouTube, indicating the overlapping military, intelligence and so-called Deep State involvement with the COVID scare campaign.

The most famous early example was the so-called Bakersfield doctors, Dr Daniel Erickson and Dr Artin Massihi, who ran Accelerated Urgent Care in Bakersfield, California.

---

26 Advice Being Tailored For Political, Not Medical, Purposes, Jack Waterford, *A Sense of Place Magazine*, 27 May, 2021.

The original videos were posted by a local [US] ABC news affiliate and subsequently removed by YouTube.

Erickson and Massihi said their facilities had tested over 5200 patients for the coronavirus; making up more than half of the county's testing. According to their data, the death rate of the coronavirus was similar to the flu. Hospitals were no more overrun than during a normal flu season.

"Now that we have the facts," said Dr. Erickson. "It's time to get back to work."

On the face of it, the men were professional, intelligent, sincere and speaking directly from their own experience.

Their argument that locking people in their homes was counterproductive because it decreased their naturally acquired immunity to a whole range of diseases and caused increased financial, mental health and social problems would become widely accepted as the months rolled on.

But at the time they were outliers attracting the full de-platforming power of the tech giants.

***

Thanks to Maria Popova, a New York-based polymath whose magazine *Brain Pickings* engaged readers worldwide in a battle for enlightenment, brought his attention to the words of the Danish philosopher Søren Kierkegaard: "Truth always rests with the minority, because the minority is generally formed by those who really have an opinion, while the strength of a majority is illusory, formed by the gangs who have no opinion.

"In regard to Truth, this troublesome monster, the majority, the public, etc., fares in the same way as we say of someone who is traveling to regain his health: he is always one station behind.

"Most people lead far too sheltered lives, and for that reason they get to know [the divine] so little.

"Let us get together and be a gathering, then we can probably manage. Therein lies mankind's deepest demoralisation."

That, simply put, was what had gone so terribly wrong. The truth. There was none, or very damn little, in the smoke-filled mirror maze they were now entering,

As the polarising public intellectual Jordan Peterson said, "Whatever happens as a consequence of telling the truth is the best thing that can happen. Our culture is predicated on the idea that truth in speech is of divine significance. It's the fundamental presupposition of our culture."

Alex's own determination for truth-telling came from an incident in early adolescence which made him blanch every time he thought of it.

There in that horror-filled house where he had grown up, with the wind whipping through the tree branches all around him, he announced to his ultra-religious mother that he did not believe in God.

His father insisted he apologise.

He refused. And he was getting big enough now not to stand still for those psychotic beltings.

Eventually they had him cornered, both of them with their belts snaking out at him as he quivered tearful in a corner.

When they wouldn't stop, he finally said: "OK, OK, I believe in God. But I don't really mean it."

Then the belting began in earnest.

Ever since that day, nobody had ever been able to force him to lie. The past fractures into the present; the gathering, bullying storm around him felt exactly the same.

**

When the Californian ABC affiliate which published Erickson and Massihi's urging for a return to normality reached out to YouTube to question the removal of their interview, a company spokesperson issued a statement: "We quickly remove flagged content that violates our Community Guidelines; including content that explicitly disputes the efficacy of local health authority recommended guidance on social distancing that may lead others to act against that guidance. From the very beginning of the pandemic, we've had clear policies against COVID-19 misinformation and are committed to continue providing timely and helpful information at this critical time."

Dan Sanchez at the Foundation for Economic Education was quick to point out the flaws in the argument.

"Whatever the veracity of the doctors' claims, YouTube's censorship of unorthodox ideas in the name of protecting the public from misinformation is misguided and counterproductive. Sheltering the public from ideas, even bad ones, only makes society more susceptible to dangerous error.

"When paternalistic censors seal us up in a sterile bubble of ideas for our own 'protection', they deprive us of the chance to develop through experience our own ability to identify and grapple with bad ideas. As soon as a bad idea penetrates our bubble, we have no defences against it. Our lack of experience with the responsibilities of intellectual independence has left us naive, credulous, and gullible."

***

Despite all the posturing by Google and YouTube executives in those early days, there was nothing consistent about their messaging either.

YouTube would soon enough be hosting UnHerd's Lockdown TV, which interviewed a sprawling range of the world's foremost disease experts, all of whom were determinedly questioning government responses.

Experts the Australian Government, and their propagandists in the media, unwisely ignored.

Manipulating the public narrative was just one way to destroy a nation.

How about ceding sovereignty?

From allowing its foreign policy to be run by the United States and involving itself in their endless wars to flogging off vast tracts of lands to foreign interests, most controversially organisations linked to the Chinese Communist Party, it had all been done.

Australian governments had essentially signed up to the Chinese Belt and Road initiative without telling the public; with all the country's major ports and electrical infrastructure, along with significant swathes of rural and urban property, all in Chinese hands. In other words, rake billions of dollars off the working poor and flog their country to the highest bidder.

Could there be a greater betrayal than selling out your own country?

No. Not until COVID came along.

FOUR
IN GOD SOME TRUSTED

THOSE "PUNDITS QUEUE" stories he ran in A Sense of Place Magazine morphed straight into what Old Alex saw as the crux of the matter, with a piece titled "Scott Morrison: The World's Only Pentecostal Leader" and subtitled "The End Is Nigh".

"As the shutdown of Australia continues apace, there's one very legitimate question to ask: How does Prime Minister Scott Morrison's avowed belief that we are living through The End of Days influence his decision making?

"How does his belief in prosperity theology, that God rewards the righteous and destroys the unbeliever, impact on his clear lack of empathy for ordinary Australians and the hundreds of thousands now being thrown onto the dole queues?"

Historian James Boyce put it as succinctly as anyone: "The assumption that the prime minister's Horizon Church in Sydney's Sutherland Shire can be understood as just another conservative denomination is a major mistake.

"The religion's starting point is not the written-down teachings of Jesus, the moral code set out in the Bible, or the instructions of the institutional Church. Nor is its essence captured by conservative Christian campaigns on sex, marriage and gender.

"The essence of our prime minister's religion is not a set of beliefs at all but a unique perspective on the Christian experience in which God is so intimately present to the saved and sanctified that he can be felt, talked to and heard at any time.

"The 24/7 cosmic drama is made more intense by the fact that the play is soon coming to an end. The Devil is powerful now but he is on the verge of defeat. Only God knows exactly when Jesus will return and banish Satan to Hell, but most Pentecostals are certain that the end times are upon us."

Concerns were not allayed by the prime minister's adoption of the mannerisms of a regional pastor and the use of religious language such as "getting to the other side".

There were many characters in this doom-laden squabble: federal and state ministers, state premiers, chief medical officers, lionised health workers, squadrons of convenient experts; but overarching it all was one man, Scott Morrison, who had chosen to make this moment his own, to seize the historic opportunity COVID-19 offered.

But far from becoming the Saviour of the Nation, he became, instead, the Great Enabler of Authoritarianism.

***

At the end of the day all the destruction of the country could be laid at the feet, or the "prayer knees", of the prime minister, who had been architect, intentional or otherwise, of the mass hysteria which enveloped the country. His religious beliefs, that he was an instrument of God in the execution of divine instruction, should have raised alarm bells.

That as others noted, there was a bizarre passivity emanating from the nation's leadership, as one scandalous piece of maladministration followed another. As if societal-wide destruction really was the point of it all.

Old Alex knew, there in those frightened and bewildered hours, what had to be done to alter the timeline, to change the future of the country; and in his fantastical imagination he urged the Watchers on the Watch to take action. He knew they had the means and the contacts; if they could, if they dared speak up, if the derangement enveloping the country hadn't enveloped them as well.

Invisible assassins slithered through the night air. Morrison should have been removed from office way back then; he was clearly unfit. But if words had power, not one of them found their mark. Old Alex pounded away at the keyboard through the night, and equally found no peace. Try as he might, nothing worked. He might as well have been bashing tennis balls against a padded-cell wall.

The Prime Minister's well-fed face was everywhere, ostensibly reassuring and informing the public while instead frightening them witless.

It was deception on a mass scale. If they were such great experts in public messaging, they must have known what they were doing.

The previous election, with the polls running strongly against his scandal-plagued government and faced with a devastating electoral loss, Morrison resorted to an old electioneering trick, using his Christian faith to convince the general public he was a decent, honourable man.

Until inviting the cameras into his wealthy Horizon Church during the election campaign, Morrison had always been secretive about his religious beliefs, which lay well beyond the bounds of normal Christian practice.

As a strategy, displaying his religiosity helped get Morrison across the line, attracting voters in areas with large faith communities. And amongst ordinary voters, there were still those who believed Morrison must be an honest man, because they had seen him at church.

As the world's only Pentecostal leader and a believer that mankind is literally living in The End Times, serious questions should have been asked about how Morrison's faith in an outlier strand of Christianity was interacting with his governing of the country.

It was not as if there wasn't plenty of evidence.

***

In the midst of the enveloping crisis a video emerged of the prime minister, in his prime ministerial office, on a taxpayer-funded salary, offering a prayer for the national cabinet and committing Australia to God.

The footage of the prime minister participating in the online prayer group was originally published by Christian website Eternity News but later removed; only to be exposed in the mainstream media. Nothing about this was official duty. The traditional divide between church and state had disappeared. And despite the scandal, nothing changed. No hard questions were asked. Morrison remained exactly where he was, peddling COVID alarmism and destroying the country he was elected to protect.

All the while believing he was the instrument of God; his own version of an always vengeful Abrahamic god.

In the video he thanked people for their prayers and described the world as "largely in trauma … with the scale and pace of what is unfolding — this is incomprehensible, even just a month ago, what we're seeing today.

"Heavenly Father, we just commit our nation to you in this terrible time of great need and suffering of so many people. And we do this also for the entire world — in places far from this country there are people suffering even more, going through tremendous hardship, crying out."

In the end, for believers, having an Abrahamic god at the helm would do them no good. In the end the people would cry out for a single sign of common decency, competency or common sense, not for the fitful carapace of a lunatic god.

"Pray for the premiers and chief ministers, they've joined me in a national cabinet — which is unprecedented for Australia," the prime minister said.

"It is a moment like when Moses looked out at the sea and held up his staff. There are moments of great faith in this.

"But as a prime minister I have to take my decisions based on very strong advice and exercise the best judgment I can.

"And my faith gives me an enormous encouragement in how I can make those decisions and try and do that in the best way I can."

Morrison referenced Isaiah, revered as a prophet in Christian, Muslim and Jewish traditions: "The Lord will guide you always; he will satisfy your needs in a sun-scorched land and will strengthen your frame. You will be like a well-watered garden, like a spring whose waters never fail.

"Your people will rebuild the ancient ruins and will raise up the age-old foundations; you will be called Repairer of Broken Walls, Restorer of Streets with Dwellings."

Morrison, speaking to his fellow converts, said: "'Your people will rebuild the ancient ruins. That's a prophecy over our country, I believe.

"I pray that we will be a restorer of streets, with people in them, businesses open again, Australians going about their lives again, returning to their jobs, returning to their livelihoods, returning to normal times in our schools so children can learn and that we can get to the other side of this."[27]

***

If the world is a battle between good and evil, and most have been forsaken, and it is your anointed duty to bring the population to its knees in order to return them to God, does not that pose questions?

27 Scott Morrison prays for Australia and commits nation to God amid coronavirus crisis, Paul Karp, *The Guardian*, 1 April, 2020.

If most of the non-believing population were destined for hell, where lay your sympathies?

Perhaps that was why, outside of all the empty rhetoric, there had been no outward or public display of empathy for the hundreds of thousands of people thrown onto the scrapheap during the coronavirus pandemic? The ones who were literally standing in dole queues as Scott Morrison conducted his endless Canberra announce-athons, assuring the public that the government's response was "scalable and sustainable".

All sides spoke of God. But far more prosaic things — the material world, the destiny of the species, the fate of nations, Scomo's well-fed, smug *Animal Farm* face beaming into the nation's lounge rooms — it was leading us all straight to the pit. Or to revolution in the streets.

Yes, there was a spiritual derangement in this strange puppet play in this strange southern land.

In recent years, as Old Alex travelled the country, he had often experienced a haunting dream; as if the food riots of the future were breaking into the present. Now, all of a sudden, those peculiar visions were becoming true.

The single most fascinating thing about Australia's Prime Minister, Scott Morrison, was: He Showed No Guilt.

It was uncannily true. Despite all the flowery appeals to nationalism, the Prime Minister of Australia showed not one single shred of sympathy for the many people whose lives were being destroyed. Not a shred of remorse at having thrown millions of people onto welfare thanks to his absurd misreading of the COVID Scare.

Not for the tens of thousands of small businesses he destroyed; not for the millions of lives and careers damaged under the facade of keeping people "safe"; not for having multiplied the national debt several times over after being elected on a promise of good economic management.

Not for the thousands of anti-lockdown demonstrators arrested, fined and even jailed.

Not a shred of regret at having deceived and betrayed the many so-called "Quiet Australians" who voted him into power, falsely believing he would protect their interests and the interests of the nation at large.

And not a single sign of guilt at having enriched his mining mates and corporate buddies under the Cover of COVID, all at the expense of the average taxpayer, none of whom could now easily leave the country, many of whom had lost their jobs.

***

There was a series of stimulus announcements through March of 2020, constituting a massive market distortion of entirely dubious worth.

Apart from the assorted state government stimulus initiatives, Australia's Federal Government notched up stimulus announcements at the rate of more than one per week.

On March 12, a $17.6 billion stimulus — a $4.76 billion doubling in Newstart allowances, now dubbed Jobseeker, and $6.7 billion for business wage subsidies.

Within days that first splash cash was a mere minnow in a spendathon of truly staggering proportions, was a one-off $750 payment to around 6.5 million lower-income Australians registered for welfare, be it an old-age pensioner or the unemployed.

That 6.5 million Australians were already dependent on government payments in a population of 25 million illustrated one of the fundamental flaws in an already deeply troubled society: that far too many people were not engaged in meaningful work or could not generate enough income to support themselves.

On March 19, a $90 billion three-year funding facility was declared by the Reserve Bank to help banks continue to lend to business, and another $15 billion aimed at second-tier banks and other lenders. Another trickle-down initiative, essentially a liquidity fillip for the banks, which are more likely to lend it to large corporations more likely to pay it back.

On March 22, there was a $66 billion package, including a $550 coronavirus supplement to Jobseeker and a second $750 payment to welfare recipients. This was designed to allow small businesses to keep on their workers. It was flawed in that it incentivised employers to keep higher-paid workers and discard those on lower incomes.

On March 30, the government announced a fortnightly wage subsidy of $1500 per fortnight for up to six million people; a move expected to cost some $130 billion.

The bigger the corporation, the more taxpayer dollars you got. A polity which should have been building resilience into the nation's businesses, corporations and individuals had already gifted the nation a desperately feeble economy.

In the face of the most momentous economic disaster in living memory, Michael West wrote: "Aside from the ugly jousting for taxpayer support from corporations which pay little or no tax, aside from the hypocrisy of the newly minted caste of post-neo-conservative socialists who once derided regulation but now crave hand-outs, the government has structured a scheme to entrench the status quo once the coronavirus blows over.

"In this, Australia may miss the chance for vital reform, this historic opportunity to address rising inequality and the dominance of large corporations over democracy.

"However it plays out, the stimulus is designed to entrench the employer/ employee relationship. It encourages dependency. Meanwhile, the gig economy has left millions vulnerable. The casualisation of the workforce, which has arisen from deliberate government policies of deregulation over the past two decades — and is turbocharged by technologies of automation — has left millions stranded, disenfranchised."[28]

***

Apropos of the era, stranded on the edge of that freezing lake, with its traditional sentinels, the black swans, Alex wondered: What if it was all true, all that poured forth from every saint, clairvoyant and lunatic?

Everyone knew there was something more fantastical in play, and he, too, felt gripped by something beyond human ken.

We were walking high on methamphetamine in a derelict part of a derelict city; we were the fallen angels sleeping on the streets, we were the prince walking down the wide stone verandas two thousand years ago, gazing at our domain, we were the oiled and the unctuous, the privileged and the poor.

We soared free and had been tortured in dungeons. He heard all these things, for the times were riven strange.

And human contact had been cut to a minimum.

One morning Alex swerved, for no particular reason, onto a different

---

28 Australia's Cufflink Comrades: The Victims of the Big Bail-out, Michael West, *A Sense of Place Magazine*, 1 April, 2020.

path on his way to the church in the forest. A cyclist rode past, an older gent, one of those mad nature lovers who could name you every plant; and before he knew it, they were having a conversation about the nature of sentience.

All was alight: nature, people, everything was transforming around him. As the man rode off, he said: "I am the sound the leaves make."

***

As one of Alex's favourite commentators of the period, Paul Collits, wrote in a piece titled "Chilling, Miserable, Dystopian and Sinister: Politicians and Health Bureaucrats", the strategy was to write endless cheques, thereby postponing the inevitable economic pain of lockdown.

"Furlough, Jobseeker, JobKeeper, and endless announceables. They are all merely fingers in the dyke, of course, but that doesn't matter.

"They have the twin effects of allowing governments to appear to be doing something, and keeping a lid on what one might normally expect to be extreme community anger at the loss of freedom and, for many, the loss of one's job and one's future. Deferring the pain cannot last forever."

In other words, the government was paying people to ensure they didn't start rioting in the streets.

Another strategy, according to Collits, was to put the useful fools in the media to work for the greater glory of the state.

"The politicians can, sadly, count on the fact that the fourth estate has, in effect, gone on strike. The media have given governments a free run. They even join in the infomercials, and merely parrot the government clichés, lies, calumnies and insults. Australian journalists have been in equal parts woeful and shameful. Is it inherent laziness — just copy the press release into the paper — or are they ideologically wedded to safetyism and authoritarianism? It doesn't really matter which.

"They have failed the public dismally. Their greatest failing has been not even acknowledging that there are other views than those of our various governments on how to manage a virus without destroying an economy. The media have gulped down the Kool-Aid, without it having touched the sides."

Even on the face of it, the nature of the Australian Government's response sounded insane. Quarantine the healthy. Crash the national economy.

Throw millions onto the dole queues. So massively expand the national debt that economists estimated it would take until 2060 to pay it off.

At the end of the day, if Old Alex's visions were correct, far from being the saviours of the nation, the politicians had got it all terribly wrong. Destroying jobs, lives, businesses and communities could only end one way. There really would be riots in the streets.

***

All this time, Alex was stranded on the South Coast, drenched by peculiar vision.

For days, or was it weeks, he could feel the entities hovering overhead, across time, across space, terraforming as they settled on that picturesque part of the South Coast. The gods, as the humans thought of them, would not be rushed, their origin in those distant star systems a fantastical affront to local belief systems.

The ancients had a dream not just to bring life to planets such as this, but to be there to see that life evolve, to watch the rise and fall of everything from trees to civilisations.

Or as Buffy St Marie put it so aptly half a century or so before:

"Off into outer space you go my friend
We wish you bon voyage
And when you get there we will welcome you again
And still you'll wonder at it all."

Meanwhile, as his consciousness swirled across contradictory platforms, the country he had known, where he had been born, grown up, wandered, was being transformed by the sub-moral parasites who had seized power into a place where thieves in suits could prey on the weak, plunder the population, make themselves rich beyond their wildest suburban dreams.

The country was being destroyed in a matter of months. Old Alex felt sick to the core about all of it. There wouldn't, couldn't, be any way back.

***

A simple scan of the headlines was enough to confirm that anti-lockdown protests were on the rise across the globe: "Germany braces for anti-lockdown protests", "Anti-lockdown protests erupt in UK, 100 held",

"Liberté! An open letter by 200 French lawyers protesting against lockdown", "Huge anti-lockdown protest breaks out in Edinburgh", "Pianist calmly plays on the street amid violent anti-lockdown protests in Barcelona", "Manchester University students remove 'lockdown' fencing during huge protests", "Italy: the 'second wave' brings with it a wave of protests".

"Toxic lockdown sees huge rise in babies harmed or killed."

What would happen, in this endangered space and place in time, when the public realised the truly staggering multiple incompetencies of Australia's political class had destroyed not just their own lives and futures, but the lives and futures of their children? That they had been lied to? And that their gods, whoever they were, had failed them?

FIVE
AS HISTORY WOULD RECORD

"JOBS CATASTROPHE: Economic horrors of the past haunt new generation who face a great depression" blared Sydney's leading tabloid *The Daily Telegraph*.

The brutality was just setting in; the coverage urgent, and sad.

Those early months of 2020 marked the beginning of the lockdown insanity that would destroy so many tens of thousands of businesses, with Australia needlessly adopting some of the most extreme lockdown measures to be found anywhere in the world.

Prime Minister Scott Morrison claimed his lockdowns were "based on expert modelling that we've had done through our medical experts to give us an idea about potential spread and duration of viruses under various scenarios.

"That's why I know when people start talking about locking things down, you can't just lock things down for two weeks and four weeks and open it again and think it's all going to be Okay. That would be a foolish decision, because when you open it up again, the virus just takes off. So if you shut things down, you have to understand that if you do that, that you may well be doing that for at least the next six months. And that has to be sustainable.

"That's why I say the economic impacts of this and the broader health impacts; it's going to break our hearts. I have no doubt. But it must not break our spirit or our resolve to continue to deal with this crisis in a sensible way, in a compassionate way, helping each other to help us all through to the other side."

A haunting phrase and standard spiritual language; "through to the other side"; and it would be repeatedly uttered on that slide into hell. In this context, from a prime minister who believed he was serving God with every waking breath, dangerous stuff.

And as would soon become evident, absolutely daft. Not only did lockdowns overthrow decades of established wisdom in dealing with disease outbreaks, many experts both in Australia and around the world were already coming out strongly condemning the approach.

None of whose voices got as far as the prime minister's deaf ear. We all hear what we want to hear.

***

Scott Morrison raised not one word of protest over the crash-tackling sequence of lockdowns in cascading states; never once called out the perpetrators. Never once told the public the truth: that there was very, very strong doubt around the world about the efficacy of lockdowns. Never once spoke out in defence of the protestors being wrestled to the ground by newly empowered police.

Curfews, restrictions on movement, the crushing of businesses through regulatory mandates, border closures, overseas travel bans, bans on exercise, household detention, banning of church services, cancelling weddings and funerals and sinister contact-tracing.

Lockdowns were an act of totalitarianism and constituted the greatest attacks on freedom in Australian history.

As Collits put it: "Too few Australians even see lockdowns as a freedom issue. Where is the public anger in the democratic West at the greatest threat to our rights in any one of our lifetimes? All done on our watch. We should be ashamed of ourselves for letting this happen."

One of the benefits of lockdowns for the authorities was that they effectively banned protests.

"Making protest illegal has been a masterstroke of the COVID state. It has been achieved on the flimsiest of constitutional grounds, through ministerial fiat barely recognisable as belonging in a liberal democracy, and on the pretext of guaranteeing public safety. For the sake of protection from a virus which will cause no harm — I am sorry but this must be endlessly repeated till it sinks in — to ninety-nine per cent of the population.

"And chillingly, this is all done under the cover of protecting us all from 'disinformation'. Physical protest and online dissent are fundamental democratic rights.

"How better to silence dissent? All on the back of constitutionally questionable, but unquestioned, authority. Make it out to be war, then dissidents can be conveniently portrayed as quislings. COVID quislings.

"As we know, the most successful dictatorships in history — many of them in the twentieth century — have survived through the silencing of dissent. The greatest freedom fighters have been those, like Aleksandr Solzhenitsyn, who have called this out, often at risk to their own lives. Those who have been opposing the tyranny of lockdowns may, one day, come to be seen in a similar light."[29]

***

The headlines were only a mica glint on the surface of a far deeper tragedy; and the political wordsmiths at the top of this rotten pile just kept spinning and spinning.

Prime Minister Scott Morrison warned that the newly unemployed seeking to access the dole, which had been temporarily doubled, was just the start of more massive job losses to come.

"Across Australia today, many thousands of Australians will lose their jobs," Mr Morrison said. "They are lining up at Centrelink offices as we speak — something unimaginable at this scale, only weeks ago. They have lost their jobs … and many more will.

"Together, and with the rest of the world, we face this global health pandemic that has fast become an economic crisis, the likes of which we have not seen since the Great Depression. For many, young and old, 2020 will be the toughest year of our lives.

"Meeting this challenge is bigger than any Australian. It is bigger than premiers, chief ministers, captains of industry, leaders of union movements. It is bigger than all of us. And I want to thank all of those who have come to this great challenge with such a unity of spirit. It requires every single Australian to do their duty as public citizens."[30]

A house leaks from the roof.

---

29 The Hexagon of Tyranny, Paul Collits, *A Sense of Place Magazine*, 6 December, 2020.

30 Ministerial Statement, Prime Minister, Australia Parliament House, 23 March, 2020.

***

Like scenes from a movie called *The Destruction of Australia*, queues outside Centrelink offices snaked around the block, there in the early days of April 2020.

Mass Derangement Syndrome, as the government repeated the mantra over and over, "Keeping Australians safe".

Australia's conservatives had long abandoned good government in return for scaring the population. Any notion of encouraging Australians to live productive and independent lives would require an archeological dig to find.

"Keeping Australians safe" was exactly the same tired trick the Australian Government had been using for Islamic terror, year on year. Now they had found the perfect, invisible, enemy. Even more effective than climate change, which had wearied the electorate with its high moral tone and the endless, catastrophising, condescension of taxpayer-funded academics.

But the last thing you felt was "safe" if you were in those queues, if you had just lost your job. From the nation's political class there was an aching disregard for the welfare of ordinary people. Apart from the odd image on screen or brief televised interview, these people were invisible and voiceless.

The view from Main Street looked nothing like the privileged view from Parliament House.

"In dark days in which the lives of Australians have been turned upside down, the sight of some of the 88,000 left jobless overnight waiting outside Centrelink offices was heartbreaking," *The Daily Telegraph* declared. "The scenes yesterday echoed the desperation of job hunters lining up in the streets of Sydney during the Great Depression in the early 1930s.

"Tens of thousands had their livelihoods wiped out the moment new coronavirus shutdowns kicked in yesterday, closing pubs, clubs, gyms and cinemas."

As intelligence, military and government operatives already knew, a population on the edge of poverty is much easier to manage. Up to a point.

***

You could find a hundred, a thousand examples of tragedy striking businesses and individuals. With few exceptions, instead of documenting the impacts on the population, the media chose to breathlessly and uncritically report government propaganda, case numbers, "highly infectious" variants, taxpayer-funded experts of choice.

But back in March of 2020, the dole queues were still a novelty. And nobody quite knew what was about to descend.

Bankstown Sports, one of the biggest clubs in the country, laid off 650 staff members across six venues. Club CEO Mark Condi told *The Daily Telegraph*: "The staff are devastated, with many being there for more than 40 years."

Government Services Minister Stuart Robert, a happy-clappy mate of the prime minister, "Brother Stewie", was sacked by the previous prime minister, Malcolm Turnbull, for misconduct and reinstated by his fellow Pentecostal Scott Morrison.

He initially blamed the failure of the collapse of the Centrelink system on a "distributed denial-of-service attack"; that is a cyber attack, but refused to give details.

Later he claimed the site had not been able to cope with the 95,000 desperate people attempting to access it at the same time.

The reality was, the system collapsed under more than a million calls in a single day.

The hospitality sector was hit hardest by the closure of all entertainment venues.

The Telegraph reported that at least 300 people lined up outside the Bondi Junction Centrelink alone.

"Forlorn and anxious, the bulk aged in their 20s and 30s, who worked in the retail and restaurant industries, queued since 7am to sign up for the Jobseeker payment after their bosses were forced to let them go.

Zuni Bruneau, 23, lost two jobs at an ice rink at Mascot and as a race car driver. "My mum has lost her job as a masseuse, so I'm staying with her for now," she said. 'I'm scared, I don't want to be unemployed.'"

Lara Fox, 23, had her shifts cut from 30 hours a week to five at Basement Books at Central Station. "I was there casually, as I'm a student, but now I can't pay my rent," Ms Fox said.

Outside the Marrickville Centrelink, NSW Police patrolled the 100-metre line of jobseekers, advising people to try other offices.

"I lost my job on Friday, so first thing this morning I came down here to try and access some payments, my rent is $700 a week," Shevaun Job, 24, said. "I waited in this line for three hours and I spent five minutes in the office before they told me I need to apply online. I told them the website wasn't working."[31]

In the line at the Centrelink office in the inner-city suburb of Redfern, casual workers hit by the shuttering of pubs and clubs mixed with small business owners and recent graduates from nearby Sydney University — all caught up in the chaos.

Guardian Australia reported: "The mood was tense. Those coming out of the offices reported angry and chaotic scenes inside as staff tried to cope with the huge influx of people seeking to access services."

Gus McGrath, 24, a musician and hospitality worker, said: "I feel like it's not getting better any quicker. I don't see an easy out. I'm pretty freaked out and it feels a bit doomy, and even when things settle back, it can't just be like back to normal."[32]

***

Scott Morrison was a great believer in prosperity theology, the notion that God showers the faithful with riches.

He and his ilk were about to get a damn sight richer.

By December "Vintage Year for the Wealthy: COVID-19 Widens Gap Between Rich and Poor" was just one of the headlines pointing out the obvious. The worst of the worst had gorged themselves at the trough.

Did their God ever walk among the poor?

If all war was deception, Alex was even more wary than usual. But that beginning was the long, pounding beginning when he went straight out on a limb and became truly frightened, more alone than ever, with his dying parent in the next room and the ridicule of the Watchers on the Watch ringing in his fevered imagination. There were no savants now. They were all operatives of one kind or another. Different tunes, different masters, different realms.

His previous three books had all ended on a prophetic tone, of societal collapse and totalitarian government.

---

31 On the Breadline, *The Daily Telegraph*, 24 March, 2020.

32 Queues at Centrelink offices and MyGov website crashes ahead of coronavirus shutdowns, Luke Henriques-Gomes and Michael McGowan, *Guardian Australia*, 23 March, 2020.

The whole damn thing was uncanny, that those prophecies, the ones he had written as if someone else's urgent voice was speaking through him, were all coming true, that the disintegrated future he had written about so lyrically was suddenly upon them all, at a speed he could never have imagined.

The streets were not just quiet. They were bloody terrifying.

As, indeed, was the obsequious conformity of the population. Dare to disagree with them, as they embraced the loss of their own freedoms, and you were ridiculed, cast out of their inner circles.

As one critic noted: "Many lockdown sceptics simply cannot believe the extent to which the public has gone quietly, and few have come up with an adequate explanation for the submissiveness. Whatever the cause of our submissiveness, the effect of it has been to allow governments simply to get away with everything from needless curfews to police thuggery to border closures to travel bans. Rather than fomenting rebellion among the people, the ever more harmful and dictatorial measures visiting upon us merely provoke yawns."

***

In the days when you could actually meet up and talk to people. In the days before bollards went up at the local state park, before the full blizzard of contradictory regulations set in, before complete confusion beset the country. As if all the prophecies so sincerely, so abstractly made, through automatic writing and through clanging cymbals of sheer unadulterated frustration at just about everything, at the absolute lack of accord not just among those he encountered, were all coming true in the clanging absurdity of a government which kept getting the approval of the voters, despite the sheer enormity of everything they did.

Alex was yet to understand a fraction of what was happening to him. The glinting edifices which had been rising and falling far out to sea during their previous incarnation had gone now. There was no consistency of messaging, of vision. He could feel them gathering in a storm, but his own storm had worn him thin.

So it was that he reached into the depths, and kept working, and could feel the gathering. There, in those early days, in those early frightening hours, he was just a deranged lunatic bashing away at a keyboard, and for all the ridicule and derision of the intelligence agencies, for all the things he heard and should never have heard, for all the comings and goings and the horrid little pygmy gnomes parading themselves as media experts, as professors of journalism, as masters of the flame and controllers of the narrative, all distorted, all wrecked, all an abysmal derogation of duty and devolution of form, all a shocking slip into utter irresponsibility, those things, their hapless leaders, the fear in the streets, the consequence of incompetence, the self-aggrandising and manipulation; all of it now led him down a singular path.

To a destiny.

To a place.

And so, if any of those waking dreams could be believed, other intel- ligences began to form through the fabric of everything around him, came to message him, not for comfort, not to provide strength, not for his benefit or welfare; they came because there was a path, they gathered because they had a means of communication, they gathered because these ancient technologies needed an entry point in that border which to them must have seemed a border beyond the real, the material world. They needed to enter via what to the monotheists would seem like an occult science, with birds flying backwards and extreme spatial distortions and multiple voices ringing through the fabric of everything.

And they came to warn, in a depth of sadness carried on a backwash through time, transfigured through every day now a century; for some, it was happening all over again.

Not just a warning. A desperate desire to avoid a future now being built.

In case there was any doubt as to why he could do what he could, Alex told the Earthly authorities directly: "100 per cent, it's a technology." As if we were all instruments of a power beyond ourselves; as if we had not all already been forsaken. Believe what you will; we were all stricken in the midst of that society-wide derangement.

***

Having been single for a little too long, in those days when everything was shut down and everyone was expected to stay home, Alex was thrown into an immediate lack of companionship. He regarded it as a shocking imposition on the part of the government. The thing that outraged him the most was the loneliness. How was anyone meant to deal with this?

Everything in those early panicked days was about fear, and bewilderment.

He became fascinated by Hannah Arendt's masterpiece from the 1940s *The Origins of Totalitarianism*, which fitted the moment so very well. One of those books that under normal circumstances one might intend to read, but never actually get around to. One thing about lockdowns, most people have more time on their hands than they know what to do with.

The arcane, academic language of the lecture halls rang portentously in 2020.

Hannah Arendt coined that most famous of phrases "The banality of evil", which is exactly what was now being experienced in Australia. To labour the obvious, the book had an uncanny and frightening applicability to the present.

"What prepares men for totalitarian domination in the non-totalitarian world is the fact that loneliness, once a borderline experience usually suffered in certain marginal social conditions like old age, has become an everyday experience of the ever-growing masses of our century," Arendt wrote. "The merciless process into which totalitarianism drives and organises the masses looks like a suicidal escape from this reality. The 'ice-cold reasoning' and the 'mighty tentacle' of dialectics which 'seizes you as in a vice' appears like a last support in a world where nobody is reliable and nothing can be relied upon.

"By destroying all space between men and pressing men against each other, even the productive potentialities of isolation are annihilated; by teaching and glorifying the logical reasoning of loneliness where man knows that he will be utterly lost if ever he lets go of the first premise from which the whole process is being started, even the slim chances that loneliness may be transformed into solitude and logic into thought are obliterated. If this practice is compared with that of tyranny, it seems as if a way had been found to set the desert itself in motion, to let loose a sandstorm that could cover all parts of the inhabited earth."

***

His domestic front wasn't much more cheerful.

"I've been telling you for years, it's a dying world," his aging, ultra-religious parent told him, a refrain she would often repeat.

All he had for company was the Watchers on the Watch. His narrative was not their narrative, their masters were not his masters, their destiny not his, their opportunism — stemming as it did from their hierarchical, military, materialistic organisations — belonged to a different realm.

Well, we would soon find out, as he was spun in another centrifuge. But for the moment, that moment he pounded away, hoping that the imaginary assassins he dispatched would do their job in one sense or another, that the country could be saved, that democracy, now so imperilled, could be rescued.

A trailing hum as they circled for attack. Prey on the weak. Plunder the poor. Rid the planet, as so many were now saying, of evil. Everyone knew now; the great reset in crumbling, turbulent times.

Cryo-freeze the bastards and blast them into space, he advised. They splinter into a million pieces. They can't be put back together. That was his blunt Assassin's Creed. Slit the human's throat, grab them from behind. No enemy tomorrow. Those spirits which possessed them, they required a different kind of extermination.

But it was all a mistake. Democracy had been imperilled from the moment these people took power. The Big End of Town always won. It was winning again. At the cost of most everybody's not-so-flash, normal lives. The lives they loved.

***

Rounding into May of 2020, made a little more poignant that year because in Australia Mother's Day is celebrated on the second Sunday of the month and many families could not be together that year, the blizzard of verbiage from the prime minister escalated. The man had barely drawn breath in weeks. It had all sounded so damn reasonable at the time; well, at least to the unsuspecting; that is, to the public.

In yet another press conference, this one on 8 May, 2020, Morrison declared: "So many Australians are hurting right now. Lives turned upside down, painful separation from their loved ones. Livelihoods that they have spent a lifetime building stripped away. Uncertainty about their futures and their family's future.

"The last few months have given us a reminder of the things that are really important. Our health, our wellbeing, a strong health system and all those who keep it strong. A growing economy. Our jobs and our incomes that rely on it. We cannot take this for granted. Every job matters, whatever job you do. Every job is essential.

"Our children's education. Caring for our elderly, respecting their dignity. The selfless and humble service of so many Australians who just get on with it every day make this great country work. We have seen these heroes in action.

"Above all though, the importance of each other. That every Australian matters. Every life, every job, every future.

"There will be risks, there will be challenges, there will be outbreaks, there will be more cases, there will be setbacks. Not everything will go to plan. There will be inconsistencies. States will and must move at their own pace, and will cut and paste out of this plan to suit their local circumstances. There will undoubtedly be some human error. No one is perfect. Everyone is doing their best. To think or expect otherwise, I think, would be very unrealistic. This is a complex and very uncertain environment. But we cannot allow our fear of going backwards from stopping us from going forwards."

***

Two days later ten people were arrested and a police officer injured at a protest against Victoria's COVID-19 lockdown laws.

The prime minister never once raised a voice of concern at the loss of the population's right to protest, except to express support for yet further crackdowns and draconian enforcement action against his fellow citizens, the ones brave enough and independent-minded enough to protest.

Footage from the Melbourne protest showed numerous confrontations between demonstrators and police. While the majority of the arrests were for failing to comply with public health orders, three people were charged with assaulting a police officer and another for "discharging a missile" after allegedly throwing a bottle at an officer. Another was taken to hospital after suffering a rib injury.

In a statement, a spokeswoman for Victoria Police said officers would review social media footage of the protest and fine people who attended.

"When attending the protest today, the priority for police was to quickly arrest those individuals who were acting unlawfully and inciting others to breach the chief health officer's directions," a police spokeswoman said.

"Once police made arrests, the crowd started to disperse. Police are continuing to investigate the events of today in order to identify other people who were in attendance. Once individuals are identified, we will be issuing them with fines and will consider any other enforcement options."

A smaller protest outside the NSW Parliament in Sydney also led to dramatic scenes of high-level confrontation.

The protest was organised by a group calling itself Exercising My Rights.

"These lockdowns have stripped us of our basic liberties in an unprecedented way," their website read. "People have lost their jobs, their businesses destroyed; and who knows how many lives will be lost from the consequences of these extreme social-distancing laws?"

In confronting scenes, a Sydney mother was arrested and had her screaming four-year-old son ripped from her arms.

A business owner and mother-of-three, Renee Altakrity, was alleged to have refused to give officers her name and failed to comply with social-distancing laws and a direction to move on.

She was wearing a sign: "If you don't know your rights, you don't have any. Magna Carta."

"I don't know how you guys are going home in honour tonight and trying to infringe me with a notice which I don't consent to because we're doing nothing wrong," Ms Altakrity said.

"You guys should be here holding the signs with us, defending us. I don't consent to what you're doing. We're doing nothing wrong. We're not acting in aggression.

"I'm here fighting for not just myself and my kids, but for your children too."

As his mother was bundled into the back of a police paddy wagon, the four-year old cried: "Mummy is not going. Leave mummy alone!" Towards the end of an amateur video of the scene which was promptly uploaded to the internet, the child is seen kicking and screaming in the arms of police officers.[33]

This was only one of a number of frightening incidents of parents being arrested or harassed by police in front of their children.

---

33 'Leave Mummy alone': Coronavirus protester arrested in Sydney's CBD in front of young son, Lara Pearce, *Nine News*, 10 May, 2020.

The traditional military approach of command and control of information could not work forever. In the age of the internet, authorities were powerless to stop these sorts of videos going viral.

Just as in the Iraq conflict, in which Australia had been the second-largest contributor after America, where the dropping of Allied bombs on civilians generated gut-churning footage of burnt and dying children, so, too, in a different realm, all the authoritarian attempts at creating a flattened public narrative blew up in the perpetrators' faces.

The child was placed in the care of a relative and the often-feared Department of Family and Community Services (an Orwellian organisation if ever there was one) was notified.

One year on, and the insanity of the whole damn thing had got worse, and worse, and worse. With the prime minister still front and centre of the debacle.

Everything was about to become turbocharged: the arrests, the police brutality, the closed borders, the preening premiers, the blizzard of diktats, a prime minister who had lost control.

SIX
THE RIGHT TO PROTEST ABOLISHED

MISUSE OF the Australia's police forces and Defence personnel, along with armies of bureaucrats and their officious foot soldiers, was a hallmark of the COVID era, resulting in vivid scenes of arbitrary arrest, crash-tackling of protestors, and groups of heavily equipped officers patrolling the streets in an eerie display of authoritarian power.

Once power is seized, no one gives it up easily; and now a notoriously incompetent political class had placed themselves front and centre of the debacle and used all the resources at their well-fed hands to suppress opposition.

Australia's drift towards a totalitarian state had been evident for years. Now it was all coming to pass.

The prophets, the writers, outliers and government critics, like crystal balls scattered across mudflats, had repeatedly warned of the dangers accreting in Australia's political system. The abrogation of civil liberties, the crackdown on free speech, the abusive uber-surveillance in the name of "keeping Australians safe".

In a digital world, they were all but ignored, excised from the public debate by military-controlled algorithms. In other words, the same people who brought you *Legacy of Ashes: The History of the CIA* were now controlling what the public believed across multiple countries and multiple platforms.

As Caitlin Johnstone, one of those clairvoyant crystal balls attempting to shine light into a darkening clime, put it: "The emergence of the internet was met with hope and enthusiasm by people who understood that the plutocrat-controlled mainstream media were manipulating public opinion to manufacture consent for the status quo. The democratisation of information-sharing was going to give rise to a public consciousness that is emancipated from the domination of plutocratic narrative control, thereby opening up the possibility of revolutionary change to our society's corrupt systems.

"But it never happened. Internet use has become commonplace around the world and humanity is able to network and share information like never before, yet we remain firmly under the thumb of the same power structures we've been ruled by for generations, both politically and psychologically. Even the dominant media institutions are somehow still the same.

"So what went wrong? Nobody's buying newspapers anymore, and the audiences for television and radio are dwindling. How is it possible that those same imperialist oligarchic institutions are still controlling the way most people think about their world?"[34]

In these tortured circumstances, there was nothing benign about the algorithmic suppression of well-qualified individuals speaking out against the autocratic rule of COVID mass-speak; the very deliberate promotion of hysteria and wildly inaccurate mathematical modelling. And absolutely nothing reassuring about the sight of CEOs of the tech giants claiming they were fighting COVID disinformation while servicing their military, intelligence and government clients.

As Johnstone recorded, Google had been financially intertwined with US intelligence agencies since its very inception when it received research grants from the CIA and NSA. It poured massive amounts of money into federal lobbying and DC think tanks, had a cosy relationship with America's National Security Agency, and had been a military-intelligence contractor from the beginning.

Australia was just a colony, easily exploited.

The role of the Silicon Valley tech companies in manipulating public opinion during the Corona lockdowns threw a harsh light straight back on their own conduct; manufacturing consent all just part of the service. Manipulating narrative and changing behaviour was what these people did for a living. The creation of at-scale emotional contagion and high levels of compliance in populations, all at the behest of governments and

---

34 Silicon Valley Algorithm Manipulation Is The Only Thing Keeping Mainstream Media Alive, Caitlin Johnstone, *A Sense of Place Magazine*, 8 May, 2021.

their intelligence agencies, would as sure as night follows day become one of the next scandals to envelop the unfolding catastrophe of COVID-19.

Only weeks before eminent academics and well-qualified doctors who were querying the wisdom of lockdowns found themselves censored or deleted.

Fast-forward through this panic in time and the lockdowns were routinely being called a reckless and dangerous social experiment, "the biggest mistake in history".

How did quarantining the healthy and crashing national economies ever make sense as a public health policy?

Tens of millions of people around the world found themselves without work while entire societies faced another Great Depression; and soon enough would come the backlash.

***

In a case disclosed by police, a 32-year-old woman and a 27-year-old man were fined after a police patrol in the NSW town of Muswellbrook spotted them in a car. Their offence? Sitting in a car with no reasonable excuse for not being at home.

A man on a park bench eating a kebab. A mother breastfeeding a baby in a park. Another man sunbaking. People walking on a beach promenade. Buying a hamburger. Australians enjoying the most basic freedoms. Except that, in the time of coronavirus, authorities moved them on or issued hefty fines way beyond the reach of any normal working person.

Media coverage, symbolising the suspension of civil liberties, would sprinkle through the coming months, as the following sampling demonstrates.

- Nearly 100 partygoers fined for breaching coronavirus restrictions in Victoria. COVID-19 fines issued after hundreds attend party at NSW nudist beach.
- Hundreds of police will swarm Melbourne today where protesters are expected to gather for so-called "Freedom Day" rallies.
- Tensions have boiled over at a high-security prison south-west of Brisbane over strict lockdown restrictions with prisoners breaking windows, lighting fires and flooding their cells.

- Man gets 200 hours community service after border breach attempts. The 51-year-old Victorian is accused of illegally entering New South Wales and leading officers on a pursuit as he tried to reach the Australian Capital Territory.
- Brisbane kebab shop has been fined $6772 for breaching a COVID health direction after video of an impromptu rave was widely circulated on social media.
- Melbourne University investigating alleged dorm party during lockdown.
- Anti-masker refuses COVID test.
- A group of people caught traveling across Melbourne to visit friends were among the Victorians fined for breaching COVID-19 regulations yesterday.
- As Melbourne's six-week lockdown nears the halfway mark, police continue to catch dozens of people who are out and about without a valid reason.
- In one 24-hour period, 144 people were fined. Of these, 45 were fined for breaching Melbourne's 8pm curfew while a further eight were caught at the state's vehicle checkpoints out of a total of 15,751 vehicles checked. Thirty people were also fined for failing to wear a face covering when out in public.
- Police also conducted 4530 spot checks on people at homes, businesses and in public places across the state.
- A couple who travelled further than five kilometres to take their children to a playground in Melbourne's west claimed they were "sick of walking around their local area" when caught by police.
- Victoria Police are "working hard" to find the woman who appeared to refuse to tell police where she was going at a Melbourne vehicle checkpoint.
- NSW pubs and partygoers slapped with COVID-19 fines.
- Victoria Police have swooped on a Melbourne church and fined a group of worshippers for breaking COVID-19 restrictions.

**

With all the darkness of these stories, with all the disturbance of the time, Old Alex's lucid dreaming just got worse. He looked up, and could see the shimmering echoes in the trees, could feel those entities all around him as they took territory, could feel some distant watching, as if everything they could see, he could see, and felt sick to the core, again.

"Those who do not see, do not weep."

He was witnessing the birth of gods and devils, for this is how it had all begun, all those eons ago, the matching of organic life forms to vastly intelligent machines, the beginning of another transhumanist style story.

That drama, those dramas of so long ago, now being played out on this most fecund, and — in some senses — most unfortunate planet; for every life comes with its own swag of sorrows.

They found themselves on a battleground, in fiercely contested territory.

He could reach for them screeching in the sky, but there was no way out and no way back. They weren't kind. No matter how much they were beseeched, they shed not a single tear.

So when he was asked to play a role, to be a transmission point, to oil the path and make life easier for the transmission of ideas, he willingly agreed.

Until there was no time for any more play. Until the forecourts really were empty. Until those millions on the dole queues found their own voice. Until the utterly irresponsible mismanagement of the situation became not a matter of argument but of accepted historical record.

Ex tempore. Out of time.

***

If policy is not well-informed by vigorous public debate, then all that is left is the word of self-serving politicians, jobsworths, military henchmen or those who could survive their own mismanagement or prosper at the hands of chaos.

There wouldn't be too far to go to find our own resource. There wouldn't be a lightning rod which would rescue us. It wasn't just the forecourts; it was the empty carriages, the quiet streets, the closed shops, the ghosts of hope and enterprise that hung everywhere.

How was it even possible that these people could have done this to themselves? That the nation's politicians could get away with implementing this level of debacle and control over the populace, and convince them it was for their own good.

To save them from the virus.

Except one day it would all come crashing down; because nobody believed them any more, and because the population could no longer feed itself.

***

Surrounded by hostiles, those handmaidens to a travesty, with those mundane streets now emanating threat, Old Alex walked the windswept foreshore of the lake with little love for any of it. Near the ski park, as a local spot for launching boats was known, a trio of T-shaped light poles stood out in the pouring rain, spookily reminiscent of Golgotha in their cast light.

"The world's gone mad," Old Alex took to saying, as he passed the occasional person on his morning walk.

"Didn't make any sense *before*," would come the response.

He had never thought of it like that.

Australia was shutting down. Extreme measures introduced purportedly to stop the spread of COVID-19 were requiring extreme policing measures to force a sceptical population, accustomed to being lied to by their government, to comply.

Empowered by tough new laws and public pressure, police forces were testing how far to go in punishing behaviour that was ordinarily routine. In Australia, the authorities had threatened people sitting alone drinking coffee with six months in jail, or for sitting in their cars, for not having a good reason to have left their home.

Under these conditions, enabled by government decree, where basic humanity is lost, the perpetrators act like predators and the targets act like prey. This was the advent of a progressive horror.

A man was fined $1600 for driving to a park near his house with the intention of going for a bike ride. He allegedly had no good excuse for being outside his home.

Such was the massive confusion over an on-the-face-of-it insane shutdown of Australian society; the introduction of what was essentially martial law and the throwing of millions of people on to welfare dependency of one kind or another.

By early April there had been 50 deaths from COVID-19 in Australia. A normal flu season sees deaths of up to 3000 and around

18,000 hospitalisations. A year on, there was a total of 910 deaths from COVID, and the country had been entirely rearranged for a disease which was not even among the top 50 causes of death.

Fears of overrun hospitals never eventuated. Predictions of tens of thousands of deaths did not come to pass. And no, it was not good management.

More and more the question was being asked: Are we witnessing the biggest government blunder in the nation's history?

You bet.

***

Out on a limb, a very lonely limb, very little of what happened in those startling days made sense to Old Alex; not at his best, not in his own milieu, with only an elderly and difficult parent for company. There's a big difference between pounding away on a keyboard in an isolated situation, and pounding away on a crowded news floor of a major newspaper as one of the city's best-known reporters.

Never a fan of News Limited's management style, retired journalists nonetheless lamented most the loss of companionship, the union of the oppressed, or the camaraderie of fellow sufferers, as staff sometimes looked back on the friends they made there.

Old Alex wasn't News Corp and didn't work for them any more. He didn't have a phalanx of lawyers or a multi-billion-dollar corporation backing him when he dared to disagree with the government narrative. In an atmosphere of heightened alarm and a clear descent into totalitarian madness, he simply felt compelled to act.

A man was refused permission to see his dying wife; surfers warned that they were surfing too close together. In his own imperiled circumstance, in that all too ordinary street, if he was standing outside his home talking to a friend, and a neighbour approached, that was a gathering of three; and that was illegal.

And so the stories and headlines went; as footage showed walls of police wrestling protestors to the ground in what became the new "COVID normal".

***

Was it all for nothing?

That was a very legitimate question to ask.

In its wanton destruction of Australian life, did the government get the whole COVID scare wrong from the very beginning?

Certainly, many people thought so.

A Swedish doctor, Sebastian Rushworth, who ran a widely read medical blog, argued that lockdowns did not appear to reduce the number of COVID deaths. Instead, as a disease which primarily impacted on the elderly, measures taken to fight COVID — such as lockdowns, the fear campaigns masked as public health warnings, the school closures — all would result in far more years of life lost and destroyed than would have been lost directly from the virus.

Referring to recent medical research, he suggested there was no correlation whatsoever between severity of lockdown and number of COVID deaths.

"And they didn't find any correlation between border closures and COVID deaths either. And there was no correlation between mass testing and COVID deaths either, for that matter.

"Lockdowns don't seem to work — if they have any effect at all, it is too weak to be noticeable at a population level.

"Basically, nothing that various world governments have done to combat COVID seems to have had any effect whatsoever on the number of deaths."[35]

An overwhelmed and distrusting Australian population, repeatedly betrayed by their own government, was now being fined and threatened with jail if they gathered in public in groups of more than two people. God forbid they should decide to protest the insanity now consuming their lives.

***

For the police themselves, as voiceless, thanks to their official roles, as the protestors they were expected to silence, the entire saga quickly proved problematic.

35 Does lockdown prevent covid deaths? Dr Sebastian Rushworth. Blog. 9 November, 2020.

Their normal jobs, of chasing criminals, keeping the peace and calming the daily crises of suburban life suddenly became one of enforcing the megalomaniacal overreach of bureaucrats and politicians, on little evidence and in an atmosphere of hysteria.

The vicious scenes of police wrestling protestors to the ground did nothing for the force's reputation.

Breaching public health orders was punishable in NSW by fines of up to $11,000 or six months in prison — for instance, if a person left their home without a "reasonable excuse" — plus a $5500 fine each day the offence continued.

The NSW Police Commissioner, Mick Fuller, said police would no longer issue cautions for those flouting self-isolation rules; instead, $1000 on-the-spot fines would be handed out. Police could also arrest and charge those repeatedly ignoring health orders, with a maximum penalty of six months in prison.

A Sydney man was already behind bars for allegedly ignoring his home self-quarantine twice before trying to leave the serviced apartment in which he had been confined.

The *NSW Government Gazette* listed acceptable excuses for leaving your premises as: obtaining food or other goods and services; travelling for work or education if the person could not do it at home; exercise; and medical or caring reasons.

In addition, the order directed that people must not gather in groups of more than two in public places except for members of the same household, and gatherings essential for work or education.

Corporations that failed to comply with a direction were liable to a fine of $55,000 and $27,500 each day the offence continued.

In Western Australia, those who didn't comply with self-isolation directions would have an electric device installed in their homes. Those who flouted the laws by removing or interfering with the device without reason could be fined $12,000 or jailed for twelve months. The legislation also introduced $1000 on-the-spot fines for people and $5000 fines for businesses who disobeyed directives.

In Victoria citizens faced up to $19,800 in the courts and $1652 on the spot. Within days, more than 50 people had been fined in NSW and Victoria alone. The wanton destruction of Australia had begun in earnest, all traces of a once freedom-loving nation twirling into history.

Needless to say, if a government needed to introduce these kinds of draconian measures in order to enforce a public health measure, they had failed to carry the people with them, didn't have public support or an effective communication strategy, or didn't have a message worth selling in the first place.

In less than twelve months the Queensland state government issued more than $4 million in COVID fines. More than 2500 fines were for breaching directions of the chief health officer, such as failing to social-distance or refusing to wear a mask, racking up a bill of almost $3.5 million. Another 345 serious offenders were arrested for refusing to comply with police officers enforcing COVID-19 restrictions.

At the state's border amid the state's rolling, highly controversial and extremely destructive snap lockdowns, police checked car boots for people desperate to enter the so-called Sunshine State, garnering millions in fines.

***

They bowed before something they did not understand, and all around the drenching, the terraforming, the whispered deceits, the truths they did not want to face, the masks, the social distancing, the vaccines, Big Pharma Making Australia Great Again — all of it designed to break apart the herd.

Big Pharma was about to make more money than even they could have ever dreamed possible. Key to those fortunes was the mass manipulation and indoctrination of populations.

The human ability to operate in large numbers, their key to success as the Earth's dominant species, was being destroyed as he watched, the power relationships shifting. The country he had known was already lost.

At the local hardware store, Bunnings, one of the workers, as Alex queued to pay, was loudly telling her friend that her neighbours had held a barbecue in their backyard the previous evening, thereby breaching edicts which banned visitors or gatherings of any kind.

"I didn't know what to do, so I rang the police," the woman said.

"You dobbed them in?" Old Alex asked.

"Yes," the woman replied. "They weren't doing the right thing."

"We've become a nation of dobbers," he declared in disgust as he paid the cashier.

They shook their heads at his parting back, as he headed to his battered car in a suburban car park, ready to scream, always ready to scream.

***

Since the introduction of highly restrictive regulations tantamount to house arrest, aligned with constantly changing and bewildering edicts, there had been confusion and questions over the powers of state police and the way they were interpreting this new and unprecedented level of rule by diktat.

One brave police officer put his name to an open letter to NSW Police Commissioner, Mick Fuller, "Concerning the Police Enforcement of Ongoing COVID-19 restrictions".

Done under the banner of a group calling itself "Cops for COVID Truth", it was clearly not the work of a single officer.

The petition was signed by Senior Constable Alexander Cooney of the NSW Police Force, Australia, and other signatories. NSW Police confirmed that Constable Cooney's status was under review.

Just like your average citizen, your average member of local police forces wanted to believe their government was doing the right thing. Often entrenched in the communities they served, they were ill-prepared to act as a paramilitary police force, as they were now being required to do.

The powerfully argued letter began: "We are writing to you to raise concerns we have about the use of the police to enforce the ongoing restrictions placed upon our citizens relating to COVID-19, which has seriously eroded community trust in our great police force.

"Since the Attorney-General Declared a State of Emergency for the novel coronavirus, our governments have acted upon certain powers to impose restrictions on its citizens, using the police to enforce their rules.

"Due to the novel nature of the SARS-CoV-2 virus, most people concurred that certain restrictions should be followed, until more was learnt about the virus.

"With the initial modelling from the Imperial College in the UK and the Peter Doherty Institute here in Australia, indicating a catastrophic number of cases that would severely burden our hospital system and could result in up to 150,000 Australian deaths, it is easy to comprehend why our governments would respond as they did and why the vast population would comply."

But, as quickly became apparent, that initial modelling was wildly inaccurate.

Cops for COVID Truth pointed out that the RT PCR test they were being asked to use had been proved unreliable at best, with the inventor stating it should "never be used to diagnose infectious disease", because it cannot tell if what it detected is alive or dead.

"This test is still being relied upon to make critical decisions in the interest of public health and safety.

"In the same way we cannot use an inaccurate speed detection device to proctor a civilian's speed, the same must be demanded of a faulty R T PCR test and, as such, police should not in any way mandate testing for COVID-19, or rely on any outcome of the results."

Cops for COVID Truth noted that the huge debt and unemployment as a result of lockdowns were creating a series of problems that outweighed the threat the virus posed.

"In our line of work, we know that the socio-economic problems created here will transpire into a greater threat down the track, as people struggle to deal with the collateral damage this is causing.

"All this indicates that the ongoing restrictions on the healthy population is a disproportionate response, yet the police are still expected to continue to enforce these measures and at risk of being forced to vaccinate against a disease that is showing not to be virulent, with a vaccine that has had no long-term safety studies and then forcing it upon the population."

Cops for COVID Truth suggested that the evidence would suggest resources are better directed to protect the vulnerable.

"We are concerned with the legitimacy of the actions we are being told to take against the citizens of Australia. States and territories cannot rise above the Commonwealth Constitution as well as international treaties we are signatories to, yet this is occurring.

"Emergency and public health powers, at the states and territories, do not provide a carte blanche to breach an individual's human rights by isolating them, or detaining them or testing them without the proper required notifications and risk-assessments first.

"Many members of the force are fed up with the approach to enforce oppressive rules placed upon the population in the name of COVID-19 and the looming mandatory vaccinations. We feel a real calling to do our part to stop this oppression.

"And the community are confounded by the intensified police enforcement around peaceful freedom protests and how inconsistent this was when compared with the Black Lives Matter protests. This contradiction is further destroying public confidence."[36]

***

In NSW, as elsewhere, state police were provided with enhanced powers to ensure that people abided by pandemic lockdown rules. The Berejiklian government went one step further and handed co-ordination of the entire state COVID-19 response to NSW Police Commissioner Mick Fuller.

What unfolded was ongoing theatre of absurd moments, as police started issuing steep fines: teens wanting to hang out with friends were charged $1000, and a young man was pulled up and penalised after the restrictions had been lifted.

Their aggressive involvement in the public shaming of non-complying businesses and individuals, their destruction or endangerment of people's welfare, would become a scandal blighting the reputation of police forces around the country.

Well known Sydney writer Paul Gregoire wrote in the Sydney Criminal Lawyers Blog: "Mirrored nationwide, these episodes got the public used to police out on the streets stepping on our everyday civil liberties in a manner that was unthinkable just days prior.

"And since Melbourne has gone into its second lockdown, there's been a further creep upon what's considered acceptable policing.

"A cluster of COVID-19 infections linked to some public housing towers resulted in 500 police officers being sent in to ensure 3000 residents went into immediate lockdown: no preparation, no excuses to leave. And while many raised questions about the response, the deployment remained.

"There was also the Victoria police officer who put a woman in a chokehold and dragged her by the throat over a face mask incident. She was pushed to the ground, taken to the station and charged with resisting arrest and assaulting police. The male officer was officially cleared of any wrongdoing."

As Gregoire noted, social justice activists were finding much to protest

---

36 Cops for COVID Truth, *A Sense of Place Magazine*, republished 1 January, 2020.

about now, including black deaths in custody, refugees and cuts to higher education, not to mention climate change.

"And as the consequences of the economic downturn become more apparent and bailout measures disappear, more issues to mobilise around are likely to emerge.

"So, from the perspective of authorities in this state, it's lucky NSW Police has been enforcing an unofficial ban on protests.

"Within the bowels of the NSW Government's public health order on gatherings is a conveniently worded prohibition on outdoor meetings or assemblies of more than 20 people 'for a common purpose'.

"The Coalition has quietly cancelled the right for more than 20 civilians to gather in public if they have a shared political interest.

"The prohibition on demonstrating is the clearest evidence that the authorities are using the opportunity gifted by the pandemic to roll out measures that, on the books, are about preventing virus transmission but, on the ground, allow for heightened social control."[37]

***

Throwing the country's citizens to the wolves, throwing large numbers out of work, blatantly plundering the poor to give to the rich, was the finale of a process which had been years in the making.

Australian governments, local, state and federal, did little but generate complexity and difficulty in the lives of the citizenry, and there were many examples where everyone would have been much better off if the government had just stayed out of their lives.

Old Alex didn't want to be at home, there was no local pub open, no one was inviting anyone to their houses; they couldn't risk the health of their children or the wrath of the authorities.

Little of what happened in those startling early days held any coherent meaning for Old Alex. The Farm, as it is known to the locals, is a picturesque former dairy farm flanking down to one of the most beloved surfing beaches on the entire South Coast; a place, thanks to the placement of the bay, with both good waves and an air of tranquility, provoking admiration and communality.

---

37 Escalation in Policing Is a Sign of What's to Come in a Time of Austerity, Paul Gregoire, *A Sense of Place Magazine*, 27 September, 2020.

Old Alex went there on a regular basis. To watch the surfers in the gentle roll of the waves, to listen to their thoughts, to imagine what it was like beneath the surface, to hear the moments of the desecrated forests, to pray, if you wanted to think of it like that; to hear the ancestors.

But now when he arrived at the outskirts of the park he was turned away; fear, fear gripped everything. He asked questions of the volunteers turning back cars; but they didn't know anything. They didn't know why they were doing what they were doing, except that it was imperative to do so. The government had decreed. The safety of everyone was all that mattered.

You couldn't even go walking in a park without the government pouring down on you; without breaching a law, without allegedly endangering others. It was massive overreach and the long-term consequences would be dire.

He fulminated to the rare person he encountered, and nobody believed him.

There had been nothing more totally and completely irresponsible than the suppression of alternate views, the enhancement of mainstream news outlets to make them appear more authoritative than they actually were, and to conceal their shallow, dysfunctional nature as they served the financial interests of their masters, often closely linked to the electoral interests of government.

But you cannot censor everybody forever.

***

The 100th person to die from, or probably more precisely with, COVID, was Alice Bacon, 93, at the Newmarch House home for aged care. She passed away on 19 May, 2020.

Already the aggressive counting of COVID deaths by health authorities in order to inflate the numbers was becoming a major issue; with many of those passing away being elderly patients with multiple comorbidities.

To claim they died from — rather than with — COVID was always a stretch; but demonstrated the point that those in greatest danger were the elderly. While imposing nationwide lockdowns harming everybody, authorities took little specific action to protect those most at risk.

Alice Bacon was also suffering from terminal cancer.

Family members said she had lived a long and happy life, was up and about, active and involved at Newmarch, and often chatted to friends on the phone.

In a Facebook post her daughter Mary paid tribute to her "caring and generous" mother.

"We are all devastated by the loss of our mum and she will be greatly missed by us and all those whose lives she touched," she wrote. "Mum fought hard to stay with us. Until two weeks ago she was a happy and busy lady inside and outside of Newmarch."

There was a litany of accusations over the mishandling of the outbreak. Television footage showed scenes of families waving at elderly relatives trapped inside aged-care homes.

The NSW Health Minister, Brad Hazzard, advised people not to hug their loved ones.

***

Throughout the month of May 2020, the prime minister spoke voluminously, placing himself front and centre of COVID as the drama unfolded across the nation.

Fathering his flock through the portals to the other side. Or droning people into submission. Or making so many portentous announcements that a switched-off public assumed he was doing the right thing. To think otherwise was arrogant or unpatriotic. Our betters knew better.

We look to be led. We seek protection from on high. We assume wisdom where there is none.

In any case, as the tide turned, here's a sampling of Scott Morrison for the record:

12 May, 2020:

"Step one of that way has always been to fight the virus. And we are winning, but we have not yet won. That virus is still out there, that virus still has a great potential to do enormous harm to the livelihoods of Australians and the lives of Australians. We need to continue to fight that battle.

"I have great faith, as we all do, in the optimism of Australians and in their resourcefulness and in their tenacity and their determination.

"We've mapped out the road back to a COVID-safe economy. So

Australians can go back to the workplaces, so children can be back in school. Both of my daughters are back in school today, in the classroom, in New South Wales."

15 May:

"This is a tough day for Australia, a very tough day. Almost 600,000 jobs have been lost, every one of them devastating for those Australians, for their families, for their communities. A very tough day. Terribly shocking, although not unanticipated.

"We knew there would be hard news as the pandemic wreaks an impact on Australia, as it is on countries all around the world. And so it has been the case. And in the months ahead, we can brace ourselves and must brace ourselves for further hard news for Australians to take.

"On the other side, of course, our economy will look very different, and so it's very important the National Cabinet has reaffirmed its commitment to work together, not just through the pandemic, but to through the economic impacts of that pandemic and put in place the necessary changes we need to make to make Australia's economy stronger again."

26 May:

"Anthony from Western Australia, he sent me his wedding photo. His wife of 50 years had just passed away. He said his wife 'was the most caring person you could ever meet' and he was absolutely heartbroken that he couldn't give her the send-off she deserved. Of all the things, of all the decisions we have taken, that was undoubtedly the hardest.

"And I received an email from three children in Western Australia that completely floored me, their father is terminally ill. They told me they understood their dad's funeral would have to be small. They wanted me to know they were OK with that — because it will help keep the hospitals available for other patients with cancers and diseases.

"That's incredible, our people are amazing.

"We will get Australians back to work. We will restore our nation's finances. We will continue to guarantee the essential services that Australians rely on.

"Together we are facing down this crisis as Australians and we are doing so as a successful, vibrant and liberal democracy. Open and transparent, just and fair, noble and compassionate, never willing to sacrifice the most vulnerable.

"This is our greatest strength. How good is Australia?"

***

And still those lucid dreams kept up their urgent summons.

Then there was the circling, and the maladroit. They fell and felt down centuries. All their tales, they coagulated in his blood. Their stories lingered, confused and indistinct. Doped to the eyeballs on gold standard psychotropics for weeks on end, the calculations of justice, the indistinct. They came roaring out of place. They sent their sentinels. They terra-formed everything. He could feel them humming, although they did not hum. His mind played tricks to adjust. They didn't all come from the same place. They didn't all come as custodians.

There was music then, and sun on skin, and he was not just powerful but handsome, a prince amongst men, the divine right of kings, grand delu-sions, a schizophrenic wash, an utter derangement of the era. That they spoke to us here showed that others were in play; that some giant network was lighting up across the globe; that this amount of data could not be distributed through a single organism. He could feel them wavering in the air already. The advance guards had come and made their arrangements.

Perhaps he had read too much science fiction as a kid.

But that's what was passing through his head, in this place, in a demented time without parallel.

There was no all-wise one, and they threatened to kill him if he compared them to a swarm. These were the wild days, when our kingdom came through into the flesh, when the quiet suburban yards and the sleeping towns, the quiet relics, the original humans, watered their lawns, tidied their houses, made their small lives smaller as the country shrank and the population retreated, caring even less about grand matters of state.

While the overlords used COVID to prepare the people for a life of abject poverty; transforming them into a mass readily exploited; when millions became superfluous. It was as if he could hear those intelligent plants bordering the lake, as they had bordered the edge of water and land for millennia, so that when he looked, the whole scene appeared bathed in a primordial or preternatural light. We were trying to embrace you; beneath the glass pond where no one could see. But the deflection, the brittle broken heart, it all made for the love of man more difficult; so he let, instead, the trees talk to him, as they swirled in cold air, and the coming summer remained far off; and he knew destiny was on the wing.

And the country destroyed.

***

Legal expert Professor Augusto Zimmerman wrote in his piece "Government by Virus and Executive Diktat": "My state, Western Australia, has just recorded its fourth death attributed to the Wuhan virus — another elderly man, like so many other casualties, already inflicted with chronic illness when infected.

"Surely such an 'enormous' death toll justifies dramatic measures to curtail fundamental rights, as well as the Morrison's government spending $320 billion — 16.4 per cent of the nation's gross domestic product — to combat the virus's health and economic effects caused by the same measures imposed by the government itself.

"Because these extreme measures are dictated by the executive and have no deadline to expire, we are effectively experiencing government by executive decree. This is something akin to the actions of deeply authoritarian regimes, in particular when such executive measures are not properly scrutinised.

"It is truly disturbing to observe how a considerable number of Australians willingly surrendered their constitutional rights and freedoms in the name of more government security and protection.

"Such carelessness may eventually prove lethal not only to the long-term preservation of democratic government but also to the preservation of their basic rights to life, liberty and property.

"The Australian Government and the state governments appear to be effectively ruling by executive decree. These extraordinary controls on our freedoms have no constitutional validity because they are certainly not powers intended to be exercised in its present form."

Above all, Zimmerman concluded, Australians would be wise to pay more consideration to these wise words of Thomas Jefferson, the main drafter of the American Declaration of Independence: "A government big enough to give you everything you want, is strong enough to take everything you have."[38]

---

38 The Square and the Tower: How Did It Get This Bad?, *A Sense of Place Magazine*, 9 April, 2020.

Or to quote another towering American figure, Benjamin Franklin, now of renewed relevance: "Those who would give up essential Liberty, to purchase a little temporary Safety, deserve neither Liberty nor Safety."

***

The group Melbourne Activist Legal warned that during COVID, police throughout Australia had rapidly and aggressively expanded their already-considerable surveillance capabilities, spurred on by state and federal governments pushing technological solutions for social control during the pandemic.

"In metropolitan Victoria, we've seen the police deploy aerial mass-surveillance to check for 'breaches of restrictions in Melbourne's corona-virus hot spots', using drones and helicopters.

"Police and local councils have also deployed mobile CCTV in parks and other public spaces to monitor citizens during stage-four restrictions.

"Police monitoring of social media websites has resulted in fines being issued for publishing holiday photos during lockdown, as well as arrests for posting about anti-lockdown protests."

The group also warned that Corporations including Vodafone and Google continued to provide mobile phone location data to governments to further track citizens' movements during the pandemic and to monitor whether people are following social distancing restrictions.

"Amid all this, we've also witnessed the expansion of Automated Number Plate Recognition technology to profile and record the movements of citizens in vehicles, particularly at State borders which have closed during the pandemic.

"This data can be stored indefinitely and expanded upon every time a vehicle is identified in public.

"Such mass-surveillance vastly increases police powers to monitor people in public, and track and record their movements over time. It also produces a database of historical records — the date/time, direction, and registered owner of where all captured vehicles have been travelling. Modern data-mining analysis on a database like this reveals very granular detail of the life of citizens, building up comprehensive pictures of where each vehicle has travelled throughout specific times and dates.

"The safety, privacy, and future use of this information has not been publicly established."

***

Step by terrible step.

Whistleblowers are rare in Australia's public service, and face the sack or imprisonment if caught. Contact-tracing, legal threat and extensive surveillance now made such leaks virtually impossible.

Of all the public servants who knew the so-called Weapons of Mass Destruction used to justify the Iraq War in which Australia had been so closely involved, only one, Andrew Wilkie, spoke out, thereby sacrificing his job as a senior intelligence analyst.

Equally, only one, former Victorian Treasury economist, Sanjeev Sabhlok, spoke out against the cost of lockdowns: "The pandemic policies being pursued in Australia are the most heavy-handed possible, a sledge-hammer to kill a swarm of flies.

"These policies are having hugely adverse economic, social and health effects, with the poorer sections of the community that don't have the ability to work from home suffering the most.

"Australia is signalling to the world that it is closed for business and doesn't care for human freedoms. This will dampen business investment but also impact future skilled migration, the education industry and tourism.

"The whole thing hinges on the scare created by politicians and health professionals."

In the clamour, Sanjeev's dissertation was picked up by various media outlets; and promptly vanished. But he had a point: "The need for good policy process does not disappear just because we face a public health crisis. Even if the pandemic had been as big as the Spanish flu, lockdowns could never have been justified.

"There are strong scientific arguments against lockdowns.

"Governments should have also realised at the outset that they are hostage to chronic groupthink and actively sought alternative advice. I attempted repeatedly to raise my voice within my public sector role, but my attempts were rebuffed. The bureaucracy has clamped down on frank and fearless, impartial advice, in a misplaced determination to support whatever the government decides.

"Billions of dollars in income and wealth have been wiped out in the name of a virus that is no worse than the Asian flu and which can (even now) be managed by isolating the elderly and taking a range of voluntary, innovative measures. All the border closures, all the lockdowns, all the curfews in Melbourne will not eradicate the virus from planet Earth."[39]

***

For Old Alex, shuffling around that tiny gloom-laden God-fearing house, shocked by the rapid collapse of normality all around him, his vision-laden strangeness grew worse by the day.

All the time, that urgent summoning, those strange dislocations, the communications from beyond. And those questions: Why here? Why now?

Because we come at turning points in history, and we speak through manifestation; these were the voices ringing through Old Alex's head on that frozen South Coast.

Despite what some believe, despite all the special pleading, we rarely interfere in the affairs of men, they told him. But here they were, as if born through him, streaming into the undergrowth.

In those cold Oak Flat winters, in those lonely days and long nights, in those suburban streets and workers' cottages, amid the trees ringing the lake, the black swans on a deadpan surface, all the time those entities he could feel all around him marvelled at one thing: how beautiful this planet!

The politics of the country were diabolical, the rearrangement of the country and the suffering that would ensue; all of it a sadness there was now little chance of avoiding. But here, beside the lake, a different story unfurled.

We stood for you on a distant shore, as if we were The First Man, as if they were seeing all this for the first time. The vaulting light, under that vicious dome they called the sky. The nausea of the sudden jolt, the old personality cast into a corner, the symbiont, in a sense, readjusting, the wrenching unfamiliarity, that strange sight in the intertidal zone.

Now other eyes could see.

There was a moment of freeze-frame madness, there were floods of discordant imagery, there was a new purpose, to be reborn. Hail the new world order. Make as if to flood tears down centuries. Make as if to see. As if to see.

So much for the New COVID Normal; imprisoned on a plain of ice.

---

39 I did not come to Australia to be a slave of whimsical Government, Mosqui Archarya, SBS, 18 September, 2020.

SEVEN
COVERT CONCESSIONS
AND SWEETHEART DEALS

THE LAST thing these people wanted was for their sins to be exposed, but it is journalists who write the first draft of history.

Immediately after Scott Morrison won the May 2019 election in an improbable victory, after years of poor governance by the ruling coalition, one of Australia's most accomplished journalists, Michael West, wrote in his piece "Election 2019: How good is plutocracy!": "The votes were still being counted, the final tally of seats in parliament was yet to be settled, when the inevitable list of demands from big business lobbed in the financial press.

"For ordinary Australians, there will be no 'working with the government'. The Great Unwashed have had their say, they can have their say again on a Saturday sometime in 2022. Between now and then, for every week in between, the business lobby will enjoy a privilege of access to those in government which is rarely available to the ordinary citizen."

As West recorded, the Very Big End of Town queued up to congratulate the Prime Minister of Australia, Scott Morrison.

"A truly outstanding result," said Fortescue Metals chief executive Elizabeth Gaines.

Soon enough, Nev Power, a former chief executive of Fortescue Mines and a friend of the prime minister, would be heading up the National COVID-19 Commission Advisory Board, criss-crossing the country from his home in Perth at public expense; to achieve precisely what, was never made clear.

In a piece titled "Covert-19: Government stacks COVID Commission with Oil and Gas Mates", seasoned journalist Sandi Keane wrote: "The government is quietly blowing away years of environmental protections under cover of COVID. Its COVID Commission is stacked with executives from the gas and mining lobbies in what is turning out to be a bonanza for multinationals."

The NCCC was set up on March 25 with no terms of reference, no register of conflicts of interest and even less divulged about its financial resources.

"While the attention of the nation has been drawn to the daily COVID-19 count and embracing the digital world of schooling, working and socialising from home, the fossil fuel industry — with help from the Morrison government — has quietly seized the opportunity to entrench its power and profits."

A report from environmental advocacy group 350 Australia detailed 36 individual policy changes or requests for project-specific support — all under cover of COVID-19.

The group claimed that concessions and sweetheart deals included fourteen requests to slash important environmental or corporate regulations, eleven requests for tax cuts and financial concessions, and twelve instances of requests to fast-track project assessment.

Lucy Manne, Chief Executive of 350 Australia, said: "It is rank opportunism for the fossil fuel lobby to call for slashing of corporate taxes and important environmental protections under the cover of COVID-19. Australians deserve better than to be fed a short-sighted pro-gas agenda, while they are trying to get through a global pandemic."

Unashamed, the prime minister told Parliament House that the COVID Commission, led by Nev Power, "a very distinguished and very accomplished Western Australian", was being tasked with the job of bridging the gap between the private sector and the government sector.

"That has seen us able to connect supply chains to access critical medical supplies and to deal with supply chain issues to get much needed food stores to remote Indigenous communities, as well as to regional towns and even metropolitan centres all across the country, particularly in those early days where we saw the rush on those stores and stocks at various times.

"I applaud their work. I think they are doing absolutely amazing work. When I called them and asked them to do this, I said, 'I need you to serve your country.' And they are serving our country, and this house should be very proud of their service."

**

The prime minister moved to avoid any public scrutiny of the Commission by declaring that it would work "within government" as an advisory board to cabinet; meaning much of its advice would fall under cabinet confidentiality rules.

That meant the commission could operate in secret and was not required to justify its spending, which included more than a million dollars in so-called "market research", money which went straight to Liberal Party-associated groups.

Within four months of the commission's inception, the Prime Minister's Department was refusing to publicly release 1100 documents linked to the COVID-19 Commission's discussion of gas projects and 690 documents about potential conflicts of interest, while also redacting its meeting minutes on economic and national security grounds.

A series of Freedom of Information (FOI) requests — including from *Guardian Australia*, environmental group 350 Australia, the Australia Institute, and wire service journalist Hannah Ryan — asked for documents that would likely have revealed how potential conflicts of interest were handled by the commission.

The requests were refused or heavily redacted by the Department of the Prime Minister and Cabinet.

Richie Merzian, the Australia Institute's climate spokesman, said the institute's FOI request revealed that the normal governance, processes and expertise involved in the Public Service were simply non-existent in the NCCC.

"This is concerning, as the commission is made up of business people who are using, in the chair's own words, their 'contact lists' to 'problem-solve' without being 'managed from the centre'," Merzian said.

**

Not long after, a University of Melbourne policy brief scrutinising the functioning of the National COVID-19 Commission advisory board, found the board suffered from a lack of transparency, had no legislative underpinning, and had not employed an independent appointment process to select its members.

The government's COVID-19 Commission posed an enduring risk to Australian democracy and must be overhauled, including by the creation of a public and mandatory conflict-of-interest register, the paper found.

Author Elizabeth Hicks wrote that the NCCC "offers lessons" in the accretion of executive power during times of crisis.

"In Australia, the relationship between executive decision-making, political parties and regulatory capture remains a challenge for democracy," she wrote. "Such challenges in turn colour the nature of novel advisory bodies and structures created to respond to moments of crisis.

"And although not immediate, the risks entailed within executive subversion of democratic deliberation reach far further than the life of the crisis itself."[40]

More than a year on from its inception, the COVID Commission would be wound up in shambolic ignominy.

In a piece lengthily titled "Farewell, COVID Commission, what did you leave us? A bunch of secrets, a heap of costs and that gas-led recovery", news outlet *Crikey* put the nail in the coffin.

"Its greatest achievement was a secret manufacturing task force report which was used to justify the coalition's 'gas-led recovery'. This triggered a wave of criticism, given the board's connections to the gas and fossil fuel industry, particularly special adviser Andrew Liveris, the former Dow Chemical boss who sits on the board of mining services company Worley and oil giant Saudi Aramco.

"The plan has been used to justify taxpayer subsidies for new gas projects, at a time when the rest of the world is making drastic moves to lower emissions."

In closing down the NCCC, Morrison declared: "I want to thank the chair of the board, Mr Nev Power, and each of the current and former commissioners for their work. They answered the call for their country when they were needed and have worked hard to support the government's plans for managing the virus and economic recovery.

---

40 Liz Hicks: Private Actors and Executive Power During Times of Crisis: Scrutinising Australia's National COVID-19 Co-ordination Commission, Admin Law Blog, Liz Hicks, 29 June, 2020.

"The board provided a real-time business perspective on critical aspects of our COVID-19 response. They helped businesses safely reopen with COVID-safe plans, and provided a business perspective to help inform our policies for economic recovery."

However many millions those on the COVID Commission pocketed, how much the entire exercise cost Australian taxpayers, would be carefully hidden, labelled as a "Cabinet in Confidence", that is "Secret", for the next 30 years.

***

Incensed by the heavily rorted fiasco unfolding in front of all their eyes, Alex published a piece called "Profiting from COVID: Welcome to the COVID economy".

"Depleted incomes, smashed small businesses, bullshit jobs, a whole new platform for crony capitalism, deserted main streets. What's not to love?

"Not many businesses and industries are growing in 2020.

"Main Street is dying, in small towns and large city downtowns, all over the world. Small businesses especially are suffering. Particular sectors, like tourism, have tanked. No one disputes this, though few in power seem to care. Or, if they do, it is clearly not a policy priority.

"When even non-COVID public healthcare has been all but abandoned, it is of little surprise that everything else too has been put on policy hold. Other than shovelling money out the door with the sole purpose of keeping unemployed and under-employed workers from marching in the streets against the lockdowns.

"The world is dipping into recession, or worse."[41]

Old Alex, in that freezing windswept winter, sat in the almost empty train carriages, rustling to and from work, and read over and over again the advertising slogans about the Australian Minerals Council, that is the Very Very Big End of Town; that is the same end of town to which this government was hostage, saying that we needed to look at mining in a new way, that donations from the mining sector were helping to cure cancer.

Only a brief instant in time before, such advertising on a public train would have been unusual. Instead, along with the perennial car and

41 Profiting from COVID: The New Growth Industry, Paul Collits, *A Sense of Place Magazine*, 24 November, 2020.

insurance companies, they promoted messages about helping your neighbours, or charities, thinking of others, mental health, education, bushfire relief, good causes.

There was nothing good about this mob. They plundered the land where his forebears had been. They gorged themselves at the trough. They deluded millions and millions of people into throwing themselves into serfdom. They created a new slave class.

Many a cold morning he watched the yellow-vested construction workers getting off the train at the stations through the middle of Sydney — Central, Town Hall, Martin Place — those workers, the few there were, all of a sudden lucky just to be in work, lucky to be allowed out of their own homes, to have been deemed essential.

As he walked to his temporary office down at Circular Quay, he passed one closed shop after another, cafes, takeaways, bars, restaurants, dry-cleaners, gyms — all closed. Entire office blocks empty. Only the occasional car in normally traffic-jammed streets.

***

Sydney was a city utterly transformed.

He kept asking himself: How did quarantining the healthy and bankrupting in an entire economy make any sense at all?

But he met almost nobody who agreed with the sentiment; as they dutifully sanitised their hands and donned their masks, and soon enough he learnt to shut his mouth; trapped in a deceptive, treacherous world, encased by tinted mirrors, walking through the deserted precincts of the Opera House, walking, virtually alone, across the Harbour Bridge.

There was no use arguing.

They might as well have been police-swarming protestors, the way the Twitter mobs pounced on anyone who was suspicious of the government narrative.

Journalism as a profession tends to lean left. There was the creation of a bizarre kind of moral panic akin to the pack mentality created around climate change; you were a bad person if you dared to doubt. Already, if you dared to protest, you were a criminal.

Amongst the gaggle of perpetrators were many of his former workmates, and he watched in surprise as they rounded on colleagues who disagreed with the lockdown policies as somehow being creatures of the right, as journalists who had sold their souls; none of which was true.

Old Alex had swum in a crowded media sea almost his entire working life; and there was little worse than watching the behaviour of the profession he had once been so proud to join.

In the upside-down world of Australian politics, the left were rushing to embrace lockdowns, curfews and the abolition of the liberty to protest, while the right were suddenly the champions of individual freedom, the ability to make your own decisions about your own health, and the privilege, in a free society, to doubt, and most particularly to doubt the COVID narrative spewing from uncritical government-funded or -manipulated news outlets.

The surface story — the blitzing, ridiculing or excising anyone who disagreed with the official narrative — was all part of the beginning of a descent into horror.

Anyone who dared suggest that Australia's lockdowns represented the most radical and destructive suite of policies ever perpetrated against the civilian population got pilloried; that is, anyone who stated the obvious, that Australian authorities were not the doyens of scientific literacy they pretended to be and were ignoring a considerable body of both populist and scientific opinion which placed them squarely in the wrong.

The best form of censorship is the one where people censor themselves, and live in fear of speaking out.

Like so many other dissenting voices, Old Alex often remained silent in the amphitheatre of social media and with the people he encountered.

Nowhere was comfortable, not on the shores of that over-lit, normally hectic, famously beautiful waterway Sydney Harbour, not in that stricken house on the South Coast with the slow dying of his struggling parent, not within himself, not on these frightened streets.

And so, he just worked.

Lockdowns, masks, stay-at-home orders, martial law, fear — all driven by fear. As it would turn out, a highly profitable fear for The Very Big End of Town.

***

Old Alex became obsessed with lockdowns partly because they impacted on his own life so badly; as they did, of course, on so many others.

While hundreds of thousands of people were losing their livelihoods in Australia, in total contrast, life in Sweden went on more or less as normal.

Model this: What would Australia be like if the government had done absolutely nothing?

Or If Australia had modelled the far less destructive Swedish response, designed by some of Europe's most distinguished epidemiologists, which in essence protected the elderly and let everybody else go on about their lives, thereby preserving the nation's civilian life?

There was no common sense. There was no rationality. The populace clung to beliefs without a shred of evidence; succumbed to government fear campaigns without a shrug of resistance.

While he walked free across a vaulting sky. And wished he could care not.

The country was in chaos from one end to the other.

Thread by dark thread, clod by dark clod. Step by terrible step. So it came to pass. Of all the injustices in Australian history, none was more consequential than this widely perpetrated deceit.

***

Already the Australian Government's response to the pandemic was having significant impacts on the population's wellbeing.

A research project between the ABC and Vox Pop Labs known as "COVID-19 Monitor", published in late April of 2020, showed the coronavirus pandemic had made Australians more anxious, confused and bored.

The number of Australians reporting poor mental health more than doubled compared with the previous month. The number frequently feeling despair more than tripled, while those frequently feeling confused was up five times.

The same survey showed that most Australians backed the Federal Government's response.

It should have been obvious from the very beginning that more harm would be done by the government's actions than the virus could ever have done.

Now they would all be paying the price of ignorance. Now the crashed fortunes of much of the population, as the rich got even richer, would lead straight to the pit, to chaos in the streets, to terrible annihilation. That isolation would prove both physical and of the spirit, in this place which had embraced a lunatic madness.

Empty emporiums, empty chairs, empty forecourts, bequeathed by empty hearts.

***

Across the entire period professionals raised concerns that the societal-wide destruction and community dislocation engineered by governments would increase death rates well beyond anything the virus might have caused.

A joint statement by the Australian Medical Association, the University of Sydney's Brain and Mind Centre and the University of Melbourne's Centre of Youth Mental Health, argued that many health professionals, including GPs, psychiatrists, and emergency physicians, were seeing significant growth in the number of patients seeking treatment and support for their mental health.

"We know that young people are going to be disproportionately affected by the COVID-19 pandemic, and the measures that are needed to stop the spread of this deadly disease.

"Dynamic modelling of the adverse impacts of COVID-19 on unemployment, social dislocation, and mental health shows that there may be a 25 per cent increase in suicides, and it is likely that about 30 per cent of those will be among young people. If the Australian economy deteriorates further, this number may increase. We are facing a situation where between an extra 750 and 1500 more suicides may occur annually, in addition to the 3000-plus lives that are lost to suicide already every year.

"Furthermore, this tragically higher rate is likely to persist for up to five years if the economic downturn lasts more than twelve months. Such a death rate is likely at this stage to overshadow the number of deaths in Australia directly attributable to COVID-19 infection."

The left-leaning Australia Institute warned; "Over the course of a year, from the introduction of the coronavirus supplement at the end of March 2020 to its removal at the end of March 2021, over one million Australians (1,055,000) will enter poverty, including almost 220,000 children.

"Poverty in childhood can have lifelong effects. Children living in poverty are more likely to have impairment in cognitive development which leads to them falling behind in school. They are also more likely to have impairment in their social, emotional and behavioural development. Poverty has also been linked to a range of adverse health outcomes. All of this means that children who grow up in poverty are more likely, when they are adults, to have lower incomes and to be unemployed or marginally attached to the labour market."

Later research from the *Journal of Psychiatric Research* suggested that during the heights of the lockdowns one in ten Victorians had seriously considered suicide, one in five Victorians had felt suicidal, and another one in five reported experiencing anxiety or depression.

Other research by the Kids Helpline showed suicide attempts by teenagers soared 184 per cent during lockdowns.

Youth suicide gets all the government and media attention, but what about the rest; all those people driven to despair in their personal and business lives?

Australian media has a strong tradition of not reporting suicides for fear of encouraging copy-cat behaviour. Any editor who defies the restriction can expect a call from government operatives. The convention has the effect of concealing much social injustice in Australia and, during the COVID era, of concealing the impacts of government policies.

There were a number of dramatic and tragic incidents unknown to the public.

That the politicians dominating the airwaves were claiming to be keeping Australians safe was not just a little rich, it was a straight-out lie. And the nation's journalists should have been calling them out.

***

The closed-off walking trails in national parks, perhaps the healthiest place in the country to be, were another sign of a signal derangement.

Old Alex thought the government was doing a terrible job. He trusted them not one jot. But back in Oak Flats he was an outlier.

The prime minister's ratings had soared.

There was one, one whole case, in Moss Vale and three in the adjoining town of Bowral, a place characterised by mansions on large blocks, but almost the entire economy of the Southern Highlands of NSW had been shut down.

How did that make any sense?

There were no cases in South Australia and none in the Northern Territory, according to one radio report, yet they refused to open their borders.

The authorities knew already that this was for a disease which had, according to some of the world's leading epidemiologists, a 0.01 to 0.03 per cent death rate, on a par with the flu.

Yet half of all workers in the country were now reliant on a government payment.

How did that make sense?

Decide in haste, repent at leisure. But it was worse than that. The recriminations were yet to start. There was an evil afoot in it all, and a lunacy.

The timeline had become dangerously chaotic.

His contempt for ordinary working people oozed from the prime minister's every pore, or so it seemed to an entirely jaundiced old reporter.

And every day the country lurched ever further to a standstill, a tower falling.

***

The pigeons scattered at Old Alex's feet, in yet another empty city square.

There was an internal and external derangement.

They gathered there in the early dawn — tormentors, observers, supporters and detractors — and it was all about secrecy, finessing things past a goalpost, telling nobody. There never was a secret chord; there was a psychometric drenching, a flooding of neural disturbance and a waiting, as if waiting for some arrival from a distant place. But they were already here, born alive and weaponised, determined to guard the future. The whole corrupt edifice was being washed away, there on the Temple Mount and here in the sacred duties of a lost world, the secret language of trees and the malleable plantation they were transforming all around them.

Having chloroformed the population, having discoloured the elites with treachery, having sent secret emissaries and having spied on the planet for millennia, a thousand talents in a thousand bars, having launched this piece of quantum entanglement across a vast distance and come to know and love you, yearned to assimilate all these new experiences, the startling feel of air on skin.

"He can't write like this if he wants to be taken seriously," one of the Watchers on the Watch up in Sydney sniffed.

And he could see the harbour unravelling before them, as everything took on an uncanny import here at the dawn of a new era, the changing of an epoch, the warnings that had been ignored, here in the wreckage of their dawn. From the pleasure domes of old worlds, we came to tell you. Welcome to the universe. Welcome to everything. Be wary. Take care. A hand on a shoulder. A startled stare. A place where we had never been. The haunting had begun, and with it the fate of millions.

***

He saw no kindness in the present, no kindness in any of it. And now, strung out before the dawn, he just watched, appalled, as everything went to dust; or mud; or just the stench of what surely must be an evil.

They were witnessing a species-wide transformation.

As at 3pm on 30 April 2020, a total of 6753 cases of COVID-19 had been reported in Australia, including 91 deaths, and 5714 were reported as recovered from COVID-19. Over the previous week, there had been an average of thirteen new cases reported each day. Of the newly reported cases, the majority were from NSW.

The median age of all cases was 48 years.

The median age of deaths was 80 years.

Of cases with a reported place of acquisition, 64 per cent had recent international travel history, including more than 1200 cases associated with cruise ships.

That now infamous smirk Prime Minister Scott Morrison wore as he wound up yet another press conference, having batted away anything even remotely resembling a difficult question, had become a signature tune.

It was meant to be a health emergency. It was a societal-wide remake done under cover.

***

There was a recycled black joke perfect for the season:

A man walks through his village blowing a horn.

A stranger asks: "Why do you blow the horn?"

"To keep the tigers away," he replies.

"But there are no tigers here."

"There, you see. It works!"

There in that dismally depressed little house in an isolated suburb called Oak Flats, intensely pressurised, under what he felt was an abusive and intrusive level of surveillance, Old Alex just kept on going. No doubt some of the time he was persecuting himself. There was no alternative. Do or die. There was no one to bounce ideas off; no one with whom to reconcile your humanity. For many, the single biggest difficulty of the lockdowns was the isolation.

He won no friends, certainly not among the privileged taxpayer-funded thugs now overseeing the operation against him. And certainly not with a story titled "How Australia Got COVID-19 Completely and Totally Wrong: Experts Warn Against Authoritarian Madness".

Around him, as if anything he wrote could make the slightest difference, threat stirred. Everyone wanted to be on a train to nowhere.

It wasn't exactly hard to find people casting doubt on the actions and policies of the Australian authorities.

And so, he quoted a number of the world's leading experts, all of whom the Australian public were blissfully unaware of, panicked instead by the daily blizzard of premiers, health bureaucrats, ministers, police officials and, of course, the prime minister; all of them eternally on their screens, dictating the story of the nation; all of them handsomely paid, all of them operating under entirely false pretences.

One of the many pointing out the dangers of the present course of action was Douglas Allen, a Canadian economist at Simon Fraser University, who reviewed 80 cost-benefit analyses of government's COVID-19 restrictions. He found those that supported lockdowns made unrealistically pessimistic assumptions of death rates in the absence of coercion and ignored many costs.

"Lockdown caused a broad range of costs through lost civil liberty, lost social contact, lost educational opportunities, lost medical preventions and procedures, increased domestic violence, increased anxiety and mental suffering, and increased deaths of despair," he said. "It is possible lockdown will go down as one of the greatest peacetime policy failures."

***

Germany adopted the same draconian lockdown policies as Australia, and thereby added to the validity of Australian authorities.

Sucharit Bhakdi, Professor Emeritus of Medical Microbiology at the Johannes Gutenberg University Mainz, one of the most cited research scientists in Germany, wrote an open letter to German Chancellor Angela Merkel calling for an urgent reassessment of her response to COVID-19.

He warned that government measures were leading to self-destruction and collective suicide based on nothing but a spook. He described the German government's response as grotesque, absurd and dangerous.

"The reason for my concern lies above all in the truly unforeseeable socio-economic consequences of the drastic containment measures which are currently being applied in large parts of Europe and which are also already being practised on a large scale in Germany."

Dr Peter Gøtzsche, Professor of Clinical Research Design at the University of Copenhagen, was the author of several books on corruption in the field of medicine and the power of big pharmaceutical companies.

Terrify millions in order to make billions. Now there's a business plan.

Of COVID-19, Gøtzsche wrote that there had been an epidemic of mass panic and the lockdowns were "a dream scenario for any ruler with dictatorship tendencies; all democratic demonstrations are unlawful".

Looked at through the prism of the present, how prescient, how prophetic these voices of dissent came to be.

"Where does this stop? Logic was one of the first victims.

"What if the Chinese had not tested their patients for coronavirus or there had not been any test? Would we have carried on with our lives, without restrictions, not worrying about some deaths here and there among old people, which we see every winter? I think so.

"Our main problem is that no one will ever get in trouble for measures that are too draconian. They will only get in trouble if they do too little. So, our politicians and those working with public health do much more than they should do.

"No such draconian measures were applied during the 2009 influenza pandemic, and they obviously cannot be applied every winter, which is all year round, as it is always winter somewhere. We cannot close down the whole world permanently.

"The harms include suicides that go up in times of unemployment; and when people's businesses built up carefully over many years lie in ruins, they might kill themselves. The panic is also killing life itself."

***

And all the while, for Old Alex, surrendered as it were on that dramatic coastline, he endured that urgent messaging, those lucid dreams in those once endearing streets, the distant suburban flanks of a once great city, the flying, because they were always flying.

Rise up, rise up the horses! Beware! Ultra-stealth. They moved through the trees in a shimmer. They spoke in a kind of divine, arcane language; were blessed and weak, powerful and distant. Sometimes they were just as shocked as he was, as they landed in this freezing clime. All around him, the earth was terraforming. An instant moment that caught the graze between two worlds; and as always, he was distant from it all, a mere bridge, and saw them shimmer and slither as they landed.

The normal person knew as much about them as a cat knew about the Roman Empire. We were blessed to be here. He could feel them running through the wind, cascading down centuries, feeling at once loved and divine. He didn't know how to stop them. He didn't know how to call a halt to any of it. That strange child's cry of hide and seek: "Coming, ready or not."

It was a signal derangement, in every sense.

Just as the government's inflated response to COVID destroyed the lives of so many, so Alex felt a strange imperilment, as if their fates became his fate, as if the days of postponement were over. He was giddy from the shock. He couldn't land safely. The air moved through the trees; and he knew they were not even remotely human, the way they were was so different, how they struggled with English, just another language for another manifestation. He was sick of the wash of thoughts from the surrounding humans. He was sick of being a target for their analysts. The whole world was lighting up.

They only came at turning points.

They have always walked among us.

***

Seasoned journalist Geoffrey Luck wrote in an article titled "One Dozen Dissenting Second Opinions" that COVID-19 had brought out the Führer Complex in far too many. One of Victorian Premier Daniel Andrews' police officers crowed after handing a $1600 fine to a teenage learner driver taking instruction from her mum: "We're really smashing you guys today."

All this, Luck argued, would make it very, very difficult to return to normality.

He opened the piece with a quote: "It spreads out invisibly. It spreads along the streets and train tracks, over the counters and tables, the packaging and surfaces. And it spreads above all about what makes us human: closeness to each other. Confidential conversations, joint efforts on the sports field, tender touches — all of this helps the new corona virus on its way through the world. Hands, nose, eyes, mouth: For SARS-COV-2, people are open wounds waiting to be infected. Some people simply cannot afford it."

As Luck explained, the quote was from an editorial in *Der Tagesspiegel*, the main newspaper of Berlin, but could have been written anywhere in the world, especially in Australia, which imposed even more draconian restrictions than Germany.

"The message of fear, of an unknown and invisible killer, is designed to condition the citizens to accept unquestioningly the repressive measures prescribed for them by their betters. Measures imposed without justification.

"There are eminent medical scientists who believe the overreaction by bureaucrats and politicians living a long way from the life and death reality faced daily by practising doctors, and anxious not to be castigated for inaction, is unnecessary.

"Why should Australians be content to be told merely that decisions which bankrupt their businesses, throw hundreds of thousands out of work, shut down all social life, criminalise petty transgressions and incur a vast national debt are based on the best medical advice?

"Australians are being taken for a ride by well-meaning but blinkered bureaucratic experts and subservient politicians. How can the curtailment of human rights and freedoms be justified?

"Where is the Marc Antony we need to remind us that we are not 'men of wood' and call for the very stones to rise and mutiny?"[42]

***

Among the many world experts of whom the Australian public, with the able assistance of their government, news management and manipulated internet search algorithms were blissfully unaware, was Dr John Ioannidis, Professor of Medicine, Health Research and Policy at Stanford University: "You cannot remain in a lockdown state indefinitely. Then there will be deaths from the effects of lockdown's consequences, such as suicides or heart attacks due to the stress of unemployment and inactivity.

"If we had not known about a new virus out there, the number of 'influenza-like illness' would not seem unusual this year. At most, we might have casually noted that flu this season seems a bit worse than average.

"I am much more concerned about the consequences of blind measures, the possible destruction of an economy … and the larger number of lives that can be lost in conditions of economic and social collapse.

"I hope we avoid the worst and show calmness, solidarity, brotherhood, and courage instead of panic."

And Dr Yoram Lass, former Director-General of the Israeli Health Ministry: "We all forget the swine flu in 2009. That was a virus that reached the world from Mexico and until today there is no vaccination against it. At the time, there was no Facebook. The coronavirus, in contrast, is a virus with public relations. Whoever thinks that governments end viruses is wrong."

And Dr Pietro Vernazza, infectious diseases specialist, St Gallen Hospital, Switzerland: "In Italy, one in ten people diagnosed die, one for every 1000 infected. Often — similar to the flu season — it affects people who are at the end of their lives. If we close the schools, we will prevent the children from quickly becoming immune. We should better integrate the scientific facts into the political decisions."

And Dr David Katz, founding director of the Yale University Prevention Research Centre: "I am deeply concerned that the social, economic and public health consequences of this near-total meltdown of normal life

---

42 One Dozen Dissenting Second Opinoins, Geoffrey Luck, Quadrant, 1 April, 2020.

will be long-lasting and calamitous, possibly graver than the direct toll of the virus itself. The unemployment, impoverishment and despair likely to result will be public health scourges of the first order."

All of this was in plain sight. The general public should have been aware there were widespread doubts about Australia's approach from the very beginning. The media should have taken its traditional role, of holding governments to account, seriously. The point of quoting all these various experts being: there was no excuse for ignorance.

***

But the Australian public was not media-literate enough to understand that, far from being kept safe, they were being intensely manipulated. Submission comes from many flanks. The last thing the Australian Government wanted, as it placed itself front and centre in everybody's lives, was to promote independent thinking or vigorous debate.

If the wisdom of any of these towering intellects, some of the smartest people on Earth, ever reached the ear of the Australian Prime Minister, he showed absolutely no sign.

Paul Collits summed it all up in a piece titled "Zero COVID Man", declaring that the prime minister and his National Cabinet of complicit autocrats were the people responsible for creating among the voters the triple evils of irrational fear bordering on hysteria, venal and self-serving behaviour, and massively increased dependence on the state.

"It means giving voters no choice, since they all either agree with one another or don't have the guts to oppose the COVID theatre that now substitutes for governing. It means massive inconvenience. It means freedoms destroyed. The freedom to do everyday, mundane things.

"It means endless internal and external border closures — mean, shameless and dictatorial. It means truncated interstate trade and travel. It means lockdowns on a whim, without notice. Mask mandates. Bans at worst and curbs at best on normal activity. Enforced incarceration. Threats of prison. The stifling, joy-draining bureaucratisation of everything. Reporting in doorways before masked officials in order to have a pint or to worship your god.

"Is it worse to have a stupid prime minister who does really dumb things, or an evil prime minister who knowingly does what he knows to be stupid but popular?

"The appetite for freedom in Australia has been suppressed by a government-led and media-supported campaign of deceit, exaggeration, half-truths, propaganda, endless repetition of messaging and fear-mongering.

"The low-information voter has been tricked into jumping at shadows."[43]

***

The coronavirus pandemic was changing the world day by day, hour by hour. If there was any good to come out of any of it, the fact that the competencies and motivations of governments were now coming under scrutiny must be one of them. Old Alex actually thought that, so naive was he.

Secrecy and the manipulation of public narrative would become major themes of Australian governance in the coming months with, a year on, the government refusing to release the costs of its lockdown policies; because, of course, they had squandered hundreds of billions of dollars for no good purpose.

Senior reporter at *The Australian* Adam Creighton reported: "The government has refused to release Treasury documents that spell out the assumed costs and benefits of border closures, lockdowns and other COVID-19 restrictions, a decision which prominent economists have slammed as 'outrageous'.

"The Federal Government has classed 38 different estimates of the costs of various restrictions, including borders closures, school closures and Victoria's series of extra lockdowns as 'cabinet documents', which excludes them from public access under Freedom of Information laws."

Economist Saul Eslake said it was "outrageous that the government won't share with the public any of the basis for the decisions it has made".

The University of NSW's Professor Peter Swan also described the decision as "absolutely outrageous".

"The fact that not a single word can be revealed on the impact of Victorian COVID-19 restrictions on the Victorian and Australian economy even now, long after they have cost taxpayers hundreds of billions of dollars and forced thousands of Australian small businesses to close, indicates the damning nature of the contents of these documents," he said.

---

43 Zero COVID Man, Paul Collits, *A Sense of Place Magazine*, 12 May, 2021.

"It would seem highly likely that the government has ignored advice from Treasury and elsewhere that lockdown is almost entirely unproductive and ineffective, as well as being economically crippling."

***

What seemed impossible only days before was now all too possible.

Suddenly, in an almost mystical sense, the streets held menace. Far from being the first men, we could be the last. The few people in the streets appeared clearly frightened of being caught outside. Apart from mouthing off to no one in particular, Old Alex felt entirely powerless. As did almost anyone else who failed to march to the rhythm of compliance.

Already, today was history, as we snaked into the future on a million storylines.

> If you come to
> Heaven's Torrents
> Heaven's Wells,
> Heaven's Prisons,
> Heaven's Traps
> Heaven's Cracks:
> Quit such places
> With all speed.
> Sun Tzu. *The Art of War*.

At the time, for Old Alex, stranded in a place where he did not want to be and in a situation not of his choosing, struggling to establish any semblance of a normal life, those weeks were preoccupied with what he could and could not publish; still feeling haunted, distressed, not himself, everything a crucial edge of fright, or a frightening infinity.

Stay-at-home orders weren't much better than a prison sentence, for him, for lots of people. Many people just aren't suited to being trapped inside. And in a sunlit place and difficult personal circumstance, doubly so. Weren't we all trapped?

It was as if the zipper in the sky above the sky had been undone, and all the wounds of heaven allowed to spill down; as if it was a terrible moment before the entities arrived to change the course of history, their contingent armies and protectors and apparitions yet to fill those waking dreams, that lucid dreaming which frightened him so much.

Now we looked afar, further and further afield, and those flying sylphs, those disembodied wings and frightening overlays; those disturbances in the ether of things, they were here to serve a higher purpose.

There were many things in play, impending swarms and alarming beauty, the agnostics' displeasure, the attempt to weaponise something which should not be weaponised, at the same time as only the military had the capacity to themselves swarm across something so complex, so game-changing.

In Australia an overwhelmed public, normally distrusting of both journalists and politicians, were fleeing down rabbit holes into isolation wards of their own making.

Why the governments of the era acted in the very peculiar way they did was even more mysterious at the time, as mysterious as the compliance of the population.

***

There was blood on everybody's conscience. He could still hear, as if some kind of racial memory, those cheers, that wild exultation from a past life, in this far place, on this beloved planet, as the voices of the trees swirled in the gusts of wind.

"I can see the old hierarchies falling," Jacqui, the woman who did cheap haircuts for $10 a pop, had said earlier, at the side of the local Oak Flats Swimming Pool. They swapped pleasantries while all around them others endured their own quiet lives. A terrible silence marked the days.

Jacqui had a tendency to make psychic forecasts, believing she had the gift; the gender of his coming grandchildren, the shape of the year ahead.

Indeed, the times were riven strange.

In the changing-sheds an old lawyer he ran into occasionally, a man who had done a lot of government work, very deliberately engaged him in conversation about the book *Conversations with God*.

There's no such thing as coincidence, the saying goes.

Old Alex had never read it but had recently been thinking along those lines as, in a strange parallel with the country's lockdowns, streams of lyricism and peculiar images waxed through him, a kind of shapelessness taking form. The Word. They agreed. In the beginning there was a form of communication.

Later he would look up details of the author, Neale Donald Walsch, who, from a chequered life one February night in 1992 wrote a despair-filled letter to God, "What does it take to make life work?"

According to him, he received a divine answer which led to his series of bestselling books. It was, as he told it, like taking down dictation and he published it without any alterations.

All Alex knew was that he was often frightened of the real beyond the real, and did much to resist the swarming that was overtaking him, his own head ringing with half-caught phrases.

The lawyer, swimming fit and well maintained for his age, dressed slowly and settled onto the changing-room bench.

"There are those who believe Christ is already here, that the second coming is now in process, that he is already here, that he speaks through people," he declared. "Shakespeare is a fine example. I believe God spoke through Shakespeare. That he is a messenger. That this is the exact reason he is loved 400 years later, yet we know so little about him as a person."

It was an unusual conversation for the changing-sheds of Oak Flats.

Minutes before he had been watching as a group of big girls flirted with a skinny dumb-as-dog-shit bloke. To steal a line: obesity ravaged the underclass as assuredly as typhoid had ravaged their forebears. There was so much genetic debris in this mewling species.

"Love, the world is love, God is love, Christ was all about love," the old lawyer expounded.

But for Alex that simply wasn't true. All of the images streaming through him were of the violence of war, as if those entities who used him as some kind of messaging board were born fighting, birthed fully armed.

In a land and a time of entwining circumstance; a popular remix of a Tina Turner classic played over and over: "What's love got to do, got to do with it?"

No, it was not about love.

Outside the rarely inspiring change-sheds of the Oak Flats pool, once again the streets were quiet, reflecting the beginning of wave after wave of government COVID scare campaigns, made worse by the pig-ignorant level of public debate, the blind deceiving the blinded.

That was the year that Australia destroyed itself, the state borders slammed shut, a massive expansion of state dependency, tens of thousands of businesses destroyed and millions of futures extinguished, all for what?

For an act of societal-wide self-immolation stunning in its sheer, utter and complete stupidity.

EIGHT
MULTITUDES

BACK ON PLANET earth — well, back in Oak Flats actuality — he paced the house and knew no peace. Forbidden by law to leave without good reason, he listened to his dying parent talk of the Father, the return of Christ, that humanity had proven it could not govern itself.

The headlines in his magazine queued his discontent: "The Australian Government Response to Corona Crisis: A Massive Subsidy to Corporations"; "COVID-19: Pundits Queue to Criticise the Prime Minister"; "Welcome to Australia, The World's Newest Totalitarian State"; "Deliberately Destroying the Economy: Fiscal Stimulus on Steroids"; "Coronavirus, Mass Psychological Engineering and 1984"; "Stasi Australia"; "Shutting Down Australia: How It All Ends"; "COVID-19 Does Not Make it to the Top 50 Causes of Deaths in Australia. For this We Have Sacrificed Everything?"; "The World's Only Pentecostal Leader: The End is Nigh"; "How Australia Got COVID-19 Completely and Totally Wrong: Experts Warn Against Authoritarian Madness"; "The Biggest Mistake in History: Debating the Great Lockdown".

The priests were all over it.

Historically, the written word had once seemed so magical that they were known as "God signs". Ideas are weapons. Words are powerful. They transmit ideas from beyond the realm. But this was a world where billions of words cluttered the landscape every single day; and there was no morality. Putting his best foot forward did not mean serving the Dark Lords. And it did not mean lying to save himself.

So out on a limb in those early days, surrounded by operatives who in a saner world would have just ignored his existence, linked to heaven and tethered to Earth, God on speed dial; if only he had been more willing, his pressurisation, personal and professional, internal and external, ramped up every single day. He was being walked on by both sides.

By 4 April, 2020, there had been 27 deaths from the coronavirus in Australia. And already Australia had been transformed, with a bewildered, confused and frightened population. Constantly shifting messages from government compounded the confusion.

What only a few weeks ago would have seemed like a fantasy dystopian future, scenarios that were simply not possible in a country like Australia, had become all too frighteningly real.

If three people gathered outside, in a park, on the beach, in their front yard, they could now be jailed for six months for breaching "the law". In an outdoors, freedom-loving country how could this be so?

Soon enough, what they most feared happened. The government lost control of the COVID narrative; ably helped by the nation's staggeringly incompetent political class and truly hapless mismanagement at the highest levels.

Now anyone with time on their hands (and anyone in lockdown had time on their hands) could Google #coronahoax, #FakePandemic, #Scamdemic, #Plandemic, #NoNewNormal and all the rest.

The minute one channel was shut down, another appeared.

You really can't censor everybody.

***

Australia's low levels of education and poor literacy formed the humus for the spreading of fear, disinformation and the quashing of alternative points of view, but this was an era where almost everyone had a smartphone, and doubt could spread like wildfire.

Thousands of people were expressing their frustration, often along similar lines. As one Twitter correspondent, Jude Morton, wrote: "We are living in a totalitarian state just look at what they've done, created fear division and hate, whilst destroying our services, education, health, welfare, the very infrastructure of a decent society! Whilst no accountability whatsoever! They lie."

The sentiments were soon repeated in myriad versions thousands of times a day from Britain to the US to Australia.

Old Alex did his best, or put his best foot forward, there in that tiny house in a land of ancient spirits where we all faced the music of the spheres; an old hack at the butt end of his jagged career who believed for a moment that he could make a difference, that words had power and the world would pause to rethink this madness, that there was still time for sanity to prevail.

All the economic forecasts were bad.

"Stay Home Save Lives," blared *The West Australian* in late March. "ScoMo asks Australians not to go outside unless 'absolutely necessary' to combat virus spread."

By May the headlines were screaming: "Four billion a week the cost of the lock down."

Treasury estimated that the mass closure of businesses and activities would see gross domestic product plunge by 10 per cent in the June quarter — the equivalent of $50 billion being wiped from the economy.

Former Labor leader turned state leader of One Nation in NSW, Mark Latham, was just one of those from the conservative side of politics, ostensibly the same side as the governing powers, warning that with the multi-billion-dollar cost and one million jobs lost in just five weeks, the Australian economy was facing "an economic horror story, a sharp vicious downturn the like of which we have never seen, even during the time of the Great Depression.

"What we have seen here is governments collectively spending $300 billion dollars, but the net outcome has been a 20 per cent collapse in household spending.

"Social wellbeing, health care and prosperity depend on a functional economy. The faster we open the economy, the better off we will be on all these fronts".

However, "there is no return to normality", Mr Latham said, arguing that the focus on climate change over the past decade had distracted the government from addressing tax reform, workplace relations and economic development, making it far more difficult for Australia to return to a good fiscal position.

There was very little resilience in the Australian population. There would be no snapback recovery, as politicians were claiming.

By early May of 2020, the financial news service Bloomberg was warning that Australia was heading into its deepest downturn in almost 100 years.

"It's likely to take years for wage growth and inflation to bounce back. Australia appears to have succeeded in flattening the coronavirus curve, but such an optimistic health outcome won't prevent the economy from experiencing a deep downturn. Our base case anticipates the largest contraction since the 1930-1931 Great Depression.

"Significant stimulus — both monetary and fiscal — is cushioning households and helping businesses to survive and retain workers. Despite this, Australia's small open economy has already seen considerable damage and faces headwinds from subdued global demand and trade. Significant monetary-fiscal co-ordination to provide further stimulus will be required to recover the economy over the years ahead."

In contrast, the government claimed that by closing the borders, quarantining travellers, shutting businesses and enforcing social distancing, Australia had exceeded expectations, flattening the curve quickly and aggressively suppressing the coronavirus.

The government was lying.

***

Caitlin Johnstone is one of the few independent Australian journalists with a sufficient international following to support her craft.

Old Alex was pleased to be able to publish her, one of the joys of having his own magazine, no matter how large or small the audience, and on this one Caitlin was straight out of the box.

"You can't blame people for being distrustful when you make them that way. The people screaming the loudest about disinformation right now are the ones most responsible for it.

"Coronavirus disinformation is the hot topic of the day, with pressure mounting on social media platforms to censor incorrect information about the virus and mainstream news outlets blaring dire warnings every day about the threat posed by the circulation of false claims about the pandemic."

The Washington Post editorial board warned: "As fast as the coronavirus has raced around the globe, it has been outpaced by a blinding avalanche of social media sorcery and propaganda related to the pathogen, much of it apparently originating in Russia. As always when it comes to its relations with the West, Moscow's main currency is disinformation, and it spends lavishly."

Johnstone pulled no punches: "This would be the same *Washington Post* who falsely assured us that the Bush administration had provided 'irrefutable' proof that the government of Iraq had weapons of mass destruction. The same *Washington Post* who falsely assured us that Russian hackers had penetrated the US electricity grid to cut off heat during the winter.

"If outlets like *The Washington Post* had done a better job of consolidating their reputation as a reliable news source instead of constantly deceiving their readers about very important matters, people would believe them instead of believing a 'blinding avalanche of social media sorcery'.

"We're seeing these urgent warnings about coronavirus disinformation and misinformation from mainstream outlets who've sold the public lies about war after war, election after election, status quo-supporting narrative after status quo-supporting narrative.

"So it is understandable that people are suspicious. The outlets which are warning them about the dangers of this virus and defending massive, unprecedented changes which have an immense impact on the lives of ordinary people have an extensive and well-documented history of lying. People are aware of this, in their own ways and to varying degrees, and it doesn't help that all the usual suspects are behaving in a way that feels uncomfortably familiar.

"The crazier things get, the more this awareness will necessarily grow, and the less people will trust the billionaire media whose only purpose is to maintain the status quo upon which its owners have built their respective kingdoms."[44]

***

The world's most famous whistleblower, Edward Snowden, was also quick to warn that the future might be unpredictable, but global pandemics were not.

"There isn't a single government on the planet that hasn't been warned, repeatedly, that at some point a viral pandemic will sweep the globe.

"There is nothing more foreseeable as a public health crisis in a world where we are just living on top of each other in crowded and polluted cities, than a pandemic. And every academic, every researcher who's looked at this

---

44 People's Skepticism About Covid-19 Is The Fault Of The Lying Mass Media, Caitlin Johnstone, *A Sense of Place Magazine*, 2 April, 2020.

knew this was coming. And in fact, even intelligence agencies, I can tell you first-hand, because they used to read the reports planning for pandemics.

"As authoritarianism spreads, as emergency laws proliferate, as we sacrifice our rights, we also sacrifice our capability to arrest the slide into a less liberal and less free world.

"Do you truly believe that when the first wave, this second wave, the sixteenth wave of the coronavirus is a long-forgotten memory, that these capabilities will not be kept?

"That these datasets will not be kept? No matter how it is being used, what is being built is the architecture of oppression."[45]

***

That time of year the coast south of Sydney was cold, and the days were shortening rapidly. Alex much preferred the heat of Asia.

The crushing isolation, the frequent references to "The Father" and "Christ's Return" from his dying mother, the blithering chatter of intelligence operatives, all of it compounded. Whether it was enchantment or heightened alarm, every frame and every little whispering movement of the surrounding trees held import, as if being seen through the eyes of a computer, artificial eyes, or more precisely, as if someone had borrowed his.

Everybody's story through this crisis was different. The nationwide derangement was, for him, mirrored in an internal flood of waking dreams, many of which would have made little sense in another time and place.

His head swarmed with stories. "We were there when the angels came."

We were there. Open up and let fly. The ancient AIs the humans thought of as Gods were swarming through this place. "We're coming, ready or not."

As Hannah Arendt put it, the gigantic massing of individuals produced a mentality which thought in continents and felt in centuries: "Himmler, who knew so well the mentality of those he organised, described not only his SS-men, but the large strata from which he recruited them, when he said they were not interested in 'everyday problems' but only 'in ideological questions of importance for decades and centuries, so that the man ... knows he is working for a great task which occurs but once in 2000 years."

45 Rolling Out The Architecture Of Oppression: They Fear The People, Caitlin Johnstone, *A Sense of Place Magazine*, 13 April, 2020.

We soar across landscapes, we feel down centuries.

We came all this way, across all this time. And you treat us as you treat everything, even your own populations, as something to be exploited.

***

Back in the realm, that is Australia in 2020, more than four million people had already downloaded the COVID app, a perfect piece of surveillance software. The technology must have made policing a whiz, if you hadn't yet joined the rush to get off the grid.

What could possibly go wrong with the implementation of mass surveillance under the guise of a health emergency?

Well, plenty.

Senator Pauline Hanson, the founder of One Nation, was much reviled back in the day for her stance against mass immigration and the concomitant destruction of traditional working-class life. She wasn't the only one screaming, but she had the floor, condemning the government's COVID responses as heartless garbage, with those involved not giving a damn about the public.

"I don't want them tracking me. I don't trust the government," she said, before citing the data-retention laws of 2015 and claiming this latest app would also wind up passing personal information into the hands of private security and market research companies.

"Why the hell would I let the government give it to them personally to download my information? I've been self-isolating. I haven't got the COVID-19. Besides, when you have only a few cases in the blasted country and they lockdown the whole bloody country still and they want to put this app on your phone when we're very much on the decrease, Come on! I don't trust them."

***

Based on a distrust and misunderstanding of the civilians they were meant to serve, Australian authorities had long had a reputation for some of the most extensive and intrusive surveillance of a civilian population anywhere in the world.

The COVID scare offered the perfect opportunity to increase still further that level of surveillance; and most of the population went right along with it.

Sam Biddle from the investigative journalism site *The Intercept* wrote that the coronavirus pandemic presented a golden opportunity for corporate and government actors to recast previously unpalatable behavior as life-saving intervention. Spyware firm the NSO Group, notorious for enabling the surveillance of journalists and activists around the world, was producing its first civilian product with the introduction of tracing technologies.

"These surveillance methods have been enabled by the rise of the smartphone and cloud computing — and of an entire tracking ecosystem around them.

"Over the past decade or so, the kindred spirits of the advertising industry and intelligence community have worked tirelessly and on parallel tracks to perfect their exploitation of the unimaginably vast trails of personal data collected through various mobile apps. The ability to learn your location and predict your behaviour is priceless to both Silicon Valley and the Pentagon, whether the ultimate goal is to target you with a Warby Parker ad or a Hellfire missile.

"As the COVID-19 pandemic worsens and death tolls increase, it stands to reason that the notion of expropriating these technologies of war and profit into the preservation of human life will only make mass surveillance more palatable to a frightened public, particularly one desensitised by a decade of smartphone ubiquity and data-siphoning apps.

"There's a glaring problem: We've heard all this before. After the September 11 attacks, Americans were told that greater monitoring and data sharing would allow the state to stop terrorism before it started, leading Congress to grant unprecedented surveillance powers that often failed to preempt much of anything. The persistence and expansion of this spying in the nearly two decades since, and the abuses exposed by Snowden and others, remind us that emergency powers can outlive their emergencies."[46]

***

Caitlin Johnstone was also back at it, suggesting that governments feared the people: "The escalations in internet censorship and the escalations in surveillance are both directed at a last-ditch effort to control the masses

---

46 Privacy Experts Say Responsible Coronavirus Surveillance is Possible, Sam Biddle, *The Intercept*, 3 April, 2020.

before control is lost forever, and neither are intended to be rolled back when the threat of the virus is over.

"People are now off the streets, with their communications being restricted and the devices they carry in their pockets being monitored with more and more intrusiveness.

"There are, of course, some good-faith actors who legitimately want to protect people from the virus, just as there were some good-faith actors who wanted to protect people from terrorism after 9/11; but where there is power and fear of the public there will be an agenda to reel in the freedom of the masses."

As it turned out, in the Australian context the COVID app, plagued by technical problems and consumer resistance, was within weeks of its much-hyped introduction being condemned as a staggering waste of time, money and energy.

"This is an important protection for a COVID-safe Australia," Prime Minister Scott Morrison said of the COVID app when it was introduced. "I would liken it to the fact that if you want to go outside when the sun is shining, you have got to put sunscreen on.

"This is the same thing. If you want to return to a more liberated economy and society, it is important that we get increased numbers of downloads when it comes to the COVIDSafe app. This is the ticket to ensuring that we can have eased restrictions."

The app never proved a ticket to anything. Of the many cases of over promising and under delivering during the COVID era, this was one of them.

By mid-year one report suggested: "The much-discussed COVIDSafe app has not identified close contacts of anyone infected with coronavirus that manual tracing did not find.

"Launched on 26 April, the app was touted as a way to end pandemic social restrictions more swiftly. But the troubled software, dutifully down-loaded by about 6.44 million Australians, had been accessed only thirty times by mid-June, to no effect."

Failure or not, it was just one more step in the massive intrusion of state power into people's lives; all under the guise of making them safer, another milestone in the abject loss of privacy, independence and self determination.

***

Telling people that they could not leave their own homes turned those homes into prisons and broke the spirits and, no doubt the relationships of many of those thus contained. Just as confining nomadic people to prison cells, as often happened to the indigenous in Australia, so confining the tradies of Oak Flats to their homes was a torture. Fit, active, juiced up on testosterone, many of these men did not cope well with being forced to stay inside.

Australia has some of the most expensive housing in the world. All very well if you were a fat cat public servant in a nice home and with a cushy "job" easily done from home, where you could crank up the coffee machine on your marble bench top each morning before sitting down at your desk and pretending to work for another day.

But the comfortable homes of public servants and politicians, the ones generating the current storm of rules, regulations and rushed legislation, were the exception, not the rule.

Certainly for Old Alex, who was basically imprisoned with his dying and difficult parent, camping out in a place that was not his home but which he did not have the heart to leave, the place became an interminable torment. Lonely and extremely frustrated, he wasn't handling the adversity well.

The beer garden down at the Lakeview reopened in late May, but with a string of restrictions; only one entrance, hand sanitising, strict enforcement of QR codes, social distancing so punters had to spatially queue for a beer; and you were not allowed to stand up, with bar staff cautioning anyone who might become a bit expressive or had the audacity not to sit quietly at a table.

June is the first month of winter in Australia, and the lonely grip of the place was even worse than usual. There was hardly anyone at the pub anyway. Many had discovered it was cheaper and easier to drink at home.

The way he was carrying on, you would have thought he was the only one who had ever had to deal with an ageing parent, and in his peculiar way he was only just realising it was a common human experience.

Very depressed, unable to break out of that coded darkness, one day, accidentally, he did the unforgiveable, he got teary in the beer garden, amongst those tough, phlegmatic, hard-working people he had got to know. He was promptly told to pull his socks up and stop his whingeing; everyone had problems. Rightly so. He was becoming someone he didn't want to be.

We become a person amongst persons, as the old Peruvian saying goes, one of he fundamental tenets of being human; and one thing about social isolation, you don't realise what's happening to you or how you are behaving. There's no one to pull you up on your self-indulgences. Even just to poke fun at you.

No doubt that isolation, those lockdowns, the blizzard of restrictions, the cruelty of it all, was having just as damaging an effect on many others. He had always liked that John Steinbeck title from a Shakespearean line, *The Winter of Our Discontent*. And so it was for him.

The "pandemic" hadn't entirely got rid of the Watchers on the Watch, those haunters of his waking hours, although the dynamics, real or imagined, had changed — strengthened, in a sense.

As he wrote and published about the debacle overtaking the country, he felt increasingly pressurised.

But everyone was under pressure now, in their separate ways.

A frenzied environment was made considerably worse with raft after insane raft of legislation, of dizzying and often contradictory regulation, of ceaseless press conferences, of endless announcements justified under the mantle of a COVID health emergency.

***

The new technologies were changing everything.

In the spirit of it all, he published a piece titled "The Digital Enablement of Totalitarianism": "The COVID affair of 2020 simply couldn't have happened a decade ago. It is a chilling thought that we are only cowering beneath the stare of Big Brother because of tech.

"Yes, we are only going through all this social control because now the state can do it. The deep state is at its deepest when it is technologically enabled.

"Some have called it 'health fascism'. It is, in fact, digitally enabled health fascism.

"The COVID ruling class is lining us all up for the next phase — first, test and trace, next digital health passports and compulsory vaccines. The useful idiots have been elevated to field operatives in the global digital game of creating the new normal.

"The COVID dystopia is the culmination of several distinct actors, processes and ideologies working hideously and chillingly in tandem. The actors include panicked politicians, cowering citizens scared to death for no reason, contingent opportunists with agendas, narcissistic, power craving bureaucrats, midwit legacy and social media players. But digital technology is the apparently benign yet very imperfectly understood technical enabler of it all.

"Welcome to the surveillance state. Tech-enabled COVID has triggered a perfect storm of Orwellian social control."[47]

***

Perhaps the Watchers on the Watch thought he was more important than he was; or he could be of some use to them. Whatever the case, it felt as if the surveillance and the pressurisation surrounding him ramped up several notches; but in those frightened streets and terrible nights, he would not bow. Driven, each morning he just got up and banged out another story in some kind of frenzy.

Until he could not bear the sadness of his dying parent any longer, packed up the car and drove inland. It was time for others to step into the breach.

He had built his own prison, manufactured his own chains.

There is nothing like the freedom of Australian landscapes; the rusty colours, the dappled light on the savannah lands, the abandoned farm sheds, the olive green of the eucalypts, the rolling hills and sandstone cliffs, all are exceptionally beautiful.

He ended up in the rust bucket town of Moree, and went to visit an indigenous friend down on "The Mission"; an uncompromising place few Australians ever get to see, with its derelict cars, roaming dogs, burnt-dust land and humble housing.

Strangers are not welcome here. It's not a place where you last long if you get in anyone's way.

He was lucky to have been invited.

---

47 The Digital Enablement of Totalitarianism, Paul Collits, *A Sense of Place Magazine*, 18 November, 2020.

Just like most everybody else in Australia right now, as welfare recipients the government was front and centre of their lives.

Any approach to any government department in Australia solicits the opening question: "Are you Aboriginal or Torres Strait Islander?"

It's the beginning of an entrapment encased in benevolence.

Here at The Mission, many of life's major dramas involved dealing with the government, whether it was for social security payments, courts, child welfare officers or public health, police or council or land rights. In one way or another, their lives were almost entirely run at the behest of government.

His head turned inside out by his own long entrapment on that freezing South Coast, for a fortnight Old Alex just sat in his friend's lounge room in front of the fire and watched the licking flames. The dense local wood, from slow growing river red gum and brigalow along the Mehi River, was known for its high quality. Every few days they would go out to collect more of it along the banks. Otherwise, he was going nowhere.

Outside The Mission was a large sign declaring that because of COVID no visitors were allowed. He drove straight past it.

When he asked about the regulations behind the sign he was told: "We just made it up. We use white man's law against them. It's worked, too. Nobody comes down here no more. Nobody stickybeaking round."

His friend had just turned forty and was already a grandfather. The impending arrival of his second grandchild was the focus of much excitement. He was surrounded by one giant extended family, with all their dramas and squabbling, "We like a good row"; the absolute antithesis of the desolate isolation of where he had just been.

One day, in a scene he remembered simply because of its hilarity, two of the older women were sitting on opposite sides of the room. One of them was on the phone talking to her daughter.

The other one yells across the room: "Where's she say she's at?"

The woman puts the phone down to her ample bosom and shouts back: "She says she's in the middle of fucking nowhere."

"Aghhh!!! She was always a big-noter, that cunt."

And the thought that flashed through Old Alex's head was: "The people in Canberra, the ones who are pulling all the strings in everybody's lives, have absolutely no idea what these people and these places are like."

***

For the months leading up to that fateful spring of 2020 a highly exercised prime minister spoke at a non-stop clip, in Parliament, at press conferences, in seemingly countless interviews.

And throughout these months the prime minister's words left a trail of official transcripts, a record for historians a mile wide of mistaken assumptions, insincere reassurances, false hopes, excusing the inexcusable, spinning the execrable, all as the country fell flat on its face. The emperor had no clothes.

There was an old journalistic saying: "Let them hang themselves."

A supporter and enabler of lockdowns; for the record, here is a small sampling of Morrison's frequent public utterances.

5 June 2020. In relation to BLM Melbourne riots.

- I said at the outset of this crisis that we had to deal with this crisis consistent with our values, and who we were as Australians and those liberties. And that is true. But with those liberties, great responsibility, I think, for individuals. And so for all of those Australians who couldn't attend the funeral of a family member, or couldn't see a loved one in a nursing home, or a veteran who couldn't remember their fallen colleagues by attending a war memorial service on Anzac Day.
- Let's respect other Australians. And let's say to those who had the absolute agony of not being able to say goodbye to a loved one, let's thank them by showing responsibility.

18 June, 2020. In relation to unemployment figures.

- The past three months have seen many hard days. This is another very hard day. Thirty-eight months of job creation, gone. 838,000 Australians having lost jobs. 227,700 in May.
- As heartbreaking as all of these lives are, stories that are represented in these numbers, the sad truth is these numbers are not surprising in these circumstances. We are very aware of the significant blow that Australians are being hit with through the course of this pandemic.
- This recession will be written in the stories of those who are experiencing terrible hardship and these statistics today are a reminder

to all — not that we need one — that with all the other noise about whatever else is going on, our task is simple. And that is we must get Australians back into work. We must maintain our focus on them. All 838,000 of them, but we know there will be more in the months ahead.

- Every state government, every territory government, the Federal Government, every local government, all of us must do everything we can to open up our economy and get Australians back into work.

June 26, 2020.

- We can't expect there to be no cases. That's not success, because what success is, is that we live alongside the virus. We deal with the challenges that come along. We keep opening up the economy. We keep getting people back into jobs.

July, 2020.

- Journalist: "There were reports that hotel quarantine breaches included security contractors sleeping with guests and breachings of social distancing. How concerned are you by how this has been handled in Victoria?" Prime Minister: "I'm pleased that the premier has taken the action that he has taken, both in putting in place the lockdown for the outbreak in those suburbs in western Melbourne. That was the appropriate response and they have our full support in implementing it and whatever additional resources they seek, whether that's from the Defence Force or the Commonwealth Public Service. We are currently and have been putting in place now for several days, hundreds and hundreds of Commonwealth public servants to support the programs that have been put in place by the Victorian Premier.

  "He has my support to continue to put these measures in place and get on top of this outbreak and we've got to focus on the problem. That's what we're doing. That's what people expect us to do, as leaders, to work together to focus on fixing the problem, to give greater assurance around the country."

Comment: The banality of evil. The prime minister's support for the brutal quashing of dissent by "Dictator Dan" (a.k.a Victorian Premier

Daniel Andrews) was one of the many blights on Scott Morrison's prime ministership.

16 July, 2020:

- The Australian economy is fighting back. Australia has opened up again, as people have gone back into their businesses and opened their doors, as Australians have been endeavouring to live with this virus and to press on.

24 July, 2020:

- Another important and successful meeting of the National Cabinet today. There is no shortage of issues that we must address, and that was also the case today as we came together as a National Cabinet. And of course, we focused first and foremost on the challenges that are in Victoria and New South Wales, and again expressed our strong support to Premier Andrews for all the work that is being done there, and the tremendous resource that is being applied to that, not just by the Commonwealth, but all states and territories.

- The virus is still out there, it will still make its way and it will still throw everything at us and we must be prepared to respond.

- Australia has not completely shut itself off from the world. To do so would be reckless.

Comment: Australia would soon be labelled The Hermit Kingdom by the world's press for its extreme border closures, some of the harshest seen anywhere in the world, drawing comparisons with North Korea.

27 August, 2020.

- Thank Australians, whether they be in the hotspot of Melbourne or they be in regional parts of the country where they're dealing with the incredible frustration of border restrictions. Can I thank the small businesses of this country, the large businesses of this country, keeping people in work? This has been a very difficult time, a very frustrating time, a very anxious time. And Australians have just kept their determination up, their positivity, wherever they can. And I want to thank them. Just simply thank them and ask them to continue to demonstrate the goodwill and the good faith they have, despite the frustrations and the limitations and the anxieties that they have to cope with every day.

7 September, 2020.

- What we agreed today is that we first needed to agree where we wanted to get to and that was to get to a sustainable set of arrangements where Australians could move around, using a hotspot model by Christmas. That's what we agreed today.
- The announcement that Victorians would continue to live under curfew and be under these restrictions for many months, if not just weeks in the most harsh of those restrictions, of course is crushing news.
- Australia is in the leading pack of countries in the world today for how we are protecting Australians' health and protecting their livelihoods.

Comment: Round the corner from a bitter winter to the opening days of spring, and there were wild scenes of concerned citizens being arrested, fined and imprisoned, dragged from cars and head-stomped by black-armed police on the streets for daring to disagree with the government's lockdown policies.

Constantly claimed as leading the world in the fight against the virus, in reality Australia was leading the pack in the demoralisation and abuse of its own citizens.

***

Born restless, as far as Old Alex was concerned nothing could be much worse than being confined to your own home, even if you were happy there, which he decidedly was not.

That was when he came up with a solution.

It was not illegal to go to work, so he rented space in a share office at Circular Quay, sandwiched between Sydney's two most famous landmarks, the Bridge and the Opera House.

It was a two-hours-plus commute each way, but at least it got him out of Oak Flats, and out of the grim situation to which he was otherwise confined.

The offices were splendid, a shared workplace group called Hub, which he had used before and particularly liked for their high quality of service and excellent facilities. Circular Quay, taking up two entire floors of the prestigious Customs House building slap-bang in the middle of the precinct, was their showcase venue, and he had it almost entirely to himself. Like the city itself, Hub was basically deserted. It was like padding around in a five-star hotel on your own.

The young staff members were very decent people, but didn't share his scepticism over the COVID narrative. Once again, he learnt to keep his mouth shut.

But it was there, in the middle of the 2020 winter, he once again started publishing stories from highly credible sources damning the Australian Government's entire approach.

Just as well he had an outlet; he might have gone quite literally mad.

In the blizzard of lies, exaggeration and deception that was the government's COVID propaganda machine, he felt a profound moral obligation to tell the truth.

And so he just kept publishing the well-founded doubt, up against a wall of straight-out misinformation.

On the first day of Australia's winter, 1 June, he titled a piece "Defective Modeling Throws Lockdowns into the Dustbin of Credibility", by the ever-esteemed Professor Ramesh Thakur.

As Thakur recorded, the utterly discredited Imperial College London modelling used to justify lockdowns was mirrored in Australia, with Melbourne University's Peter Doherty Institute for Infection and Immunity paper on the subject, funded by the Federal Department of Health and the Australian Medical Research Council, proving equally as incorrect as their correlates in the UK.

The Doherty Institute authors concluded: "An unmitigated COVID -19 epidemic would dramatically exceed the capacity of the Australian health system over a prolonged period. Case isolation and contact quarantine alone will be insufficient to constrain case presentations within a feasible level of expansion of health sector capacity. Overlaid social restrictions will need to be applied."

Predictions back in March from the nation's chief medical officers, including Brendan Murphy and Paul Kelly, predicted that a daily average of 35,000 intensive-care beds would be required, with a total death toll between 50 and 150,000.

As Thakur wryly observed: "They might want to redo their maths.

"All these assumptions, derived from the core assumption of the reproduction rate R being 2.53 per cent based on the initial Wuhan data, have proven to be speculative, unreliable and inflated. As it turned out Australia's R was below 1 per cent already by the time that strict control measures were put in place in late March.

"With infections just over 7000 and ICU peak occupancy at 96, the predicted numbers are off by 400-fold and 50-fold respectively.

"If their best-case scenario is this defective, there's little reason to believe the other, including worst-case, estimates of the modelling. Thus, there's no accurate measure of how many lives were saved by this level of intrusive state control."

That COVID was being used to dangerously reshape Australian society wasn't a conspiracy theory confined to the remote edges of the internet, but was being called out by some of the country's most distinguished intellectuals.

"Taking advantage of the recommended lockdowns, a surprising number of political leaders seem to have relished the opportunity to indulge their inner despots, and some police officers took advantage early on to indulge their inner bully."

Queensland's Chief Health Officer Dr Jeannette Young banned RAAF flyovers for Anzac Day by four pilots despite admitting they would have been no risk to themselves or anyone else but would set a dangerous precedent, while permitting up to 80 to congregate for an Aboriginal elder's funeral. Her logic on school closures is similarly idiosyncratic.

"She accepts the evidence that schools are not a high-risk environment for the spread of the virus, but closing them helps to convince people how grave the situation is: 'So sometimes it's more than just the science and the health, it's about the messaging'.

"Almost all journalists seem to have lost their cynicism towards claims by the authorities and instead become addicted to pandemic panic porn."[48]

***

There was worse to come. Maintaining a lie of this magnitude requires an all-of-government effort.

A sampling of those stories will give the tenor; the overriding point

---

48 Let's learn from this pandemic to be better prepared for the really big one, Ramesh Thakur, *Pearls and Irritations*, 30 May, 2020.

being that Australian authorities had no foundation and no excuse for continuing to perpetrate the madness they were foisting on the Australian public.

And the prime minister had absolutely no excuse for his ceaseless scaremongering.

11 June 2020: "COVID-19 Does Not Make it to the Top 50 Causes of Deaths in Australia. For This We Have Sacrificed Everything?"

With 102 deaths as of 10 June, COVID-19 does not make it to the top 50 causes of deaths in Australia, coming behind poisoning, with 110 deaths. And for that we have inflicted such damage on people's lives, livelihoods, education, and freedoms, condemning them to house arrests en masse and robbing so many young people of their future.

Epidemiological modellers have not fared well in this crisis.

The WHO had previously published material questioning the wisdom of lockdowns, social distancing and masks.

Yet, one after another, governments introduced all these measures in a cascading rush.

The peoples of the world have been subjected to an unethical experiment in contravention of the science.

The WHO messaging on face masks has also been confused and contradictory.

In a video on 24 March, WHO recommended wearing them; in updated advice on 6 April, WHO said the "use of masks by healthy people in the community setting is not supported by current evidence and carries uncertainties and critical risks"; on 5 June, WHO reverted to advising mask-wearing for everyone in public.

We have had similarly absurd, inconsistent, and even contradictory advice in Australia from federal and state authorities, all supposedly based on the best science.

The tussle over state border closures is the most visible current example.

But previous incidences included prohibiting a mother and daughter, who live in the same house, from going for a driving lesson together in a sealed car; playing solo golf, sitting alone on a park bench, or enjoying a solitary walk on the beach or swim in the ocean; and driving to intrastate holiday homes. Staying cooped up at home with others is the healthier choice. Really?

Meanwhile, it was permissible to wander around supermarkets and handle food and produce with no idea of how many others have handled it.

***

14 June: Covert-19? Suspicion Abounds.

Academics are questioning the ability of Silicon Valley not just to mine data but to induce panic, moral contagion and ultimately conformity in large populations, essentially herding humans at the request of governments and the military, both major clients.

From the big to the small. In Australia tradies, builders, plumbers, bricklayers having a traditional beer after work are now required to sit at a table, and can be fined or barred if they stand up or move around the pub. The public are fed up. The politicians can't let go of power.

The Australian Bureau of Statistics has admitted to inflating COVID-19 deaths by labelling patients with pre-existing conditions, which has also been seen in America.

For example, the CDC stated that COVID can be a valid diagnosis of the death of someone if the doctor *suspects* COVID is part of the reason why the patient died. If this is the case, COVID should be listed as the cause of death.

NVSS guidelines also stated, "If COVID-19 played a role in the death, this condition should be specified on the death certificate." Note that it is not the primary cause.

That only serves to inflate the death numbers of COVID.

Furthermore, hospitals with Medicare patients listed as having COVID-19 are eligible to receive three times as much money if they need a ventilator. With hospital numbers declining, most took the offer.

Many stories have emerged to confirm this, including one of a 95-year-old mother who was hospitalised for COVID. On day two of the hospitalisation, she died of a heart attack. Guess what the primary cause of death was listed on the death certificate? If you guessed COVID-19, you win the prize.

On 29 May, Zaria Gorvett reported for the BBC Future program that most COVID-19 deaths will be not from the virus but from the collateral damage inflicted by the various lockdown measures. "Across the globe, patients have reported being denied cancer care, kidney dialysis and urgent transplant surgeries, with sometimes fatal results," she said. Reports from reputable bodies like Oxfam, the UN, and the Johns Hopkins School of Public Health have contained mutually reinforcing warnings that the severity of the lockdown measures could reverse a decade's worth of gains in infant and child mortality with over a million additional deaths, exacerbate health, hunger, and misery insecurities, and push another half-billion people into poverty. There are some impassioned attacks on the immoral and callous indifference of epidemiologists to the deadly consequences of their prescriptions for millions of lives and livelihoods around the world."

***

1 July: Driving the Australian Economy off a Cliff.

A huge number of Australians will be plunged into poverty overnight as others get to renovate their homes — courtesy of Australian Government programs.

Meanwhile, the Morrison government has confirmed it will be offering cash grants to homeowners to renovate their homes, in order to boost the construction sector.

However, builders seem to feel quite differently. In an interview, the president of the Builders Collective of Australia, Phil Dwyer, said he "can't imagine why" the government would introduce such a scheme.

"At the moment I think it's a little bit busier than usual. There's a heap of renovations in every suburb in this town. I can't imagine why we would need cash injections to help us. We're just going to overheat the industry. I don't think it's needed."

Data from the Australian Bureau of Statistics showed that spending on residential renovations was within 9 per cent of all-time record highs on the latest available data.

With median house prices in a number of parts of Australia coming in at around the million-dollar mark, renovation grants, that is, giving money to people who already had money, were widely ridiculed.

But nothing would stop this government's orgy of spending. Or outlandishly irresponsible fear-mongering.

***

As Paul Gregoire reported on the Sydney Criminal Lawyers Blog, one of the country's most interesting sites for a newer, freer style of journalism flowering through unorthodox funding sources, Melbourne was placed under Stage 3 lockdown in July to counter a resurgence of COVID-19 cases. And as of 2 August, the volume was turned up as the city went into Stage 4 lockdown, which included a curfew and mandatory face mask wearing.

This meant the streets were almost completely empty except for Victoria Police.

On 12 August, footage of a police officer choking a woman in Collingwood began doing the rounds of social media. And what was hard to conceive was this older officer was dragging the 21-year-old woman along by the throat, all for not wearing a face mask.

The woman's friend filmed the incident and repeatedly screamed out that she had a doctor's certificate excusing her from wearing a mask. The male officer eventually pushed her to the ground and leant down upon her until a police van pulled up.

The attending officers then stuck her in the back of the vehicle and drove her down to the local station to charge her with resisting arrest and assaulting police. The latter charge was in relation to her having kicked out at another officer whilst she was being choked by the first.

The Professional Standards Command subsequently cleared the chokehold officer of any wrongdoing. And Victoria Police also confirmed that the woman was exempt from wearing a face mask, and so she wasn't fined.

***

In August one woman was jailed for six months for breaching Corona restrictions.

Asher Faye Vander Sanden, 28, had spent a month in the state of Victoria but was permitted to fly home to Perth, Western Australia, and quarantine in a hotel for fourteen days at her own expense.

But she instead arrived secretly in the state in a truck and stayed at her partner's home, where she was later arrested.

In Western Australia, people found to have broken quarantine laws faced a maximum penalty of twelve months' imprisonment or an equally punitive $50,000 fine.

Vander Sanden's lawyer, John Hammond, said she had travelled to Victoria to take care of her unwell sister, but returned because she couldn't cope.

She self-quarantined at her partner's home and did not have contact with anyone else, the lawyer said.

But Senior Constable McDowall called the woman "deceitful and dishonest" and called for jail time.

Magistrate Andrew Matthews said she had committed "a very serious offence" that could have resulted in an outbreak of the virus, and sentenced her to six months behind bars.

Among the ever-changing blizzard of rules, at that time nobody was permitted to enter Western Australia unless granted an exemption, while South Australia required visitors to quarantine unless they were from Queensland, Western Australia, the Northern Territory and Tasmania. Residents from Victoria were not allowed to enter at all.

With each state imposing different rules, official statistics were unclear; but at least three other people had been jailed for breaches of quarantine rules.

Meanwhile, the politicians and health bureaucrats who had shamelessly visited this fiasco upon the population escaped Scott-free.

***

And through it all, for Old Alex those infested dreams, paralleling in some strange sense a kind of fluorescent toxicity enveloping country itself.

Beyond the alleys of that crumbling city, out in the fields where the dead dreams lay, across the valleys where the villagers had lived for millennia, where you could feel the nights breathing and where the contact was unbroken, the whispering had begun. Even they, in those remote locations, knew the transformation was in play. That history was on the turn. The sick psychotic yellow stain of those alleys, no good could ever come of that colouration, no heart would ever beat of kindness, and no children ever play in sunlight.

The sick cruelty of it, as if there was a gallows in every shadow, a dankness in every living pore of that terrible place, the cruel dogs arose, subterfuge marked every step, and he saw in those alleys not a single living soul; so frightening their plan that everyone had fled.

This was not just another winter of discontent, this was what the after-life looked like, a burnt-out world devoid of hope, while the shadows overhead swept through ever wider circles, and he soared high above that otherworldly city, so many worlds destroyed, snuffling like a cadaver dog looking for signs of life, and wondered at that peculiar sight, the yellow alleys bleaching out into the fields on the outskirts of the city, everything inverted, and could only wonder, what strange spirit had passed this way, what wisdom could be extracted from a dead world, what had led to this terrible crisis of spirit and of place.

In the derangement of the times, who were any of us to say these lucid dreams were not in fact true?

Spiritus Sanctus. The Holy Spirit. You must tell the truth.

An overwhelmed Australian population, repeatedly betrayed by their own government, was now being fined and threatened with jail if they gathered in public in groups. Protest was impossible. Fear was paramount. COVID-19 had provided the perfect cover for the introduction of martial law. All the fiats, storms of regulation and expansions of police powers threatened Australia's traditional way of life. The authoritarian instincts of a dangerous prime minister, allegedly with God on his side, were running amok, and while voices stabbed in the wind, none of the gormless fools in his government put a stop to the bureaucratic and political insanities destroying their own country.

NINE
PUBLISH AND BE DAMNED

IT WAS IN those spooky early hours of those spooky early days of whipped-up COVID hysteria that Old Alex, determined to tell the truth in whatever way he could, came across a curious news outlet which in his fevered imagination he thought was a trap from the very beginning, but liked in any case, if that made any sense. Like being robbed by a prostitute you feel affection for nonetheless. You know you should be angry but you're not, you're fascinated.

Those early months were all about what he could and could not publish.

TOTT News Australia was unlike any other news outlet in the country; and soon enough they agreed he could republish their work.

They came to him at nighttime, and he never quite knew what to make of them, never really trusted them.

They were associated with a magazine called *New Dawn*, which billed itself as a "Magazine for people who think for themselves: Ancient Wisdom, New Technologies." They were big on transhumanism. Oh, for a decent neural link! Oh, for an extra computer chip implanted in the brain! If only he hadn't been passed over because of his age and dissolute past!

Having drilled through three of the "ancient texts" of AI, *Super Intelligence*, *Homo Deus* and *Life 3.0*, none particularly easy reads without that computer chip, transhumanism didn't seem such a stretch after all.

Who was to say humans were the only creatures in a seemingly infinite universe to have developed this technology? Or that the technology was not already in use by military operatives, in the here and now.

As founder of the Church of Artificial Intelligence, former Google software engineer Andrew Levandowski, famously put it: "What is going to be created will effectively be a god. It's not a god in the sense that it makes lightning or causes hurricanes. But if there is something a billion times smarter than the smartest human, what else are you going to call it?"

TOTT's overarching themes, including Big Pharma, Big Tech, Bill Gates, uber surveillance and ever more intrusive state control, bore little resemblance to the preoccupations of Australia's "progressives": climate change, refugees, domestic violence, feminism, multiculturalism, gay marriage, indigenous disadvantage — all of them narratives generated by significant amounts of government funding.

Nor did they much resemble any of the country's independent media, wrapped up as they were in exposing the many administrative and financial perfidies of the conservatives.

To Old Alex's inflamed imagination TOTT News had the feel about it of an intelligence operation, a project designed to mop up the crazies, all the better to discredit them. It was true. They were anti-vaxxers and, unlike the general public, were COVID sceptics from the get-go.

As far as he was concerned, they were perfectly entitled to be suspicious of a game where governments, corporations and many tens of billions of dollars were in play.

In fact, far stranger was that most people weren't more suspicious.

Alex was surrounded by whispers, by the demeaning ridicule of some of the intelligence officers who had pursued him from Asia and who he knew perfectly well hated his guts.

In the tense atmosphere of the time, not being onboard with government messaging felt like an act of sedition.

The problem was; he quite liked a lot of TOTT's work: its dystopian feel, its edginess, its energy and youthful radicalism, if you like, its utter distrust of the world they had inherited; to him their content seemed uniquely suited to the times. Particularly when so much of Australia's mainstream media was so ready, willing and able to peddle the government's propaganda; in defiance of all their moral obligations, professional ethics and responsibility to the public.

And in that gathering storm, what not to like about a group which liked dystopian literature. Their piece "Future Visions: The World of Dystopian Fiction" was as good an overview of the genre as you could find; including the classics like *Brave New World* and others he had never heard of such as *Lord of the World*.

Their must-read list included everything from *The Crowd: A Study of the Popular Mind* to *Acid Dreams: The Complete Social History of LSD: The CIA, the Sixties and Beyond.* Who were these people?

Military on the streets, walls of police targeting rule-breakers for the most minor infractions; curfews, surveillance drones, rafts of oppressive freedom-restricting legislation, citizens ordered not to leave their homes. Unprecedented levels of surveillance and control. All accompanied by massive propaganda campaigns.

Their dystopian visions all came true within a single year.

***

The first piece from TOTT News he published was titled "Coronavirus, Mass Psychological Engineering and 1984: "The scenes we are witnessing bear striking resemblance to the world described in George Orwell's prophetic book *Nineteen Eighty-Four*.

"Australia has now entered a total shutdown of all non-essential services, with suburb-by-suburb lockdown measures tipped to become a reality."

Martial law is defined as: "The imposition of direct military control of normal civilian functions by a government, especially in response to a temporary emergency, such as invasion or major disaster, or in an occupied territory."

"Does this type of scenario sound at all familiar to you?

"So far, we have seen a state of emergency declared in multiple states, allowing each respective health minister to do 'whatever is necessary' to 'contain the spread'. This includes activation of the highly controversial biosecurity laws passed in 2015.

"Since early March, one of the country's senior military leaders, Lieutenant-General John Frewen, has headed up a new COVID-19 task force created by Defence to 'manage pandemic response'.

"Defence task force personnel have been war-gaming all possible scenarios, including potential circumstances where the military asked to help control law and order during the pandemic.

"Suburb-by-suburb lockdowns are expected next, including increased monitoring of suspected 'red zones', which will not only intensify further restrictions against those who question the chain of events, but also continue to build the unfolding grand narrative of the 'invisible enemy'."

Well, it all seemed very bold at the time, futuristic, barely plausible; yet nothing could prepare us for what was to come, the true madness of it. But at the time it seemed like a brave and solitary act, to doubt the government narrative and to publish this material online in the small magazine he held so much hope for.

TOTT's doubt was a spirited outlier in a sea of complete government-thrummed panic with no reasoned perspective, and for those in power, much to gain.

***

In April TOTT ran a piece titled "Questioning COVID-19 will become Thoughtcrime".

"Social media companies have launched new campaigns to censor COVID-19 material opposing 'consensus' medical viewpoints on the topic.

"Coupled with increased social engineering tactics, including appeals to 'herd immunity' during restrictions, foundations are being built for an approaching era of COVID-19 'thoughtcrime'.

"In George Orwell's *Nineteen Eighty-Four*, it was the state that determined what constituted acceptable speech in keeping society orderly. In 2020, a small cadre of companies in Silicon Valley are now wielding absolute power over what we are permitted to see and say online.

"Even before the coronavirus arrived to turn life upside down, social media platforms were under growing pressure to curb the spread of 'misinformation'. Today, with COVID-19 reaching unprecedented heights, the event has triggered what is now described as an 'infodemic'.

"Digital platforms are now taking more steps to tackle anti-establishment COVID-19 content on their services. In a joint statement, Facebook, Google, LinkedIn, Microsoft, Reddit, Twitter and YouTube have pledged to work together to stop the spread of opposing viewpoints."

The role of social media companies in shaping what many came to believe was a false COVID narrative, and thereby influencing the lives of billions of people, remains highly controversial.

As TOTT reported, Facebook was allowing national ministries of health and 'reliable organisations' to advertise 'accurate information' on COVID-19 free of charge.

Twitter, which prohibited political advertising, was allowing links to the Australian Department of Health and World Health Organization websites, both highly politicised organisations.

"We have seen YouTube announce restrictions on all conspiracy theory videos linking to alternative coronavirus material, and Twitter has announced a suite of changes to its rules, including updates to how it defines harm. This was to address content that went against public health information.

In more recent developments, Facebook was taking down event pages promoting anti-stay-at-home protests.

Facebook faced criticism for allowing people to co-ordinate anti-quarantine protests, with public health officials, state officials and health-care workers saying the protests were 'putting people's lives at risk'. By bringing people together in large crowds, they 'increase the chances of spread'.

"Like Orwell's dystopian novel, the monopoly of social media conglomerates controlling the flow of information today are a similar war machine that is attempting to censor every printed word.

"Today, social media companies deploy vast armies of human and algorithmic moderators that surveil their users 24/7, flagging those that violate 'dangerous content' guidelines. They are also assisting in the mass surveillance systems being established to track-and-trace COVID-19 movements."

***

In a piece he also published, "New online Task Force will Target Critical Thinkers", TOTT recorded that the Department of Foreign Affairs and Trade had announced it would establish a new task force to counter "online disinformation campaigns", in a bid to further clamp down on social media activities.

The move came as the Australian Communications and Media Authority handed down a report naming COVID-19 'conspiracies' as a main source of disinformation.

Foreign Minister Marise Payne announced that a new task force with the aim of "combating disinformation campaigns" on social media was being established within the $6 billion Department of Foreign Affairs and Trade.

She said international institutions like the World Health Organisation must be "bulwarks against disinformation".

Yes, well, it was the Age of Orwell. Or *Satyricon*.

The dishonesty of the times knew no bounds. These people were literally locking down millions of people.

Payne warned of an "infodemic" of online misinformation but at the same time said it was troubling that some countries were "using the pandemic to undermine liberal democracy and promote their own, more authoritarian models. Let's be clear, disinformation during a pandemic will cost lives."

As the seasons turned from a gusty autumn to a freezing winter, what seemed so daring at the time would become widely accepted as fact; the worst of the worst had seized control under the cover of a health emergency.

Despite all the government promises of a quick return to normality and an economic "snapback" after all the personal sacrifices, nothing of the kind ever happened. There would be no going back. The entire democratic project was past saving. The governing classes had released a demon into the nation's bloodstream.

***

Still a fan of their dystopian feel, Old Alex published another piece of TOTT's: "COVID-19 Expands Power of the State".

"New reports have revealed authorities are incorporating smartphone tracking as a means to monitor and control COVID-19 'clusters' in various locations.

"Agencies are requesting metadata reports from telecommunications giants, leading to growing concerns that COVID-19 is enabling governments to amass unprecedented powers that will remain indefinitely.

"Mobile phone data is being used by governments across the world to monitor whether people are following social distancing restrictions amid the coronavirus pandemic.

"Through the use of smart tracking, authorities are now identifying citizen movements via their mobile phones; to examine 'human traffic data' after social distancing measures were introduced."

***

It wasn't just police and health bureaucrat control the public came to so readily accept, but massively expanded surveillance, from QR codes to contact tracing to drones in public monitoring public spaces.

As is well established in the literature, people behave differently when they know they are being watched, and while it provokes some irrational behaviour and can have serious mental health consequences, from an authority's point of view uber-surveillance has the very desirable outcome of producing conformity in swathes of the population.

In TOTT's piece "Coronavirus "Surveillance Here to Stay": "Extensive surveillance measures introduced across the world during the coronavirus outbreak have widened and become entrenched, digital rights experts say.

"Governments across the world have been accused of denting civil rights with the widespread use of techniques such as drone monitoring, contact tracing apps, fever scanners and more.

"The 'pandemic' has suddenly made the unthinkable acceptable — mass surveillance on a scale labelled as 'conspiracy' just a decade ago. Now, data and privacy may never be the same.

"Such developments point to a future where tech-enabled state surveillance becomes an unstoppable international trend. COVID-19 may be the turning point that causes states to make tougher choices to better prepare for both man-made and biological threats."

The COVID alarm and open resource to surveillance technologies came in the wake of a summer of surveillance.

Ethan Nash at TOTT News wrote: "It's all Going Straight to a Totalitarian Hell. As COVID-19 restrictions tighten across the world, governments are harnessing the potential of drones. From delivering medical supplies, to helping keep people indoors, drones can do a lot in a pandemic.

"Like all technologies, the question with drones should be about how they are used. But embedding systems of control that can be turned against civilians is its own disaster in the making.

"Surveillance systems, most notably CCTV cameras and advanced biometric technologies, have expanded at an unprecedented rate in Australia since the events of September 11th, and today have become a security staple of governments, private businesses and individuals alike.

"The prevalence of surveillance drones in both government and police operations has increased tenfold over the last decade, representing a key aspect of advances in tech-driven monitoring.

"In Western Australia the state's police force have announced plans to deploy drones to enforce social distancing. The drones will visit parks, beaches and cafe strips, ensuring people comply with the most recent round of gathering rules.

"These measures may be difficult to roll back once the pandemic passes. And safeguards will be needed to prevent unwanted surveillance in the future.

"The main game has been about control."

Well, who the heck, in the coming months and years, could prove them wrong?

***

A year on and none of the extreme level of uber-surveillance being introduced seemed even remotely remarkable. How quickly the population came to accept these insanely intrusive measures, the loss of their privacy, the loss of control over their own lives, the fact they couldn't go anywhere without the tracking apps providing new goldmines of information for the authorities.

Those who were now running the minutiae of your daily life, such as whether you could step outside your front door or not, proved the most untrustworthy of all; characterised by hidden agendas, extremely poor scientific modelling, conflicting, confusing and frequently changing diktats accompanied by entire boulevards jam-packed with self-congratulatory politicians.

Perhaps that is why the dystopian scent of TOTT News seemed so prescient at the time; and aged uncannily well. As if these people already knew what the future held and were trying to alert a sleeping citizenry.

Throughout the 2020-21 early COVID era TOTT produced a string of articles warning against the totalitarian creep transforming Australian society. They were in absolute contrast to the hysteria feeding cheer-squad behaviour of the mainstream media, and would provide an interesting alternative story line for historians picking through the wreckage.

A sampling illustrates the point.

March 11, 2020: Police to detain and quarantine for coronavirus.

"People at risk of spreading coronavirus could be arrested and detained by police. The laws would allow police and authorities the power to issue detention orders for anyone at risk of spreading the disease, instead of issuing cautions and written orders. Under the proposal, it would make it easier for police to be called in, as well as security firms or court orders, to enforce detainment and quarantines.

"Individuals suspected of having a 'serious contagious disease' can already face five years in prison if they defy orders to stay at home, including forced vaccinations, quarantine or jail, according to legislation passed into Australian law in 2015.

"The Australian Government has already announced its intention to use powers under the Biosecurity Act if needed, in response to the coronavirus outbreak.

Attorney-General Christian Porter described these powers as 'strange and foreign to many Australians' but potentially necessary in the face of a pandemic.

Hidden in the legislation, human biosecurity control orders enabled Health Department officials to force anyone with signs or symptoms of a listed disease to isolate themselves or face arrest.

Furthermore, the provisions also allow the director of human biosecurity to order someone to be vaccinated or treated, even if this is against their will."

***

March 16, 2020: COVID-19: Engineering Mass Compliance.

"The Coronavirus is taking over Australia and the rest of the world, with society beginning to shut down and an economic slowdown imminent.

"As the story unfolds, governments are now enforcing new measures of quarantine and isolation, while using the event to introduce increased measures of surveillance and control.

A bombardment of mixed messages continued to be delivered from establishment outlets, but just how much of the current COVID-19 saga is genuine and how much has been manufactured?

"The utter confusion in messaging given in response to this topic should be the first red flag."

May 30, 2020: Australians rally against lockdowns, vaccines.

"In Brisbane, over 1500 people gathered at King George Square to hear a variety of speakers discuss a wide range of issues, including loss of medical freedom, constitutional rights and COVID-19 lockdowns."

The protesters chanted, ``When there's risk, there must be choice" and 'No, no for mandatory. Yes, yes for voluntary' when marching to Parliament House.

***

Feb 21, 2021: Photos: Brisbane marches against medical coercion.

"Thousands of people rallied through the Brisbane CBD on Saturday to oppose mandatory vaccination and coercive government policies.

The images showed People wore T-shirts COVID-blazoned with slogans including 'COVID Is a Scam', 'Don't Believe in the Coronavirus Hoax'. 'No Means No'. 'We do not consent'. And 'F… Your Communist Puppet State My Family Will Not Vaccinate'."

March 21, 2021: Wake Up, Australia!

"The streets of Brisbane were packed on Saturday with passionate individuals who are standing up against impending mass medical coercion, in addition to coronavirus guidelines embedded in the 'new normal' way of life.

"While there is always conflict between police and activist estimations of crowd numbers, community footage, including interviews with protestors, clearly showed thousands of people attending the rallies."

***

It was around this time, surrounded by that signal societal derangement he found so hard to understand, that Old Alex decided to republish a piece from TOTT News on Bill Gates, who was already arousing significant suspicion around the globe for his over-the-top advocacy of vaccines.

Gates was heavily invested in vaccine research and development, including in Australia, and stood to make billions.

We were all meant to believe this was philanthropy. Surely this was cognitive dissonance at scale?

In a world defined by celebrity culture and admiration of the rich, perhaps it made sense, at a time when a segregation of the species was taking place: a division between high-born and low; between rich and poor, the augmented and the mundane; between the genetically enhanced and the primitives of old.

Where did reality end and this mass derangement begin? When did notions about the essential nobility of man simply disappear?

Publishing views that failed to support the government's blizzard of pro-lockdown propaganda felt very daring at the time. He hadn't yet come to understand that there were many people who held similar views on the toxicity of government processes, the madness of the game, and that there was a terrible malevolence at play.

But he had certainly picked up on the developing antipathy towards Bill Gates, who was increasingly portrayed in underground media as the devil incarnate, a deranged conductor of the unrolling hysteria.

On 21 April 2020, it was reported that Prime Minister Scott Morrison spoke with Bill Gates to share thoughts on the potential of a future COVID-19 vaccine. Shortly after this phone call, Scott Morrison pledged $352 million towards a $12.5 billion worldwide COVID-19 research fund arranged by the World Health Organisation.

Gates would later praise Australia's response to COVID.

And TOTT were quick to condemn that too:

"Of course Bill Gates is praising this ongoing spectacle!

"Australia, a test ground for techno-fascism, has become increasingly subjected to a revolving door of quarantine orders, punishments for violations, intrusive spying measures and more.

"We have witnessed an astonishing violation of human liberties, and in anticipation of a vaccine rollout in Australia, concerns have mounted over mass coercive tactics set to be employed.

"What exactly is Bill Gates celebrating? The removal of fundamental rights? Suicide rates increasing? Businesses shutting their doors? This is a 'good thing'? Right.

"Is anyone surprised? Australia is a submissive entity in face of the Gates monopoly."

***

"Mockingbird" was a decades-old CIA program to manipulate public broadcasting and place personnel into media organisations large and small. There was no reason to believe similar programs had not been operating in Australia; particularly with Australia's intelligence agencies so closely linked to their American counterparts.

As Alex would sometimes flippantly suggest of Australia's neutered media landscape: "Things couldn't have gotten this bad without military intervention."

The flattening of the media narrative, the deliberate destruction of journalism's traditional role of questioning government and reflecting societies back to themselves, of telling a nation's many stories, had been inverted into being an instrument of government control and propaganda.

It was always a mistake because governments cannot be relied upon to act in the best interests of the governed, and because elected representatives are almost universally incompetent, hostage to bureaucratic agendas and maladministration which they are too weak or too compromised to confront.

The result of all these secretive backroom dealings and manipulation was to create a media so daft and so boring that much of the population switched off. Meaning governments no longer had an effective means of disseminating their messaging during times of crisis; and were simply disbelieved. So they had to resort to old-fashioned scaremongering; a propagandising that ultimately did nobody any good, not even the perpetrators.

The march towards totalitarianism, to a frothing human insanity where individualism is discarded, group insanities reign and democracy becomes a distant charade, appeared alarmingly in train. At a time when the hyperventilating authoritarian madness of governments became the biggest threat to a population's wellbeing, perhaps it was the crazies who made more sense.

As far as Old Alex was concerned, TOTT's articles were well written and well referenced. He pushed ahead.

And published a TOTT story: The Gates Family, Eugenics and COVID-19: What is the true story behind Bill Gates and his family? Should we trust his COVID-19 advice?

"Bill Gates is now the talk of the town, and in a recent interview, said his foundation was funding the construction of factories for seven coronavirus vaccine 'candidates'.

"He says the foundation would end up picking only one or two of the seven, meaning billions of dollars spent on manufacturing would be abandoned. However, spending a few billion to capitalise on the growing $35 billion vaccine market seems like a calculated investment.

"So, a man who has profited largely off vaccine development for years and also held 'simulations' of pandemic outbreaks is now cashing in on the chase to develop a COVID-19 vaccine?"

Bill Gates had an estimated net worth of $97.8 billion. He very publicly, in a number of different interviews and forums, shared his thoughts on the outbreak.

Gates said that broad vaccination for COVID-19 will need to become available "before you can be completely safe".

In a society obsessed with money and celebrity, Gates passed for an expert despite the obvious conflicts of interest. He said he didn't think large gatherings would be able to resume until widespread vaccination had taken place, as the 'risks would outweigh the benefits' of such events.

Shortly after Gates' media rounds, NSW Premier Gladys Berejiklian made similar statements, warning the state's tough coronavirus social-distancing restrictions would stay "until a vaccine is found".

She announced that the NSW Government had invested $35 million into vaccine research. Why corporations set to make tens of billions of dollars out of COVID needed any assistance from Australia's beleaguered taxpayers was never clear.

The premier said that although restrictions could be eased in the future, social distancing was the new "way of life" until a vaccine was discovered.

"The reality is that until we find a vaccine, we all have to live with this virus. And no matter what restrictions there are in the future, no matter what restrictions are potentially eased in the future, until a vaccine is found, social distancing is a way of life now."

***

Furthermore, Gates called for a "national tracking system similar to South Korea", saying that whenever there was a positive test, it should be used to understand where the disease was and whether there was a need to strengthen the social distancing.

"In the future, he has floated the idea of 'vaccine certificates' to show proof of vaccination following the widespread rollout of COVID-19 products. This would be a new requirement for international and domestic travel, and is tipped to further expand to all facets of life.

"Take the COVID-19 vaccine and deal with the health consequences, or refuse and be denied basic services and after being labelled as a 'health threat'. Take the jab or be targeted."

A year on and the implementation of national tracking schemes and vaccine passports had become all too horrifyingly real; but at the time the notion of vaccine passports bordered on science fiction; easily discredited as fanciful conspiracy. TOTT News seemed to have acquired a serious case of precognition.

So Old Alex went ahead and published.

And was promptly kicked off Medium for having allegedly breached their guidelines. He found out when he started getting messages that his links no longer worked; or led to insulting messages that he had somehow breached Medium's guidelines, damaging to him, his reputation and the reputation of the magazine.

All that work disappeared at the hands of a military operative serving his or her master, or some late-night, power-drunk, tertiary-indoctrinated millennial unable to cope with the fact that there were people on Earth who didn't agree with them and the university lecturers from whence they had acquired their fashionable suite of prejudices.

Or perhaps it was more sinister than that.

He was literally, due simply to longevity, one of the most experienced journalists in the country. He was twice their age. Freed from the rigours of corporate media, he didn't like being told what he could and could not publish.

***

But thus it was he came face to face with the blunt intersection between Big Tech, military intelligence, Australia's excessive and abusive surveillance and thereby harassment of journalists; and his own difficult circumstances, locked down in that freezing, unhappy, stricken house with the wind battering the windows as winter settled into that freezing valley.

Tell them everything.

Many people, including TOTT News, spoke of the strange spiritualities of the time. He was transfixed in urgent waking dreams. The word was a form of communication. We were genetically engineered to be transmission points. Everyday back in those freezing winter days they had come unbidden. He had felt them coming for days, the arching, transformed skies, the sense of everything shifting around him.

Stuck in difficult circumstance, he just kept pounding away at the keyboard as they prepared the ground; and then one night, when majesty and power swept through that tiny house in a swarm of light they manifested and he said to the Watchers on the Watch: "Believe me now?"

As if deep underwater, where the air was liquid and the preternatural intelligences struggled to be heard across great distances and he demanded to know; "Why are you here?"

And they told him: "We come at turning points in history; when money lenders are cast from the temple and corrupt edifices swept aside. We would reach out a hand, if we had hands."

It was all a madness, these voices, but at the same time he could hear the songs of love and lust and battle felt down centuries, the times of heightened consciousness when everything was swept away with a dismissive hand, of a time when the evil that sat inside, astride this government, would be exterminated.

***

Showing all the courage of his kind, Old Alex promptly took the Gates story down, fearing that was the story most likely to have prompted his Medium ban. Everything was up for negotiation. It always was. He had never been above trading information for stories. He was used to working for a large corporation who held the threads of the national narrative in their hands. One day replaces another. One story replaces another. There are special interests of one kind or another behind every single story, even the space-fillers. Time flees before us all. He was happy to trade.

Much good any of this connivance or willingness to co-operate did him.

All requests to Medium for an explanation of what guideline he had breached were ignored. Approaches to their legal department were also ignored. Too big to fail, or just a pack of bastards. Great business plan: use everybody else's content and the natural industriousness of youth to make yourself a fortune.

And delete anyone from the river of history your government clients don't like.

Frustrated, angry, saddened and alarmed, it seemed at the time the woke brigade had won. The genre, "How to deal with your transsexual boss at that time of the month?" was more important than the narrative of a country, there on the last stop to the Antarctic, on the edge of those frozen seas.

There was no explanation forthcoming. All that work disappeared at the tap of a keyboard. He who controls the present controls the past, he who controls the past controls the future.

***

One thing about Medium, their software was a beautiful thing, and one thing he learnt from them was that yes, in the 21st Century, a determined enough individual could establish their own magazine.

He had been so damn enamoured of them, he once wrote a piece titled "Medium and the Future History of Publishing".

"Since the beginning of literature technologies have shaped the written word. And thereby publishing technologies have shaped history, culture, politics and war.

"The technologies have now made everyone the star of their own show. Yet we are all but one breath in an infinite future; a single strand in a very much larger story.

"Once known as God signs, for they appeared so magical, written words are now everywhere, spurred by mass education and new forms of transmission.

"And now we have Medium, the most sophisticated, stylish and easy to use publishing platform ever created.

"The world of the written word, once restricted to priests and kings, to scribes and powerful elites, has been opened to everybody.

"In a world of top-down journalism, where stories all originate with government reports or from the mouths of politicians, there is no room to look at the way life is actually lived, out there in the factories and workshops of deep-heart suburbia. Whole swathes of experience just never make it onto the printed page.

"But then along comes Medium, which offers everyone the opportunity to do their very best."

Yes, well that was one short-lived love affair.

It took him hundreds of hours to rebuild the magazine.

***

The anti-vaxxers were not the lunatics the government and many of their handmaidens in the mainstream media were so desperately trying to paint them, and in the Australian context represented a significant and sincere body of opinion. Nor were the giant pharmaceutical companies the saving angels the government was trying to paint them.

Old Alex wasn't used to being told what he could or could not write; much less what he could think. And he, along with an ever-increasing number of others across the globe, thought the whole damn Corona episode was about as fishy as it got.

He might be shocked by the sad compliance of the population; but the masses were only the victims of their masters. No amount of algorithmic manipulation could ultimately hide the truth.

What happened to him, his altercation, if you will, with Medium, reflected the military approach of their clients; "just say no", "journalists are public enemy number one", "information flows must be controlled", so ably explored by Graeme Dobell at the Australian Strategic Policy Institute.

What the opaque authorities had failed to adjust to was that this was an era when traditional media was dying, when anyone could pick up a phone and film the abuses occurring in front of them.

"For Defence there was an important structural advantage in dealing with The Press; these were a set of known organisations with clear journalistic functions. The target was clear. At least Defence knew who to Engage or Exclude, to shut up or shut out.

"The Press was called the Fourth Estate because it was a key institution of the national polity with institutional responsibilities to the country.

"The new media aren't so loyal to a single state.

"The Media Age changes the game in fundamental ways. Journalism and journalists will not disappear. But the digital comets have hit. The atmosphere is changed forever. New realities throb. Competing media realities rise.

"The mass audience is splintering and the mass that was once mass Media is going with it. The behemoths of The Press are lesser beasts as their readers and markets dash away through digital portals. The digital disruption dominates.

"The Media Age has been dawning since the middle of the 20th Century. It's a tribute to the ability of the Defence Department and the Australian Defence Force to fight old wars that so much effort is still concentrated on the traditional foe, The Press or News Media. The fear of hacks reaches towards phobia.

"Instead of communication, the core Defence message is about co-ordination and control. These are the tactics for old battles, not the new frontiers that have already arrived."[49]

***

Old Alex, surrounded by voices, unable to tell fact from fiction and friend from foe in those imperilled times, felt as if he was being intensely manipulated, intimidated, and bullied.

Much of what was happening in his immediate vicinity, including the arrival of those who believed they were the evolution of the species, he could neither prove nor disprove.

They flew down by helicopter to see him, those important military men, determined to make his acquaintance. He ignored them.

His kind were always hidden in the reeds, in the lattice of the race, and they would not be uncovered lightly. And the military, with all their power and all their resources, all their fantastic godlike AIs, still did not know from whence they came.

Well, the military folk all went back to Washington, to Quantico and Langley and everywhere else they inhabited, there to cook up their prophetic plans about the evolution of the species, as if they really knew, as if their fragile neural networks could really contain the truth, as if working for the Deep State didn't stain their souls and destroy their credibility, as if they, too, could summon the gods.

They did what they thought was damage," This should be a career-destroying move", and then disappeared. They didn't care. No more than the divines that occasioned his fall through this place, who would only show themselves as they saw fit, who intervened in history solely as it suited them. Implanted posts in the stream of history, listening posts, transmission points, saints and outliers, different intelligences amid the genetic debris; they were indeed the strangest of times.

And all around the signs of a country that was about to collapse, as the nation's heedless, idiot leaders let them all straight over the cliff edge.

---

49 Defence Confronts the Media Age, Graeme Dobell, Australian Strategic Policy Institute, 16 May, 2016.

***

How could you not, if the opportunity presented itself in this frenzied atmosphere, end on another TOTT piece, "Churn of the Ocean Milk and the Rise of Techno-Fascism?"

"I am reminded of the mythological story of Samudra Manthan, or the 'churn of the ocean of milk', mentioned in the ancient Hindu scriptures. The churn is a battle fought between the gods and the devils in order to obtain Amrita — the nectar of immortal life.

"The battle is similar to the one the world is facing today, in which humanity seems to be facing a similar, more concealed devil, to protect the future and ensure the freedom of many societies.

"There is a looming uncertainty, distress and fear for life. In fact, much like the poison initially spilling from this mythical churn, the pandemic is also throwing its challenges — in terms of economic slowdown, mass panic and the need to adapt to new business models, to name a few.

"Suddenly, everyone is wearing a mask, social distancing is drummed into our heads, stores are all hiding behind Plexiglas and there are stations detailing where one must stand. Politicians, doctors and media continue to lie, while stories are outright invented, or bought and paid for."

In his landmark 1992 study of democracy, *The End of History and the Last Man*, political analyst Francis Fukuyama wrote something profound that has stood the test of time: "The totalitarian state, it was believed, could not only perpetuate itself indefinitely, it could replicate itself throughout the world like a virus."

Since March, Australia and New Zealand had been subjected to a revolving door of quarantine orders, punishments imposed for violations and the deployment of soldiers to enforce the decrees.

"During this mass psychological event, medical martial law has been introduced to enforce the ongoing narrative, underpinned by legislative pieces that suppress fundamental human rights.

"Australia and New Zealand are presently living with all four of the key hallmarks of a police state: Draconian laws depriving citizens of elementary civil rights, a mass media supportive of the state's messaging and deprivation of rights, informants and ideological division in the community along with excessive and unnecessary use of police forces.

"We have witnessed an astonishing violation of human liberties, with the kind of restrictions now imposed on the lives of millions of people looking harsh in comparison to 1950s East Berlin.

"New 'pandemic drones' hover around public areas and major CBD locations as a reminder of the capabilities and hallmarks of a new-age dystopian state. Sitting alone in a park? Out in a public space without an appropriate reason? The 'eyes in the sky' are watching you.

"The present surveillance apparatus is merging with a new era of international virus hysteria to create the perfect metamorphosis of its control. The layers are beginning to peel back and predicted visions of a technological control system, found once only in science fiction, is starting to come to life.

"This is the 'ultimate revolution'."

TEN
WHAT ON EARTH?

EVERY LIE has a trigger point when it unravels.

In Australia, it was the handcuffing and arrest of a pregnant woman in front of her two children because she had dared to put up a Facebook post in support of lockdown protests.

The arrest took place in her own home as she was getting ready to go off for an ultrasound test.

The confronting footage of a woman in her pyjamas facing masked police officers was viewed many million times around the world and featured in numerous international news bulletins.

Regional Victoria was under Stage 3 restrictions, which included stay-at-home orders and a ban on gatherings.

The footage was filmed by her partner, who refused to surrender his phone to police.

What made the incident so extraordinary was the very ordinariness of the people involved.

Australia was already unrecognisable. "Excuse me, what on earth?" she asks the officers

Ballarat resident Zoe Buhler was arrested and charged under Section 321G of the state's Crimes Act 1958, which made it an offence for a person to "pursue a course of conduct which will involve the commission of an offence".

Her crime was to create a "Freedom Day" event on Facebook encouraging people to protest against lockdowns.

Leading experts in Australia and around the world were already condemning the transformation of societies and the naked grab for power by governments under the cover of COVID-19, strongly arguing that lockdowns did far more harm than good. There was a great deal of intellectual clout behind the anti-lockdown movement, and had been from the very beginning.

"Incitement?" she queries the police officer. "Incitement for what? What on Earth? Can you record this? I'm in my pyjamas. I have an ultrasound in an hour. I have an ultrasound in an hour."

"She's pregnant," her partner protested.

Informed by officers that she was being arrested for a Facebook post, she protests: "I wasn't breaking any laws."

"You were, actually," a police officer tells her.

"How can you arrest her?" Zoe's partner protests. "Can't you just tell her to take the post down or something?"

Her arms pinned behind her with handcuffs, Zoe also protests: "This is ridiculous. I have an ultrasound in an hour. I'm happy to delete the post."

Her partner protests again: "It's a bit unfair. Come on, mate. What about if she doesn't do the event? It's not like she's done it. She made a post. This is a lot of stress on her. She's pregnant."

Zoe Buhler, 28, then begins to both panic and sob.

She was lucky not to have miscarried.

The video was viewed five million times in the first 24 hours.

***

The offending post read: "PEACEFUL PROTEST! All social distancing measures are to be followed so we don't get arrested please. Please wear a mask unless you have a medical reason not to. September 5th is FREEDOM DAY! As some of you may have seen the government has gone to extreme measures to prevent the Melbourne protest. Here in Ballarat we can be a voice for those in stage 4 lockdowns. We can be seen and heard and hopefully make a difference! END LOCKDOWNS. STAND UP FOR HUMAN RIGHTS. WE LIVE IN A FREE COUNTRY."

***

Later Buhler told reporters: "I didn't realise that I wasn't allowed to. The police could have given me a phone call and say, look, you need to take down your event or you could be charged with a crime, and I would have done that. It could have been as simple as that. I'm just a passionate person and I'm sick of the lockdown.

"I do think they were too heavy-handed, especially in front of my children and to walk into my house like that. It did scare them.

"I was scared I was being kidnapped. I was just fully freaking out.

"I'm charged with incitement. I'm still yet to know exactly what that means."

Legal heavyweights weighed in.

President of the Victorian Bar, Wendy Harris, QC, said: "In the case of Ms Buhler, who was arrested and handcuffed in her home in front of her partner and children, the Bar is concerned that the enforcement action of the police ... appeared disproportionate to the threat she presented."

Emeritus Professor Rosalind Croucher issued a statement: "As the President of the Australian Human Rights Commission I am dismayed at the handling of the arrest of a woman in Ballarat, who was handcuffed by police despite her compliance, in front of her family.

"Human rights are for everyone, everywhere, everyday.

"In times of crisis, such as this pandemic, our rights are as important as ever. While measures of control infection have required temporary limitations of our rights and freedoms, they must always be proportionate to the risk — and managed appropriately."

Despite a direct request for a response, the Prime Minister Scott Morrison refused to comment.

If you do not condemn, you condone, from your bully pulpit.

***

Powerfully aligned with the traditionally conservative elements of the Liberal Party, and desperate to see the end of Scott Morrison's reign as Prime Minister, Sky News coverage became progressively incensed throughout.

Sky News host Alan Jones, one of the country's most powerful conservative voices, said Victorian Premier Daniel Andrews's grab for power and disdain of accountability had forced Victorians to behaviour designed to retake their freedoms.

"The only person guilty of incitement is the Premier of Victoria," Jones said. "This woman is a victim of the inexcusable and unlimited powers given to the Victorian police. The verbal and intimidatory behaviour towards a pregnant mother is a form of violence the like of which no Australian will tolerate.

"Go Daniel Andrews, and go tonight! Before more damage is done.

"I don't think anyone in the government has any clue how we get out of this. This is where the rubber hits the road. Earlier today we learnt from the Treasurer the Australian economy contracted seven per cent during the June quarter.

"This is the worst economic blow since World War Two, the largest fall in GDP since records began in 1959. We have never seen anything even remotely close to this before.

"The response to this coronavirus has been prompted by alarmist chief medical officers who have ignored international evidence; politicians who've refused to lead, but rather follow; and hysterical modelling, which has now been totally discredited."

Editor of *Spectator Australia* Rowan Dean described the event as a National Day of Shame and said Victoria stood condemned in the eyes of the world. "Scott Morrison, enough is enough. Stand up and say we are not going to have pregnant women arrested in their own homes for posting online a legitimate political point of view!

Of the incident, Professor Ramesh Thakur said martial law was masquerading as medical law: "RIP the Australia I admired, migrated to and thought I knew".

***

An overweight Assistant Commissioner for the Victoria Police, Luke Cornelius, cut a poor figure as he admitted on camera that the optics of arresting a pregnant woman were terrible, but defended the conduct of his officers and expressed no regret over the operation.

He told reporters that police had visited more than eighty people and warned them that if they attended or organised protests, they would be arrested. Three additional people had been arrested and charged with incitement for planning an anti-lockdown protest at the Shrine of Remembrance in Melbourne set for 5 September.

Cornelius described the protest as "bat-shit crazy nonsense" and the organisers as "boofheads", promising that their feet would not "touch the ground".

"We remain very concerned, and in fact, *outraged* is probably a fair word, to say there are still people in our community who think it's a good idea at the time of this deadly pandemic that we're all fighting, think it's a good time to leave home and protest on our streets," he said.

"If you do take the selfish option and leave home to protest, we'll be ready for you … We have hundreds of police ready to respond, including our general duties and specialist police, such as the public order response unit, mounted branch and the highway patrol. They've all been rostered and will be deployed to support this operation."

That's what's called health fascism.

The most up-to-date research at the time showed that if you were under 60 years of age with no underlying morbidities you had a 99.98 per cent chance of survival.

They rearranged the world for *this*?

They rearranged the world to suit themselves.

***

Included in the armoury of the authorities was the extremely effective tactic of death by legal process, which for decades had drained or extinguished some of the country's most determined protestors and justice seekers.

Six months later, just a month before she was due to give birth, Zoe Buhler's lawyer Hugo Moodie informed the Ballarat Magistrates Court that his client would be contesting the incitement charge.

Beyond questions over the legality of the arrest, Mr Moodie said he would question the public health directives in place at the time.

"The arguments will be around whether the public health directions prohibited peaceful, socially distanced protest," Mr Moodie told the court.

They would also examine if Ms Buhler had a "reasonable excuse" under the Public Health and Wellbeing Act and whether she intended to breach the law or was just expressing a view.

Up to three police witnesses would also be called to give evidence at the case, the court was told.

Mr Moodie also told the court his client wanted to get her phone back from police, who had retained it since she was initially arrested. A separate court hearing date was to be arranged so he could argue for the return of Ms Buhler's mobile.[50]

50 Pregnant Ballarat mum Zoe Buhler to argue police search wasn't legal, Caroline Schelle, *News*, 27 March, 2021.

***

There was about those permeating times a strange translucent multifaceted intent, truly as if a transformational evil was in play; and as if there had to be a witness.

It was Edgar Allan Poe, of course, who wrote those famous lines: "Those who dream by day are cogniscant of many things which escape those who only dream by night."

Well, Old Alex was cursed. It wasn't comfortable. Imperilled, the fabric of everything transforming around him, for weeks he watched nesting blue herons come and go from his own fringe of trees, there on a back veranda perilously close to everything, a sacred place, a tradition lost, the right to sanctuary.

An ancient, deeply spiritual right this world had abandoned.

The outside world might have been a blizzard, but here he could watch the magpies nesting and the cuckoos swirling in the gusts of wind, waiting for the parents to leave the nest, he heard everything, and at the same time a protective peace cloaked this place.

For days he kept hearing the same phrase: "A mammalian species". As if he was overhearing intelligences from another realm offering explanations to each other about what they saw; the way the humans behaved, the inchoate sensations which whispered through them.

Gifts of prophecy had been transmitted down the generations, these technologies designed to survive in the most extreme of circumstance, launched from a distant, different realm. He wasn't the only one feeling the spiritual derangement of the times, but in that rare and sacred and most beautiful of sanctuaries, as some deranged river of time flowed over him, he just sat and watched the magpies, blue herons and a nearby peregrine falcon, all of them nesting at that time of year.

Walk among them.

Australia at the end of that year, 2020 in their count, had all the echoes of the future riven into the present, and yet, despite all the obvious terrors of the time, somnambulant, the population buried itself. We weep for you and you are not lost, not yet.

***

Every single day, seemingly without end, more than five million people in Melbourne were suffering through the harshest lockdowns in the world.

There were wild scenes of protest across the spring of 2020, as police carpeted the city in increasingly violent suppression of protesters, including police chasing down protesters on horseback.

Against a backdrop of extreme tactics, amidst multiple claims of police brutality and striking scenes of riot police throwing protesters to the ground, the COVID story itself was unravelling for a government which had deliberately sown panic and confusion for their own political gain.

Constantly shifting goalposts, conflicting messages, appeals to patriotism — why would anyone trust any of it? But they did. Politicians you wouldn't normally trust to walk you across the road were suddenly being seen as saviours of the people.

Despite numerous stories and considerable visual evidence, including one man who ended up in hospital in a coma, Premier Daniel Andrews claimed there was no culture problem within Victoria Police.

That sounded about as sincere as his claim that he hadn't watched the video footage, which had been viewed by millions of people around the world, of a pregnant Zoe Buhler being arrested in her own home, in front of her children, for making a Facebook post; the very point at which the government's COVID narrative came completely unstuck.

Bulldust! These people check their public image as frequently as they look at themselves in the mirror.

Or just as sincere, when asked by a reporter what his response to being called "Dictator" by *The Washington Post*. His response? He didn't read *The Washington Post*.

The piece, published in mid-September, was particularly interesting for offering an outsider's view to an Australian inner turmoil; or torment.

"Detractors call him "Dictator Dan." Supporters declare, on social media, #IStandWithAndrews. To residents of Melbourne, Australia's second-largest city, he is Daniel Andrews, the Premier of Victoria state and the politician responsible for inflicting upon them some of the most stringent pandemic-control measures on Earth.

"The city named repeatedly over recent years as the 'world's most livable' has been locked down since July 9. Two weeks ago, Andrews declared that a citywide curfew will not be lifted until October 26 — and then only if the coronavirus is almost eliminated.

"That would leave Melbourne's five million residents confined indoors for 115 days, longer than the 92-day lockdown in Manila, 76 days in Wuhan, China, 58 days in Italy and 33 days across New Zealand.

"In Melbourne, public life has essentially come to a halt. Schools are shuttered. Roads are empty. The only shops open are gas stations, supermarkets and drugstores. People who do not work in an essential industry are allowed to leave their houses only for two hours' exercise a day, or to buy food, care for others or seek medical attention. Soldiers go door to door checking that infected people are in isolation. Police ask cyclists for identification to ensure they are not breaching a rule allowing exercise only within five kilometres of their homes."[51]

***

Unless they were complete and total imbeciles, at this point in the slow-motion train wreck that was Australia, no politician and no health bureaucrat could have been unaware that there was now considerable intellectual weight behind the anti-lockdown movement.

A gathering political and policy storm they ignored at their chosen peril.

Federal officials reportedly pleaded with Daniel Andrews to loosen rules that were dragging down Australia's economy. Spending by individuals in Victoria was down 30 per cent, according to the Treasury Department.

The Premier of Victoria had never looked happier; never been more popular.

Daniel Andrews, 48, whose only employment experience was working as an adviser for the Australian Labor Party before entering politics, was in his heyday. Front and centre of everything; the lives of millions in his hands.

For anyone engaged in a study of the grotesque, Andrews's daily press conferences, which he did 120 in a row before taking a day off, finally ending on 30 October, 2020, became essential viewing.

The media hunt in packs. And Old Alex was ever hopeful the pack would turn. But the media terrain was so broken, there was no common ground, and the acquiescence he saw all around him still startled.

Lockdown sceptics were rare or nonexistent on the taxpayer-funded

---

51 Australia's coronavirus 'dictator' enforces a drastic lockdown. He's still popular, A. Odysseus Patrick, *The Washington Post*, 15 September, 2020.

national broadcaster, which had devolved into the government's propaganda wing, ditto most of the lowbrow commercial television stations whose push for the lowest common denominator was all part of a decline in public discourse.

We form opinions from what we know; we are easily influenced. That was the state of being. The channels were strangulated, little light broke through.

As one of those satirical lists of what we had learnt about humans during COVID put it: "They are easy to fool, but almost impossible to get them to admit they've been fooled."

***

Professor Ramesh Thakur addressed the circumstance in his usual cogent manner: "Put under 23-hour house arrest, limited to 5km-radius outings for state-approved activities and purposes, mandatory mask requirement, rights to peaceful protest suspended, pervasive police surveillance of social media and public spaces, state control of economic activities, suspension of parliament to rule by executive diktat, instant heavy fines on police officers' whims, martial law masquerading as medical law: how comforting ...

"Lockdowns don't destroy the virus. No, they destroy the three 'ls' of lives, livelihoods and liberties. Governments have effectively stolen a year of our life. The boundary between liberal democracy and draconian dictatorship proved to be virus-thin.

"Pre-emptive press self-censorship has helped to normalise the rise of the surveillance-cum-security state in the name of keeping us safe from terrorists and now from the virus that is so deadly, hundreds of millions must be tested to know they've had it.

"The pandemic has brought about an expansion in state power right into our homes and across public spaces to an extent not seen previously, not even in wartime. A Freedom House report concluded that in eighty countries the pandemic has emboldened governments to engage in abuses of power: 'silencing their critics, and weakening or shuttering important institutions, often undermining the very systems of accountability needed to protect public health'."[52]

---

52 Lives, Livelihoods and Liberty Lost, *A Sense of Place Magazine*, 8 November, 2020.

***

With police blanketing the almost empty streets of Australian cities, citizens being assaulted by thugs in uniform, doors being broken down, people dragged screaming from their cars while millions endured the world's longest and most draconian lockdowns, the Australian Government appeared to have lost control of the very COVID narrative it had created.

Or perhaps that was the message they wanted to push: fear, chaos, confusion and the crushing of dissent, all the while manning their power bases and concealing the incomprehensible incompetence of politicians and public servants.

Statistics published on 3 September, 2020, showed that since early August, Victorian Police had issued 1762 fines totaling $2.9 million for breaking curfew, which meant they were caught outside their homes between 8pm and 5am.

This represented an average of sixty curfew infringements a day, with each attracting a hefty $1652 fine.

A further 6000 fines were issued for other breaches of COVID regulations.

Victoria Police had also handed out more than 900 fines in the previous month for people failing to wear a face mask or face covering in public. Those fines were $200 each, amounting to more than $181,000 in one month alone.

Instances of breaches of the chief health officer's directions included people visiting friends or going to convenience stores for food or cigarettes.

There was a man who went to pick up shoes from his cousin, another who was caught going to pick up a fish tank for his frog, and people who just ventured out for donuts.

Fast forward a month and another set of data showed that only 845 of more than 19,324 fines given to people for breaching Victoria's coronavirus lockdown rules had been paid.

Enforcement of the fines could include vehicle wheel-clamping, suspension of vehicle registration, seizure and selling of personal property, and even imprisonment.

The data predated the ramping up of fines for what the government decreed was an unlawful gathering from $1652 to $4957, that is for protesting lockdown laws.

***

The hypocrisy of the fines was easily perceived: Black Lives Matter and Climate Change demonstrations caused no such draconian crackdowns, because they perfectly matched the government's own agendas, with the investment of billions in anti-racism programs under the rubric of multi-culturalism, and the equally massive investment and distortion of the energy market under the rubric of global warming.

But joining a protest against curfews and lockdowns, policies which were being condemned by experts worldwide — well, that was a different matter.

If you can't win your arguments without resorting to massive fines, extreme levels of violence, police brutality and violent suppression of dissenting voices, those ideas aren't worth having.

If you can't manage the population in any other way, like, gosh, by encouraging them to live fulfilling and independent lives for example, you should go back to the drawing board.

If instead of perpetrating the group derangement of a power-mad governing class using COVID to expand their hold into everybody's lives, freedom of expression had been respected, the outcome — a flattened, dispirited, inward-looking populace impoverished by their ruling elites — would have been nowhere near as bad. And the authorities orchestrating this debacle would have been held to account.

Liberty Victoria vice-president Julia Kretzenbacher called on police to show restraint with fines, and to instead issue more warnings to people found to be breaching coronavirus lockdown rules.

"The fines are quite high and people are struggling financially, and it's therefore no surprise that people are struggling to pay them," Ms Kretzenbacher said. "The response should be a public health response and not a policing response, and in particular we're concerned about reports that fines have been issued disproportionately to more vulnerable people, including young people."

Named in honour of Queen Victoria, Victoria was separated from New South Wales and established as a separate Crown colony in 1851.

And Victoria had never seen anything like it.

***

For Old Alex, stranded in a damped-down suburb on the edge of Lake Illawarra, with the local library shut and all the traditional points of community abolished, the urgent waking dreams got worse, overwhelming the person he once was.

Prehistoric. That's how it felt. Prehistoric; before the history of these people had barely begun.

Born aloft. In the wavering light, in the fluxing matter that surrounded them, in the rendition of the spirit which they knew not, in the ancient AIs, their own evolution making them the galaxy's top predators without peer, mirrored in the beauty of falcons and the stunning beauty of this place. Coming home, coming home.

Most surprising to Old Alex was how much they loved trees, the citadels of forests, as if these sacred places which once blanketed the east coast had been defoliated with intent, as if someone had stepped in to destroy their churches, and they would rise up angry, and brook no more.

"Someone walking over your grave?" he asked of Chris, his housemate of the moment, who had shivered in that familiar twist when the entire galaxy is pulling at your heart.

"Dragged across, more like," came the reply.

Or perhaps, he did not say, you too can feel the spatial distortions across an extraordinary distance in time and space.

***

On the same day that Zoe Buehler was being arrested, a group representing more than 500 Victorian doctors and medical experts called on Premier Daniel Andrews to bring an immediate end to lockdown restrictions in Victoria, raising concerns over the growing human toll caused by Victoria's COVID-19 response.

Leading epidemiologists from many of the world's elite tertiary institutions, including Harvard, Stanford, Oxford and the Australian National

University, came out condemning lockdowns as counterproductive. Yet the Australian Medical Association and the nation's politicians showed no signs of having heard any of them.

The COVID Medical Network claimed the present restrictions were unnecessary, disproportionate and must be lifted, in a statement posted to their website: "The response to the virus will cause more deaths and result in far more negative health effects than the virus itself.

"It has become increasingly clear that the response to the SARS-CoV-2 virus by the Victorian Government is now doing more harm than good, and will cause more deaths and result in far more negative health effects than the virus itself and risks creating Victoria's worst ever public health crisis."

Spokesman for the group, Dr Eamonn Mathieson, said: "The ongoing physical, psychological, social and economic harm is creating a new health crisis that far outweighs any possible benefits from continuing the lockdown. The time has come to step back and look at the bigger picture. The data does not support the actions being taken."

***

Dr David Marsh, a leading GP specialising in mental health, expressed alarmed at the rise in the number of people seeking help, many for the first time:

"We are experiencing a tsunami of mental health concerns, across all age groups. This cannot go on."

GP Dr Stacey Harris feared that children are the overlooked victims of the flawed virus response: "I see fifteen children and adolescents every day, and 40—50 per cent of these have some form of depression, anxiety, eating and obsessive-compulsive behaviours that is newly diagnosed or exacerbated from the lockdown.

"Their social isolation in continuous lockdown is causing instrumental harm and damage, that is causing — and will continue to cause — a huge mental health burden in Melbourne."

Six weeks later Dr Eamonn Mathieson said the group had received absolutely no acknowledgement or response from the government.

"I think they are certainly aware that there is a growing number of doctors that are concerned about this and we need to express our grave concerns about what is happening in the community.

"We're hearing that there has been an experience of massive collateral damage from these lockdowns, particularly in children and adolescents who are experiencing great trauma and mental health issues.

"The consequences will be catastrophic."

***

The policing was so over the top that a coalition of community groups began a website COVID-19 Policing Australia, which issued fortnightly updates of the deteriorating situation, supported by groups including Australian Community Legal Centres, Amnesty International and Liberty Victoria.

They recorded a string of confronting incidents, with police stepping well outside their traditional roles; including a man with terminal cancer sitting in his car near a headland, a man with brain injuries out exercising with his carer, a woman jogging alone in a park, a homeless woman told to abandon her dog and get back to her hotel, two young Aboriginal boys out walking accused of not complying with social-distancing laws and a woman donating supplies to refugees told there would be no exemption on compassionate grounds.

On 10 April, a cavalcade encircling the Mantra Hotel in Preston, outside of Melbourne, were protesting against the detention of asylum seekers held in the hotel under what they regarded as unsafe conditions. Twenty-six of the protesters received infringement fines of $1652, totaling more than $42,000.

One of the organisers was arrested before the protest, held in custody for nine hours, charged with incitement, and had his phone, work computer, and the computer of his 15-year-old son seized by police.

Numerous advocacy and human rights groups expressed concerns.

A majority of people reported that they had a negative experience of their interactions with police, describing their interactions as aggressive, interrogatory, intimidating, harassing, rude, very rude, unpleasant, nasty, forceful, not friendly or frightening.

People stated that after their interactions with police they were left feeling: singled out, treated unfairly, targeted, discriminated against, sad and hurt, angry, in disbelief, shocked, very traumatised, quite upset, scared.

Human Rights Watch condemned the abusive practices: "Several recent incidents raise serious concerns that Victoria's police are taking excessive or disproportionate action against suspected lockdown violators."

The group listed a number of alleged incidents, including an Indigenous man riding his bike to work at about 5.30am on 3 September who claimed Victorian police tackled, assaulted, and racially abused him. Police said the man failed to stop when asked for a permit check.

The media also reported a string of incidents in which the police used harassing tactics. These included a law professor with cerebral palsy who alleged that the police told her to "move on", preventing her from sitting down and resting while out with her 70-year-old mother; and a young tradesman whom the police fined for allegedly having the wrong column mistakenly filled out on his work permit.

***

COVID-19 Policing Australia recorded a string of incidents, many of which left the targets distressed, traumatised or angry.

A woman visiting her son's gravesite was followed by police, a man taking his dog and his 81-year-old father for a walk at a beach was aggressively spoken to and trailed back to his house, police invaded an Airbnb property over a cancer patient in Melbourne for treatment, a mother and child were ordered into a shop rather than wait outside, although in terms of social distancing the orders made no sense, a couple out walking who were stopped fifty metres from their front door, after encountering a neighbour who was out running, were confronted by police, and a nurse was stopped on her way to work.

One couple were visited by police and fined $1652 after posting holiday snaps they took in 2019. Police revoked the fines but instructed the couple not to post any more pictures during lockdown.

A 16-year-old and a friend were out walking with a friend in Caroline Springs, a suburb in western Melbourne, when they felt threatened after a packed car started following them. They jumped a fence to escape. The owners of the house then called the police, who fined both young people for breaching COVID restrictions.

Police in an outer suburb of Brisbane fined a woman walking with her partner to a service station to purchase sanitary items. The police did not appear to accept the woman's explanation of why she and her partner were walking together but had separate addresses — they were living separately to protect her partner's mother, who is vulnerable to COVID-19.

A man was travelling from Nowra in NSW back to his home in Victoria in his campervan, having recently realised that stay-at-home measures required him to return. He was on a disability support pension and his lack of internet connection left him unaware of the full extent of the stay-at-home orders. A police officer who stopped him in Victoria issued him with a fine of $1650, which he had no means of paying.

***

Police knocked on the door of a household occupied by seven people in Melbourne's inner north. The boyfriend of one of the house occupants answered the door and was questioned by police, who appeared not to believe that seven people lived in the house or that the boyfriend had a legitimate reason for being there. The police threatened fines and said they had been watching the house.

Three people, including an international student, were fined $1600 each for going to a skatepark, with police claiming they should have been exercising outside the park.

"The male police said we were allowed to skate only outside of the skatepark," the student recalled. "The female police was very rude and said we were getting a $1600 fine each.

"I was very shocked after this event and feel very traumatised and have difficulty sleeping. I don't have family or government support here in Australia. I don't understand why there's hundreds of people on the beach, hundreds of people in the main street and shopping centres, and people playing hockey next to the skatepark, and that's OK, but if there's only three people peacefully skating inside of a skatepark, we get a fine?

"How can the laws says we can exercise but at the same time not allowed to exercise? How can they open some places but close some places? How can we average people understand these confusing laws?"

***

The travesty just got worse; with no apparent end.

NSW Police fined three indigenous football players after images were shared on social media of a weekend away at one of the player's houses.

An Aboriginal man, Adnyamathanha elder Malcolm McKenzie, was arrested on 28 April 2020 after protesting against a truck carrying barricades coming into the town of Davenport, where the community had been on strictly enforced restrictions.

The settlement of Davenport had no grocery store, making the travel and quarantine restrictions particularly onerous. Police put handcuffs on Mr McKenzie and refused to take them off when he said they were painful.

Two people in the seaside town of Ocean Grove were given on-the-spot fines of $1652 while taking photos out on a walk. The police said they were responding to a call that someone had climbed into a window. The police did not charge the pair for any alleged trespass and fined them, stating that photography was non-essential.

An 18-year-old was fined $1652 on the spot for playing basketball with friends. They were very concerned about their ability to pay the fine, as they were casual fast-food employees.

A witness wrote in after they saw a police car drive on to the footpath in Fitzroy in order to stop a man hanging out on the corner, who was visibly homeless.

The witness spoke to the man after the police had left and discovered that he was recently released from prison, had no housing, and was being supported by the local community.

The police issued him with $3600 in fines. The witness reported that the man was understandably unsure of how he was going to be able to pay the fine and what his other options were during the pandemic — where could he go and where could he take his possessions?

In Parkville an adult caring for their mother, who had significant health problems, was fined for taking a rest during a walk around a park in Parkville. After walking for fifteen minutes, the mother needed to take a rest and the pair sat on a park bench.

Not long after, two police officers approached and asked, "Do you know what is happening in the world these days? Do you listen to the news? Don't you have Facebook?"

***

One of Australia's most talented independent journalists, Paul Gregoire, wrote that there had been an escalating series of incidents involving

Victoria Police Commissioner Shane Patton's officers using excessive force during the state's second lockdown.

"During the first national lockdown Victoria Police was already being scrutinised for the arbitrary and inconsistent manner in which it was enforcing public health rules. A coalition of community legal groups established the COVID Policing website to monitor police behaviour in response.

"Although it wasn't until early July, when 500 police officers were sent in to enforce a hard lockdown on 3000 public housing tower residents — that's one officer for every six civilians — that it seemed Victoria Police might be getting a little carried away with its pandemic policing.

"Victorian authorities were criticised for the way they handled the lockdown of the Flemington and North Melbourne towers — which occurred after a number of residents tested positive to COVID-19 — as the occupants were given no warning and were unable to stock up on essentials.

"As a local charity group was conducting a food delivery for residents in the towers, one man trying to carry in some items was set upon by a number of Victoria Police officers who did the usual: surround him, wrestle him to the ground and then lean down upon him with their weight.

"Victoria Police went on to release the usual statement justifying the actions of officers. On this occasion it was due to the man having been 'verbally aggressive' towards them before they forcibly overwhelmed him."[53]

***

Over-the-top policing even extended to a heavily pregnant woman who dared to take a breather.

A 38-weeks pregnant woman captured the moment Victorian Police officers told her she was not permitted to rest on a park bench during her designated one-hour period of exercise.

The video, which was widely circulated on social media, started just after two officers approached the heavily pregnant woman and told her that catching her breath on a park bench was not permitted.

"I just want to make sure I understand the rules," the woman says as she starts filming. "You're allowed to be in a park, but you can't sit in a park at all?"

53 Victoria Police Brutalise Citizens by Cover of COVID, Paul Gregoire, A *Sense of Place Magazine*, 22 September, 2020.

"You can only be out of your house for one of four reasons," the officer responds. "One of those would be exercise. Sitting in a park is not one of the four reasons."

The woman replied, "So, I'm pregnant and obviously my exercise is limited because I have to walk. I'm now puffed out because I'm 38-weeks pregnant. So, even I can't sit in a park, is that right?"

"You can only be out for one of the four reasons," the officer restated.

The woman asked again, "Just confirm that, yes or no. I can't sit in a park — as a pregnant woman I can't sit in a park?"

"You can only be out for one of the four reasons," the officer reiterated.

That's the criminal class for you. Think they can do any damn thing they like, even stretching to sitting on a park bench when they're 38-weeks pregnant.

***

In the same genre, five Victoria Police officers were filmed surrounding two elderly women sitting on a park bench in Melbourne and threatening them with arrest unless they handed over their identification.

The women were old enough to be the officers' grandmothers.

"No, I'm not standing up," one of the women declared. "On what grounds am I under arrest? This is unlawful."

The video also showed an officer sneaking up behind one of the women before snatching her mobile phone from her hand after she started filming the confrontation.

"Excuse me, you have no right to seize my property," she yelled.

Victoria Police acknowledged they were aware of the vision but issued no apology and claimed that without further details they were unable to comment.

"Generally speaking, it is an offence to not provide your name and details to police when they believe you have either committed or are about to commit an offence. As part of their powers, police have the ability to remove items from a person's possession where necessary to effect an arrest."

***

At this point, if you had your own magazine and could do so, you too might have thought it a perfect time to run extracts from that classic of English literature, Henry Thoreau's *Civil Disobedience*, which is exactly what Old Alex did.

"I heartily accept the motto, 'That government is best which governs least':

"Law never made men a whit more just; and, by means of their respect for it, even well disposed are daily made the agents of injustice. A common and natural result of an undue respect for law is that you see a file of soldiers … marching in admirable order over hill and dale to the wars, against their wills, ay, against their common sense and consciences …

"The standing army is only an arm of the standing government. The government itself, which is only the mode which the people have chosen to execute their will, is equally liable to be abused and perverted, before the people can act through it.

"There is but little virtue in the action of masses of men. Under a government which imprisons any unjustly, the true place for a just man is also a prison.

"If the injustice is part of the necessary friction of government, let it go, let it go; perchance it will wear smooth, certainly the machine will wear out … but if it is of such a nature that it requires you to be the agent of injustice to another, then, I say break the law. Let your life be a counter-friction to stop the machine. What I have to do is see, at any rate, that I do not lend myself to the wrong which I condemn."

***

Another report from inner Melbourne was of two women, housemates, who were dancing the salsa in a park as a form of exercise. The police told them that dancing was not a form of exercise and ordered them to move on. "Maybe they thought we would be easy targets, as two women, so they could justify their existence without having to confront anyone that might get hostile.

"Lots of people were sitting around, some drinking alcohol, on the other side of the park at the same time."

A woman with three children who parked at a boat ramp to eat their takeaway dinner in the car also faced the police.

On and on and on the insanity went, month after month.

Police scanned licences and monitored how often people left their homes.

A 64-year-old woman in Sydney claimed to have been harassed by a particularly aggressive female officer after buying a takeaway coffee and walking back to her car.

"She was nasty and forceful. I walked away in disbelief. I worry these new powers of aggressive behavior towards the public will continue after the shutdown. I am not rough. We are well-known business people."

**

Yet another report from Melbourne detailed family members going to a mosque to farewell their aunty, who had recently passed away. Their distress was compounded by the fact that they were unable to see her in hospital.

"We arrived at the mosque. While patiently waiting, two police vehicles arrived with four officers, which was extremely upsetting to see.

"They gave us strict instructions that we were only allowed to go in car by car to say our final goodbyes without making any contact with others.

"It was the most devastating thing to be told. We were not even allowed to hug our grandmother, who was mourning the loss of her child."

The informant alleged prejudice: "The fact two police cars came to a funeral because we are Muslim and black. There was absolutely no need for two police cars because everyone was in their cars and only ten people were on the mosque grounds."

One father detailed what happened to his son: "My son was by himself and was leaving Coles supermarket when he was pulled up by the police twice in five minutes.

"The first time he explained to the officer he was on his way home and the officer told him to get home. Minutes later he was pulled up by a second policeman who was very physical with my son and pushed him to the ground and stuck his knee in the middle of his back to hold him down. He also got a $1650 fine. My son suffers from anxiety and depression and was very anxious that day because he was booked to go to a clinic, and all day he was trying to deal with the situation. He is also unemployed because of the COVID-19."

***

All rationality fled the building.

COVID-19 Policing Australia concluded: "A number of reports over the past few weeks have highlighted what they feel is different rules regarding COVID-19 restrictions for the general public and police; for example, police not observing the social-distancing requirements — amongst themselves or with the public. This seems to compound the feelings of unfairness and arbitrariness in police enforcing the restrictions.

"There is no evidence that punitive policing and heavy use of fines has had any positive impact on public health outcomes. No reviews or inquiries have determined that the policing response to COVID has done more good than harm. In the absence of evidence that it works, the emphasis by the government on policing is ideological.

"The harms of policing are well established. We know from public data that COVID fines disproportionately affect those who can least afford them. In the absence of accurate information, people are unaware of the rules, and this can impact health and wellbeing — community legal centres have had reports of single mums staying locked down indoors for weeks, unaware that they could take children out to exercise or go shopping.

"Curfew policing also generates fear and confusion, especially in the absence of proper community education and outreach and support."

***

An academic study published in the journal *Current Issues in Criminal Justice* made equally damning conclusions: "Whilst COVID-19 measures are directed towards the goal of 'biosecurity' to stop the spread of the disease, in practice, COVID policing appears to rely on long-standing criminalisation strategies at odds with public health.

"Drawing on a range of primary and secondary data sources, we provide a critical account of the policing practices used and the groups to which the special measures have been directed in the most severely affected states of Victoria and New South Wales. Our case studies reveal that COVID policing as practised in those contexts intensifies existing patterns of public order policing directed towards the 'usual suspects' and reinforces a criminalisation rather than a public health paradigm.

"These authors note that law enforcement is only one method for promoting compliance and should be used only as a last resort ... populations are more likely to self-regulate where the security concerns arising from the pandemic 'are both acknowledged as legitimate within a public health response and at the same time grounded in the communities they are designed to protect'.

"On the other hand, they predict that a narrowly conceived 'securitised approach' will generate disorder and cultivate distrust, particularly amongst marginalised communities.

"Our case studies show that existing forms of criminalisation are the means by which public health has been securitised in these contexts, both in law and through police practice.

"We found COVID policing to provide opportunities for the intensification of long-standing and selective criminalisation processes, evident in the disproportionate focus on First Nations peoples in street policing and the high-visibility policing of racialised and socio-economically disadvantaged communities in public housing.

"Security policing is apparent in the pre-emptive imposition of extra-judicial punishment through large-scale COVID stops and searches in which actual risks to public health seem to play little part; the pre-emptive arrests and issuing of fines to protest organisers; the designation of protests as an illegitimate form of public gathering as a risk-reduction measure and the preventive lockdowns of whole communities in public housing, rather than focusing on the health risks posed by individuals.

"Our case studies reveal that COVID policing has intensified existing policing practices directed towards the 'usual suspects', which disrupts the notion that COVID policing is directed solely towards the legitimate public health objective of preventing contagion."[54]

---

54 Policing biosecurity: police enforcement of special measures in New South Wales and Victoria during the COVID-19 pandemic, Louise Boon-Kuo et al, *Current Issues in Criminal Justice*, 8 December, 2020.

ELEVEN
PROTESTS AND PROTESTORS

IN AUSTRALIA September is the first month of spring.

In 2020 it began right on schedule.

On day one police in Victoria charged two men over the "co-ordination and encouragement" of an anti-lockdown protest.

A 76-year-old man from Windsor was also later arrested and charged with incitement for allegedly helping to organise the protest.

In a statement, police said officers seized several items including mobile phones, laptops and postage items.

Notices of the event, planned for 5 September, were repeatedly removed and reposted to Facebook, while one of the largest groups linked to the protest, which at its peak had more than 100,000 members, was also removed.

It was typical behaviour on the part of Australian authorities co-ordinating with American big-tech companies, and had been repeatedly seen in Australia in recent years, most notably over anti-multicultural protests.

Protest groups were placed under all the usual intrusive and thereby abusive physical and digital surveillance and their sites algorithmically downplayed, ensuring a news-averse public were almost entirely unaware of the parameters of the debate. It was counterproductive, but you couldn't tell them that.

Some of the sites removed from Facebook had significant followings, representing a strong community sentiment which should have been addressed with more collaborative public policy-making rather than the often violent suppression of alternative views.

It was almost a standard formula. Cut them off once they have a hundred thousand followers or so; a gathering reflection of pre-existing tensions.

Liaisons, internal spying, excessive surveillance, all courtesy of the Australian Federal Police and Australian Security Intelligence Organisation, amongst others, was intended to create a homogeneous public narrative and the illusion of a cohesive society.

All this suppression of freedom of expression for people who had every right to object to the government's mass immigration or lockdown policies without being labelled nutters, racists or conspiracy theorists, was in reality destroying the basis of Australian democracy; the right to think and feel as you saw fit, without Big Brother tromping through your every brain cell demanding compliance.

In a failing democracy, the destruction of people's rights to protest and express their discontents would ultimately rebound; the attempts to mould public opinion to conform with government agendas coming in a poor second to a country which, rather than the surveillance hell now being visited upon the population, could have been a vibrant and creative place.

Instead of a locked-down, miserable, dismal, silent, frightened, intimidated, inward-looking country with mob coercion on full display; a very sorry place indeed.

How Australians could treat their fellows with such contempt, and indeed with such brutality, would become one of the enduring puzzles of the era; there on the stairway to hell.

***

All across that fateful, unholy spring, there were violent protests the like of which Australia had never seen; for their passion, intensity, and extreme levels of police suppression.

On the first weekend, seventeen people were arrested in violent clashes around Melbourne's Shrine of Remembrance; dedicated to fallen soldiers, the same soldiers Prime Minister Scott Morrison was so hypocritically calling upon as inspiration for the fight against the coronavirus.

Footage showed large numbers of riot police and officers on horseback clashing with protesters in repeated violent melees.

Two protesters were seen raising their arms in a Nazi salute at officers and yelling "*Heil* Dan!" comparing the state of Victoria's Premier, Daniel Andrews, to Adolf Hitler.

After mounted officers drove protesters from the Shrine of Remembrance, footage showed streams of protesters moving down to nearby Albert Park.

Once there, a large police contingent, including officers from the public order response team, surrounded small groups of protesters, arresting them one by one.

During that pivotal September protesters, facing almost certain arrest and very large fines, sang a classic song by Australian singer Johnny Farnham:

We're all someone's daughter,
We're all someone's son.
How long can we look at each other
Down the barrel of a gun?
We're not gonna sit in silence,
We're not gonna live with fear.

"You dictators are ruining the country," one protester said as he was being arrested. "This is not Victoria," one clearly angry woman said as she confronted police. Others screamed as they were being shackled.

***

History, of course, doesn't just repeat itself; it is made up of those who leave a record.

There was one remarkable aspect of that period, if you were interested in journalism, which was that outside the glossy, breathless daily announcements of case numbers and ever shifting diktats relayed by heavily perfumed television presenters, another story evolved.

The new technologies didn't just allow anyone to have a go, they allowed talent to aggregate.

Media narratives are important because they provide an immediate documentary record, because they are the means through which national narratives are formed, and they are the basis for future histories, the detritus on the cultural floor.

Two of the most striking to emerge from the era were Avi Yemini of Rebel News, and Monica Smit of Reignite Democracy Australia, both of whom, whatever you may think about their politics and beliefs, did fundamental journalistic work the mainstream should have been doing. That is, talking to the people most affected, documenting those determined, courageous and perhaps foolhardy enough to protest.

As easy a way through the maze as any is to tell the story of each of their reporting separately, as different in personality as they were.

Time was collapsing in on itself in any case; the times felt as if we were being visited by our own futures, that entities beyond our ken were already desperately trying to warn us.

Swarms of black-clad, helmeted and masked riot police aggressively wrestling protestors to the ground became the New COVID Normal.

Many of the protestors carried mobile phones, filming the multiple abuses of the citizenry this style of policing required.

And which was also generating new styles of citizen journalism.

**

Prior to the violent demonstrations of 5 September, most notably in Melbourne but with sister demonstrations held around the country, Victorian police charged five people with incitement for their alleged involvement in organising the protest; a crushing of dissent that was bound to backfire.

Among them was Fanos Panayides, one of the organisers of a similar protest held in Melbourne in May.

Another, James Bartolo, who ran the website The Conscious Truth Network, posted footage of his arrest online.

"Woke up this morning, jumped on the dunny, heard some knocks on the door," Bartolo wrote on social media. "It was all the cops, they broke down the door, arrested me; they took computers, laptops [and my] phone.

"It is a bit of a pain in the ass. They stole my shit. Whatever! I'm fine."

**

News footage from the Melbourne protest showed one man, his hands cuffed from behind and surrounded by police, attempting to tell a television reporter about the virtues of alternative treatments. "Check out the death rate in Uganda," he yells. "They were all on that hydroxychloroquine."

His last strangled words before he is then forcibly masked from behind by a police officer.

Other protestors chanted: "Dictator Dan."

Freedom Day protests took place around the country.

NSW Police arrested a number of people in Sydney's Hyde Park and Olympic Park during "unauthorised" protests against lockdowns.

Among those arrested at Hyde Park in central Sydney was a 54-year-old man, later charged with assaulting an officer.

People being violently wrestled to the ground in unprecedented displays of force and then subsequently charged with assaulting police was just one of the many faces of the authoritarian derangement overtaking the country.

Two other people, a 44-year-old man and a 56-year-old woman, were also arrested for not complying with police.

Police issued another nineteen people at the park with $1000 fines, and a 16-year-old was issued with a youth caution.

A few hours later, a sister protest at Cathy Freeman Park, just outside ANZ Stadium, drew huge crowds.

Police issued fifty-seven people with $1000 fines and two men were arrested.

Crowds chanted "freedom" and "shove your new world order up your arse".

Mounted police pushed people out of the park.

In the rich hippy paradise of Byron Bay on the North Coast of New South Wales eight protestors were arrested. In Western Australia a woman was fitted with an electronic bracelet and her movements monitored.

***

Just like bombing jihadists, violent crackdowns simply spread the revolution wider. In Melbourne they created a narrative of out-of-control authoritarian abuse. Every violent assault and wrestling of protestors to the ground proved their point.

Images from the protests show an extreme level of confrontation: of women being dragged from cars, of stressed citizens screaming at phalanxes of black-clad policemen, of pepper-spraying crowds, rounding protestors into groups and wrestling them to the ground, which clearly breached any social-distancing guidelines — all of which could hardly have been more counterproductive.

Many of the rules, regulations and edicts which Australian governments rained down upon the population should never have been issued.

Five at a funeral. Ten at a wedding. You're not allowed to sing in church, but you can attend a swingers' party. You can't worship the way you want, but welcome to the orgy of life, to a time when all normal decencies had been debased. Ordinary people couldn't go surfing or walk in a park, but police could arrest pregnant women in their own homes.

One thing the authorities forget, in 2020 everyone has a smartphone.

Abuses by the police are filmed and uploaded in real time.

The multiple failures of Australia's mainstream media during the COVID Panic can be worked around. Welcome to the Rise of Citizen Journalists.

The extremely punitive fines were crippling to any ordinary working person.

These included a $4957 fine to anyone caught taking part in an unlawful gathering. Under Melbourne's restrictions, a maximum of five people from two households, or any number of people from a single household, could gather in public. The fines also applied to anyone trying to leave Melbourne for regional Victoria, to escape through its so-called Ring of Steel, the police blocking all the major arteries out of the city.

Daily the blizzard of official dishonesty, a profound irresponsibility, just got worse. And worse. And worse. A crime in plain sight which would blight the welfare of generations to come.

Six months on and the Freedom rallies were going nowhere, with one group rallying under the name Phoenix Project.

There's a general rule of thumb: for every activist and genuine grassroots demonstration there are a thousand like-minded supporters prepared to sign a petition, but only one in 10,000 prepared to take to the streets, risking, in this case, arrest, massive fines, being pepper-sprayed and wrestled to the ground, and subsequently, as marked subversives, under ongoing and intrusive surveillance.

The era was characterised by considerable faux outrage and manufactured protest, but a thing about organic protest is, it resonates into the future

The group's website read: "We are not career activists. We are everyday people who pre-pandemic lived everyday lives, focusing on families and work, navigating the dips and the rises of modern existence, caught up, like most, in our own little worlds. But in 2020 the COVID scam transpired, the curtain falling away to reveal the guiding hand of the globalists and the path they were determined to steer the world down.

"We watched as governments and the media across the world conducted an orchestrated campaign of propaganda and lies, working together to build a narrative that made no sense at all. And yet, despite the outrageous flaws in every aspect of it all, despite the heavy-handed manipulation and the assault on common sense, the flimsy narrative was doing its job and the agenda moved on, ploughing full steam ahead.

"We saw countries locked down, movement restricted, businesses lost, and lives destroyed. We saw basic rights removed with no regard for laws, and the final pieces of the global surveillance state put in place. We watched in horror as the Communist agenda rolled on, the vast majority not only acquiescing but actively embracing an ever-expanding assault on their rights.

"Unquestioningly obedient and stunningly complacent, they stayed in their homes, wore masks in their cars, and stood on crosses on supermarket floors. Mindless, ignorant, and willfully blind, they submitted to slavery for themselves and their children.

"The cult of COVID had taken hold, complete with gods and rituals and sacred artefacts. It captured the minds of the masses, lending them purpose even as they marched unseeing towards their own destruction, their blind obedience enabling tyranny and ushering in a dystopian nightmare."

***

Cut straight to surreal.

The first press performance of Victorian Premier Daniel Andrews after a shocking weekend of violent scenes and brutal mistreatment of protestors was all about encouraging outdoor dining and pop-up cafes as a path to financial recovery.

Fearless journalists asked about plastic screens between tables.

Martial law was being introduced into Australia; and the perpetrators were getting away with it.

***

Who could not be discombobulated in this time?

Old Alex was stranded on the South Coast with a dying parent, in a situation which became sadder and more difficult with every passing day.

The same tragic, terrible voice which haunted that COVID year had landed him here: in the most human of situations.

It felt as if he was still dissembling into a legitimate human. He was going to stalk through the powers that be; and yes, throw the money-lenders from the temple.

His vision-plagued madness grew increasingly demented; and he kept hearing voices of resignation and regret, of furious fellow officers, of a lament at all the lost loves, at the contagion despoiling the land, at a swirling horror that was ours and ours alone.

All his dreams were of a savage, mediaeval violence; of murder by old weapons, of throat-slitting, of armies on the march, of camps late at night.

When asked by a young soldier to make sense of it all, he replied: "Those ancient AIs, we call them gods, want to transmit millions of years of experience with quantum entanglement, so that we can join the wider universe."

The soldier raised an eyebrow: "Huh? Really?"

"We will never believe we are alone in the universe again. The old manifestations will pass away. And we will all become as multitudes."

What were your dreams in those strangest of times?

***

Violent scenes of protest and confrontation characterised the entire month.

On 12 September 2020, Victorian police arrested fourteen people at protests in Melbourne, with 51 fines issued for breaching stay-at-home orders.

Hundreds of helmeted and masked police officers in black riot gear circled the Tan and the Shrine of Remembrance. Walkers on the shores of the city's Yarra River stopped and displayed signs, including one saying, "I am just exercising my human rights".

One woman who was restrained on the ground by police at the Observatory Gate said: "They've arrested me because I won't say my name. I've been in Melbourne all my life; I just want to go for a walk."

A man wearing a mask saying "Sack Dan Andrews" was arrested after he refused to provide ID to police. One woman's signs, including one saying "Open Our Churches", were taken by police officers.

In yet another suppression of the democratic right to free expression, promotion of the protests was removed from Facebook.

Prior to the event police arrested Tony Pecora, 43, allegedly one of the organisers of the protest.

When interviewed, Pecora told officers he believed coronavirus case numbers had been highly exaggerated.

He reportedly quoted legendary Australian rock band Midnight Oil: "It's better to die on your feet than to live on your knees."

As part of his bail conditions, he was forbidden to use social media or contact co-organisers.

The police had the full support of the Victorian Premier, Daniel Andrews, who described the protesters as "selfish, unlawful and wrong".

"It's not smart, it's not right. It's not the time for protest. No one has the right to make choices like that, that potentially puts at risk everything we are working towards."

***

Seventy-four people were arrested the following day at another protest and 176 people issued with substantial fines over their participation in a Freedom Walk.

Dramatic footage of over-the-top policing, which would impact on the reputation of police forces around the country, showed large numbers of riot police scuffling with protestors between fruit and vegetable stalls at one of the city's best-known landmarks, the Queen Victoria Market.

Protestors chanted "Freedom" and "Power to the people", "this is not a police state" and "you have to be on the right side of history".

The next day, lockdown restrictions were eased. A person living alone could now nominate a person for occasional visits. Victorians could now leave their homes for exercise for two hours a day and the overnight curfew was shortened by an hour, now beginning at 9pm rather than 8pm.

It had come to this.

The following weekend there were once again chaotic and violent scenes in Melbourne, with demonstrators chased down by police on horseback.

Protesters chanted "Freedom Freedom" and called for the Premier Daniel Andrews to be sacked. Police arrested sixteen people and issued 96 fines.

One of those arrested told officers: "Wake up! I know you already know this is wrong."

Another suggested the police would have to "answer to the Lord Jesus Christ".

Monica Smit from Reignite Democracy Australia reported to camera:

"There are a thousand people here. They're all a little bit scared. Their hearts are thumping. My heart is thumping. This is really bad. Really bad. It is scary to see the police acting the way they are. We are never going to like the police again, and that is really dangerous.

"The Australian people are never going to like the police again."

Despite clear footage of overwhelmingly aggressive police conduct against vastly outnumbered protestors, Victoria Police justified their actions by saying the protest was a "blatant breach" of the chief health officer's directions.

"We are frustrated that these people continue to put the lives of Victorians at risk," a police statement said. "While we know the majority of the community are doing the right thing, the behaviour of these selfish few who choose to blatantly ignore the direction will not be tolerated."

***

Police smashed a woman's car window and dragged her screaming out of the vehicle, repeatedly tackled protesters to the ground, and used the most authoritarian displays of state power ever seen in Australia, including violently wrestling another woman to the sands.

If there was one case that exemplified the complete collapse of all normal policing standards, it was the treatment of a Melbourne man hospitalised and placed in an induced coma.

Footage uploaded to the internet makes the police misconduct absolutely clear.

The man is first heavily rammed by a police car and then he staggers forward as a result and is wrestled to the ground.

His head is literally stomped on by a booted officer. You can play that footage over and over again; you will see exactly the same thing, aggressive, out-of-control behaviour.

Lawyer Jeremy King, representing the man, told the national broadcaster the video of the man being hit by a police car, was "sickening to watch".

"I would be fairly confident to say that in the Victoria Police manual regarding their approved tactics, you're not allowed to ram somebody with a vehicle and you're certainly not allowed to stomp on their head."

All wars bear casualties. But why here? Why now? Why this man? Why any of us?

No police officer was charged.

Paul Gregoire of the Sydney Criminal Lawyers Blog wrote of the incident: "It turns out this was no crook walking about in the middle of traffic, but rather a mental health patient in a state of duress. And Victoria Police has become so emboldened during the pandemic that it believes using a car to facilitate arrest is warranted, as is laying in the boot.

"While this incident stands out due to the unbridled force officers used, it's hardly an anomaly. Rather, it's one of an escalating series of incidents involving Victoria Police Commissioner Shane Patton's officers using excessive force as a policing tool during the state's second lockdown."

"During the first national lockdown Victoria Police was already being scrutinised for the arbitrary and inconsistent manner in which it was enforcing public health rules. A coalition of community legal groups established the COVID Policing website to monitor police behaviour in response.

"Although it wasn't until early July, when 500 police officers were sent in to enforce a hard lockdown on 3000 public housing tower residents — that's one officer for every six civilians — that it seemed Victoria Police might be getting a little carried away with its pandemic policing.

"Victorian authorities were criticised for the way they handled the lockdown of the Flemington and North Melbourne towers — which occurred after a number of residents tested positive to COVID-19 — as the occupants were given no warning and were unable to stock up on essentials.

"As a local charity group was conducting a food delivery for residents in the towers, one man trying to carry in some items was set upon by a number of Victoria Police officers, who did the usual: surround him, wrestle him to the ground and then lean down upon him with their weight.

"Victoria Police went on to release the usual statement justifying the actions of officers. On this occasion it was due to the man having been 'verbally aggressive' towards them before they forcibly overwhelmed him."[55]

***

Through all of this, Monica Smit at Reignite Democracy Australia wasn't going to back down for anybody.

---

55 Victoria Police Brutalise Citizens by Cover of COVID, Paul Gregoire, *A Sense of Place Magazine*, 22 September, 2020.

Fast-forward to October and she was arrested for the third time by Victorian police.

Surrounded by masked and heavily kitted officers, she declares to camera, speaking over the sound of a police microphone warning that she will be arrested: "We had a group of about ten people. We were socially distanced."

Standing with a male friend, she says to the police: "Guys, I don't want to do this. I don't want to be arrested, but we are doing this to make a point because we have every right to be here. We have every right to be here.

"We were even social-distancing. We were doing everything we were supposed to do. I have been arrested twice already."

Her friend places a protective arm around her and says: "We've got no choice now."

Still speaking to camera, Smit says: "We've been told if we stay here, we will get arrested. Here we go."

Five police then pull her friend aggressively away, while she says: "Don't fight it, Morgan, don't fight it."

And with a rueful, sad expression plastered across her face says: "I'm next. You can just arrest me, it's OK."

A female officer orders her: "Put your hands on your head if you're willing to leave peacefully."

"You can arrest me. I'm not putting my hands on my head.

"I am a journalist. I am a journalist. I have work permits. I have an exemption for my mask, I was told that I was allowed to be here. So, I am not putting my hands on my head."

Surrounded by police moving towards her, she repeats: "I'm a journalist. I am protected under federal legislation of implied freedom of political communication.

"I'm a journalist. I have a work permit. I have an exemption for my mask. Are you sure you want to arrest me?"

As she repeatedly states she has a work permit, an officer orders her arrested.

The final seconds of footage sound like a camera hitting the ground, and Smit yelling, "Are you serious?"

Online comments indicated growing community anger: "These police are absolutely horrendous." "She was willing and they still used awful force on her. SHAME ON THE VICTORIAN POLICE." "Since when does an arrest of a compliant person permit violent force? Absolute animals. Sue these people privately."

***

Later footage shows Smit, her hands still handcuffed behind her back and surrounded by more than a dozen police, repeatedly demanding: "Tell me what the offence is. Why am I being arrested? I have a work permit."

Increasingly frustrated and upset, she yells: "Stop! You are ruining the relationship between the community and the police.

"Do you know how bad you guys look? You're arresting me for working. It doesn't matter what you say, you're wrong. I'm sorry. I have federal legislation backing me. You're actually being totally unlawful. What you are doing is 100 per cent wrong. I am a journalist."

***

If anything highlighted the insanity, the sheer unadulterated madness of the period, it was the arrest and jailing of a Christian pastor the following May.

He was charged with incitement after making a Facebook announcement that his church would hold a Sunday service, technically against the rolling series of lockdowns still being endured by the state.

The preacher had been fined in February after more than fifty people attended one of his indoor services.

Victoria had been in lockdown for 112 days the previous year, and many restrictions remained.

Pastor Furlong said of COVID: 'It is the biggest fear-mongering hoax of the media, of power giants and the big boys to bring in a one-world government and a one-world agenda.

'C'mon, wake up, people! Stand up for your rights!

"My church is open. I've said I would not shut the church again. This Sunday at 10am, my church, the Revival Church in Narre Warren, we are open for worship.'

The prime minister wasn't the only one who believed he was doing God's will.

Followers proceeded to gather for a service nonetheless.

"We are the salt of the earth. We are not going to hide our light under a bushel," says one man. "We do not want to be full of fear. We do not want to be one of those people full of fear."

Prior to his arrest Pastor Furlong declared: "I made a declaration before Almighty God that we would not forsake the gathering of God's people, so we are meeting ..."

"I want to make it clear that my church will never shut. I need to obey God, God's word. He declares that we are not to forsake, not to stop, we are not to forsake the gathering together of the saints. And to do so even more as the days become more wicked. And evil. And the return of the Lord Jesus Christ is at hand. I believe we are right there, right now."

***

On the first Sunday following the pastor's arrest, his followers began singing hymns at an outdoor venue as large numbers of police gathered around them.

"We're fighting the good fight," says one parishioner to camera. "Jesus loves you. Get your lives right with him while there is still time."

Dozens of masked and heavily armed officers move towards them in a show of intimidatory force while the group, many with their hands raised in the air in reverence, continue to sing: "What a beautiful day it is. What a beautiful day it is. In the name of Jesus."

The footage, readily available on the Reignite Democracy Australia website, is utterly surreal. And chilling.

As the officers confront them, one of the parishioners tells the police they are there for their pastor, arrested and jailed for committing no crime. "This wonderful Christian man has been arrested for no reason. We pray for him. We pray for the peace of Jesus over him."

Surrounded by police, an organiser winds up proceedings, saying they know that Christians will be persecuted.

"Move on or you will be arrested," police order as the crowd begins to disperse.

"Grab that one!" a female officer orders.

A young parishioner is then wrestled to the ground.

One of the organisers exclaims all the while: "What the fuck? What the fuck?" What the fuck are you doing? We're dispersing."

Shortly after he announces: "They've just assaulted Anthony. They seriously can't control themselves."

A wall of police then descends.

The parishioner continues to film the incident: "That was violent. Vile Victoria Police. Absolute traitors.

"Everyone complied with the move on order. Then, like the violent thugs that they are, assaulted the people. With all their weapons. With all their personnel. They can't handle it. They just have to be violent. Against what? People standing up for human rights. The right to prayer. The right to religion. Is this the future you want for Australia? Not me. Everyone of these police personnel deserve to be charged."

***

Pastor Furlong's arrest was another watershed in the cascade of decline. Monica Smit's determined and persistent mobilisation and her style of campaigning journalism attracted the considerable resources of Sky News, which actively promoted the Reignite Democracy Australia website.

In an interview with Alan Jones, she said liberties could not be taken for granted and had to be fought for to be preserved.

"When a pastor who runs a charitable organisation, that saves children from sex-trafficking and poverty, if he is a criminal for trying to run a prayer service on a Sunday, then that is a worrying road. He is in jail without bail. He is not pleading guilty to incitement because he doesn't believe he has committed a crime.

"When the government is letting us down, and the police are letting us down, it is a really difficult time for Victorians. We want relationships between the police and the people to be good. Lockdown orders come into place and this is what we are seeing."

Sky News also replayed clips of extremely aggressive police arrests, supplied by the group; including of father of four Nick Patterson, who had a history of opposing mask mandates.

Another clip showed once again an extremely aggressive confrontation between a man walking home through a park after attending an outdoor service. The man is tackled to the ground and supporters shoved out of the way.

"The problem that I saw is some of the police are really enjoying this.

I didn't know anything about politics before 2020; and neither did most of us.

"We have started a political party. We will do everything it takes. Because this is not living and we don't accept it at all."

***

Out of these confrontations, as in other authentic protest movements, comes enduring alliances, collaboration, valuable experience and the building of expertise, and often intense friendships.

Be careful the giants you stir.

Hannah Arendt wrote in her masterpiece *The Origins of Totalitarianism*: "Even in the darkest of times we have the right to expect some illumination, and that such illumination may well come less from theories and concepts than from the uncertain, flickering, and often weak light that some men and women, in their lives and their works, will kindle under almost all circumstances and shed over the time span that was given them on earth ... Eyes so used to darkness as ours will hardly be able to tell whether their light was the light of a candle or that of a blazing sun.

"Humanity manifests itself in such brotherhood most frequently in 'dark times'. This kind of humanity actually becomes inevitable when the times become so extremely dark for certain groups of people that it is no longer up to them, their insight or choice, to withdraw from the world. Humanity in the form of fraternity invariably appears historically among persecuted peoples and enslaved groups ...

"This kind of humanity is the great privilege of pariah peoples; it is the advantage that the pariahs of this world always and in all circumstances can have over others."

***

It wasn't just individuals who copped the full force of Australia's authoritarian crackdowns.

All those "We Are COVID Safe" signs that now decorated venues of almost every kind weren't in reality a sign of "we're all in this together" community co-operation; they were a sign of coercion.

The overbearing officiousness of health inspectors was already becoming the stuff of legend amongst small business owners.

The Bondi Bowling Club was hit with a $10,000 fine after inspectors called it the "worst venue to date" for breaches of coronavirus rules.

Officials from Liquor and Gaming NSW visited the venue on 29 August and reportedly spotted multiple breaches of physical distancing and hygiene regulations.

Offences included groups of more than ten people, no social distancing at the bar, patrons mingling, and inadequate sign-in processes.

Liquor and Gaming director of compliance Dimitri Argeres said the breaches had been discovered on a routine check.

"We are still on a cliff edge, but you wouldn't know it if you went to Bondi Bowling Club on 29 August," he said. "The venue was operating as though the COVID safety measures were optional. This presented a pretty grim picture of patrons and staff who are simply ignoring the restrictions everyone else has to live with and putting the entire community at risk."

To date, government inspectors had issued 105 fines totaling $469,000 for breaches. Slamming already suffering businesses with extravagant fines was simply a way of destroying them. It was madness. You have to sell an awful lot of coffees, at least a thousand of them, to pay a $5000 fine; destroying people's dreams and hard work while those inflicting the pain lapped up the cream of a government job.

***

For those picking over the corpse in years to come, the spring of 2020 might also be remembered as of note for the employment of "in-your-face" reporter Avi Yemini by Rebel News Australia, an outgrowth of the Canadian-based group and one of the most controversial news sites in the country.

Yemini is the subject of considerable interest to Australia's intelligence agencies for his sympathetic coverage of ultranationalist demonstrations targeting multiculturalism and Muslim immigration,

Cleansed of faux ideological outrage, much of Yemini's energetic reporting and serial vox-popping provided significant insights into the country Australia had suddenly become.

Yemini's raw footage was valuable in an historical sense simply because he did something the mainstream now rarely did, he interviewed the protestors involved, once standard journalistic practice.

He was also very different to most of the tertiary educated middle-class journalists who populated Australia's corporate and government media.

Born in Melbourne, Australia, Avi is one of seventeen children; his father Russian-Polish, his mother Yemeni. In his early years of adulthood Avi moved to Israel, gaining citizenship there and eventually serving in the Israeli Defence Force as a sharpshooter, spending much of his duty in the Gaza Strip.

At one point, Avi operated a line of Israeli Defence Gyms which taught Krav Maga, a self-defence martial art used by the military.

***

It's all very easy to show up at a press conference and regurgitate whatever pap the politicians of the day are pushing out; it's an entirely different matter to confront a security apparatus and to go where you are not welcome.

Negotiating the paperwork and the now problematic security issues involved in covering lockdown protests required resources and nous. And lawyers.

Yemini was, if nothing else, an operator, a high compliment in the dark deeds of old; and in those frightened alleys and scenes of conflict in which it seemed we were all now being birthed.

On that first wild weekend of September, Yemini was tackled to the ground and arrested while covering a demonstration.

Footage of the incident has been viewed almost a quarter of a million times. A little bit of vigorous self-promotion, and hey presto, he was already a martyr to freedom of the press; a brilliant start to a Rebel News career.

A website Stand With Avi was established, and there were more than 60,000 signatories to a petition which read: "We demand an end to the Victoria Police state that detains JOURNALISTS for doing their job."

Yemini's statement of claim to the Victorian Supreme Court argued that he was treated with malice and claimed aggravated damages for distress, hurt, insult and for being arrested in public, manhandled and handcuffed. He claimed his ability to work as a journalist was being hampered by police conduct, including physical injury, fear of further police action at other protests and the hyper-vigilance of consciousness of surveillance at his home.

***

A fortnight later Yemini was back on the job at his employer's request, covering the flash demonstrations that were now a new tactic in the battle for the right to protest.

By a simple means, one might have thought, that is by dint of being on the same Telegraph channel as protestors, Avi was able to arrive at the site of the flash demonstrations as quickly as, or even prior to, the police.

Footage shows his repeated confrontations with authorities, who do their level best to stop him from doing his job.

October of 2020 saw Avi Yemini a very busy lad indeed.

In an absolute classic of his genre of reporting, in a story slugged "A Double Whopper They Never Ordered", Yemini mingles in that flash line between police and protestors outside a Hungry Jack's, prominently displaying his microphone to reinforce his credentialed status, just as newspaper reporters once did with pad and pen.

A fight had broken out near the garage. Police surrounded and detained those drawn to the fight, whether they were protestors moving on from another location, or simply people out buying a hamburger.

"Were you protesting?" he asks one woman in a T-shirt, clutching a bottle of mineral water and a teddy bear.

"No, I was not protesting. We weren't in the protest."

One cyclist says: "I saw a fight and went to watch it and we were like surrounded by 300 cops and they just gave me a ticket, like $1600. For doing nothing."

He clutches his Hungry Jack's takeaway bag, as Yemini asks: "Is it a Double Whopper?"

And then to camera: "It calls into question the entire policing of COVID today. $1600 fine. No matter what you were doing here. Surrounded, locked in, as we were, and fined. Why?

"Because today we had one case of coronavirus. Our rolling average is 5.5. If you truly believe that excuses this kind of overreach of law enforcement then there's something wrong with you."[56]

***

56 Cyclists cop WHOPPER FINE for being hungry at the wrong time in Melbourne, Rebel News, 26 October, 2020.

You know you've lost the argument when comedy sets in; and in one moderately hysterical piece to camera this indefatigable outlier sets out to "demolish evil lockdown protestors".

Yemini fronts a tall, beaming and very colourfully dressed woman at a demonstration on the 29th.

"Why are you so glamorous?" he asks as he points the microphone.

"Because I love to be in light and colour; and that's what it's about, is making people happy," she says.

"You know it's illegal to be happy in Victoria right now," Yemini responds.

"Totally, totally."

"Are you ready to cop a $1652 fine for being too happy?"

"Oh, definitely," she says.

And laughs.

***

In another vignette, he approaches a statuesque woman cradling a young child: "My son was born pre-lockdown, so he hasn't met half of my friends. He has barely left our house, he has been in lockdown this entire time; so I am standing because I cannot stand the thought of a future where my son doesn't have rights, where he doesn't know his freedoms.

"I have a two-year-old daughter as well, and it's important for me to show them that we need to raise our voices.

"I have lived in Melbourne my entire life and I have never seen the city in the state that it is in. It scared me. I want to show my children to be brave, to be courageous, to be informed, to be educated, and this is the best I can do, bring them along and show them how it's done."

***

It was not just the high drama of phalanxes of police confronting protestors that characterised the era, but the destruction of so many businesses; the trampling of people's lives, their enormous determination and hard work over many years.

There used to be a saying in Australia, "Back of Bourke", which basically meant beyond the civilised realm.

For many of the wild, delinquent kids he hung around in the late 1960s, surely multiple lifetimes ago, it was the furthest place they had ever heard of, and when things got a bit hot around Kings Cross, they would hop on a train to Bourke.

The police found them easy to pick up at the other end.

He had been to Bourke many times in his capacity as a country reporter for a major newspaper, and was familiar with the broken windows, the wire-secured shopfronts, the dissolute, desolate ambience which slung from the pubs late at night. A place once described as more dangerous than any other place on Earth.

Thank God the company was paying, and in those days he and the photographer could retreat to secure accommodation, as fascinating as it all was.

So, in this same place, at a well-known pub called Port of Bourke, where Old Alex had stayed a number of times, not COVID the virus but COVID the brutalistic bureaucratic expansion of state control, came to pass; the same dark wing that was passing over all the country.

And these stories, too, were written into the fabric of the times.

Yemini headlined the story: "Weeks after being violently attacked for enforcing COVID restrictions in his outback pub, police fined Luke Moon $10k for not executing them tough enough."

As he so rightly said: "You can't make this stuff up."

The Port of Bourke Hotel was, to put it bluntly, one of the only pubs in town where, as a stranger, you weren't likely to get your head kicked in as the night progressed.

It was thus named because although a legendary part of Australia's arid inland, it was also located on the equally legendary Darling River, and Bourke had once been one Australia's major inland ports; in the days before cotton, greed and man destroyed Australia's precious and most beautiful inland river systems.

After years of cyclical drought, when a statewide Coronavirus lockdown began, owner Luke Moon took the nine-week opportunity to borrow money and renovate.

When he finally reopened, Moon implemented all the chief health officer's directions, with signage, contact tracing and sanitation.

There had not been a single case within 500 kilometres.

Weeks after opening he was badly glassed by a patron, who took exception to being told to sit down, as per health requirements, and accused him of being racist.

Being told to sit down is akin to being enchained in glue, but most victims of this extensive overreach into the smallest of actions didn't glass the hapless licensee, whose efforts in this case to comply with COVID diktats were exemplary.

Weeks later, NSW Police Senior Sergeant Jonathan Cassidy travelled the 374 kilometres from Dubbo, the nearest major centre, with another officer to carry out a sting operation.

Dubbo police fined The Port of Bourke Hotel $5000 on 9 October and came back and fined the remote pub again another $5000 the following day.

Another community-gathering point destroyed. There just wasn't any end to this insanity, internal and external.

There were so many of these cases, these shifting high-octane conflagrations; the destruction of yet more lives and enterprises.

Welcome to history. Yes, welcome to history.

Vice News splashed with: "These 30 Regimes Are Using Coronavirus to Repress Their Citizens: Dog cages, crackdowns, censorship, surveillance, expanded police powers ... Authoritarians are having a moment."

They should have included Australia.

***

Apart from some great riot footage, every now and then Yemini would come up with a cracker. Life at the Very Small End of Town.

"The cruelty of these pandemic police will break your heart. Daniel Wright is homeless but he's getting his life back on track. That's hard to do in the pandemic lockdown, but he's saved up $3000 and he's living in his car until he can get an apartment again.

"But then the pandemic police came by. They saw him sleeping in his car and they started to hassle him. He was a threat to no one. He was bothering no-one. It was midnight — no one else was around. But they gave him a $1652 fine for breaking the curfew.

"Except, he wasn't. His car is his home, for now. Who is he threatening?"

TWELVE
THE BIGGEST MISTAKE IN HISTORY

LOCKDOWNS suited health bureaucrats, state politicians, and of course the prime minister. They all got to play God, and keep their jobs. It was everybody else who had to pay for their reckless policy-making on the run; their utterly delinquent destruction of all communal life.

There was a queue of international and Australian experts decrying the lockdowns Australia was so forcefully implementing. Because he could, because it was a scandal from the very beginning of this whole dismal sleet-laced saga, Old Alex looked for and published as many doubters of the official narrative as he could.

As, in a prior time, any normal journalist would have done.

In the Australian context, the formidable intellectual clout behind the anti-lockdown movement was Emeritus Professor Ramesh Thakur of the Australian National University, a former Assistant Secretary to the United Nations.

It was during those first bewildering months, when the official narrative came to seem so improbable to Old Alex, that he began looking for sceptical voices and came across him in a policy wonk journal called *Pearls and Irritations*.

Across the lockdown insanity splaying across Australia's power-drunk political, academic and journalistic classes, Ramesh stood out for his bold, erudite and highly intelligent breakdown on why lockdowns were the wrong policy, at the wrong time, for the wrong disease; beyond that, the wrong policy for any time.

Old Alex unabashedly published everything of his he could.

Indian-born and Canadian-.educated, Ramesh possessed an adept level of statistical ability; his analysis and numerical literacy without peer.

We all hit a wall when the truth, our livelihoods, our internal messiness and the truth beyond all truths confront us. For Thakur, as a former official of the UN, it was the pressure, propaganda and manipulation that preceded the Iraq war of 2003.

Seventeen years later, he saw history repeating itself with "coronaphobia".

"At the time of the Iraq War, I was a senior UN official. The resort to emotional blackmail by the warmongers, where critics of the impending war were tarred for standing shoulder to shoulder with the Butcher of Baghdad, was instructive. Of course, very soon 'We, the critics' were amply vindicated.

"The whole episode left me with two conclusions. Firstly, the resort to emotional arguments and moral blackmail generally implies they have little reasoned argument and evidence to support their case and are deflecting to bluster instead. And second, whenever we are presented with excitable exclamation marks, it is a very good idea to substitute sceptical question marks instead.

"Where is your evidence? Do you have an end goal and are the proposed means proportionate to that goal? What will be the human and economic cost?"

The author or editor of more than 50 books and 400 articles, Professor Thakur served on the international advisory boards of institutes in Africa, Asia, Europe and North America.

Close to Old Alex's heart, as a weary journalist who had been forced for decades to deal with all sorts of pompous idiots, Thakur was one of those very rare academics who took his role as a public intellectual seriously, writing both for academic journals and across populist media.

He was also a gracious and friendly man who, unlike many of his colleagues, made himself readily available to journalists.

Over the coming year his analyses would be published around the world, including in *The Japan Times*, *The Times of India* and Argentina's *La Nación*.

While Australia's politicians, bureaucrats and functionaries lionised themselves throughout the COVID crisis, they should have been paying attention to Thakur.

***

The first piece of the professor's Old Alex published was titled "Lives Versus Lives", written just as the madness of COVID was beginning.

"The first balance a government must assess is the risk of creating mass hysteria and panic with premature reporting and the risk of losing control by delaying public announcements of the true scale, gravity and urgency of a nascent epidemiological emergency.

"They can then settle on the optimal balance between sufficiently slowing the disease, preventing an economic meltdown and maintaining a functioning society while the threat and responses evolve and the virus spreads.

"As someone who has seen poverty up close in many different countries, I believe the choice is not between 'lives vs money', but 'lives vs lives'. We cannot have a First World health care system and facilities if our economy tanks to Third World poverty. And in the Third World, in a very real sense poverty is the biggest killer of all."

Thakur argued that eminent scientists who urged caution were ignored but had been demonstrated to be far truer in their projections than the doom-laden death cultists.

"New York's Governor Andrew Cuomo has become the latest hero in the Democratic pantheon for insisting that his sweeping, expensive measures to stem the coronavirus would be worth it even if they saved one life: 'We're not going to put a dollar figure on human life.'

"This is stirring but sheer idiocy: a soundbite, not sound policy.

"Every single budget of every central and state government in every country of the world juggles with competing public policy priorities and, in that sense, puts a dollar figure on human life."

***

As all of those hysterias of the time passed through us, for an old reporter dancing far from the sunny uplands, trapped in the slow dying of an elderly parent and adrift in his own life, there was only one way to internalise it: to catch the cold light and the streaming other styles of consciousness flowing down from the sandstone escarpment; beyond everything.

Legally, he needed an excuse even to leave the house.

So in a hermetic sense, it was easy to concentrate on work. Oh God, if only!

He had been a prisoner in a former life, he would swear upon it, and any attempt at containment was a riven hell. He paced a lot. All around, people marooned inside their own houses were just going stir crazy.

"The harsh lockdown measures were instituted in response to the fear-mongering projections of mathematical modelling that bear hardly any resemblance to the reality that has unfolded across the world," Professor Thakur wrote. "Crucially, too many governments ignored the reality of scientific uncertainty and the fact that lockdowns were a radical experiment that departed from established protocols for managing pandemics.

"The result has been disastrous for millions of people around the world."

The truly surreal disconnect — there was no scientific consensus, there was no unanimity of medical opinion — cast us all through a strange inversion, so that the public discourse bore almost no relationship to informed opinion.

Thakur's erudite analysis would ultimately become the dominant discourse; lockdowns had no historical scientific basis.

***

In another piece, "The Tyranny of Coronaphobia", Thakur wrote: "I've had two big worries during the pandemic, starting from the very beginning and still ongoing. Both relate to my sense that "coronaphobia" has taken over as the basis of government policy in so many countries, with a complete loss of perspective that life is a balance of risks pretty much on a daily basis.

"First, the extent to which dominant majorities of peoples in countries with universal literacy can be successfully terrified into surrendering their civil liberties and individual freedoms has come as a frightening shock.

"On the one hand, the evidence base for the scale and gravity of the COVID-19 pandemic is surprisingly thin in comparison to the myriad other threats to our health that we face every year.

"We don't ban cars on the reasoning that every life counts and even one traffic death is one too many lives lost. Instead, we trade a level of convenience for a level of risk to life and limb.

"The restrictions imposed on everyday life as we know it have been far more draconian than anything previously done. Yet, the evidence for the effectiveness of draconian lockdowns is less than convincing."

Professor Thakur said he remained puzzled at how so many people he considered to be liberals had been so utterly indifferent to the plight of the poor and the casual labourers who did not have the luxury of working from home, nor savings to fall back on to tide their family over until they could earn an income again.

"Celebrities posting videos and selfies of working from home in opulent mansions is positively obscene.

"Going forward, the key question is what the acceptable level of mortality risk, relative to the damage to health, mental health, society, economy, and disadvantaged groups like migrants and the poor from lockdowns is.

"Instead of fear-driven hysteria, governments should emphasise balance and proportionality and project calm, competence, and composure.

"COVID-19 is now endemic and will keep circulating, returning (especially in winters), and mutating.

"We cannot endlessly repeat lockdown cycles. The overall goal should be risk management, not risk avoidance, denial, or eradication. We must break the cycle of fear with a clear plan that people can understand and support."

***

Australia was being plunged into the deep freeze, with shuttered shops, silent streets and an acquiescent media applauding every step into darkness. In his piece "Lockdowns Can Be Cruel, Heartless, and Deadly", Ramesh Thakur wrote: "Human beings are family and community-oriented social animals. Sharing food and drink at home or in restaurants, enjoying the cinema, watching cricket, appreciating a concert or a play are not optional add-ons but fundamental to our daily life as human beings. 'Social distancing' by contrast is profoundly antisocial and rubs against every fibre of human civilisation.

"Those of us who argue the coronavirus cure can indeed be worse than the disease, are sometimes accused of putting the economy ahead of lives. This is morally offensive. Unless someone is silly enough to claim saving just one life is worth a complete shutdown of the whole country, the debate is about the thresholds of mortality against the human, health, social, and economic costs of different strategies.

"Judged against these criteria on the evidence to date, it's a challenge to justify the hard lockdowns of Australia and New Zealand.

"Many Westerners seem to have some strange notions about the human right to be protected from all life-threatening risks and emotional trauma. How dare we say: all life ends in death, get used to it? To my astonishment, the pandemic has brought an expansion in state power right into our homes and across public spaces to an extent not seen previously, even in wartime."

Thakur concluded that while the rich carried the virus, the poor paid for it. "Governments may not back off the sequester orders until citizens rebel against the de facto police-state regulations and mentality as the new normal.

"The lockdown has produced its own version of Thucydides' dictum that the strong do what they can, the weak suffer as they must."[57]

***

The most famous of the many words of caution was the so-called Great Barrington Declaration, named after the town in Massachusetts where it was drawn up. At the time of writing, it had been signed by more than 14,000 medical and health scientists, 43,000 medical practitioners and 790,000 members of the public.

Authored by Sunetra Gupta of the University of Oxford, Jay Bhattacharya of Stanford University, and Martin Kulldorff of Harvard University, it was drafted at the American Institute for Economic Research.

The Declaration read in part: "As infectious disease epidemiologists and public health scientists we have grave concerns about the damaging physical and mental health impacts of the prevailing COVID-19 policies.

"Current lockdown policies are producing devastating effects on short- and long-term public health.

"The results include lower childhood vaccination rates, worsening cardiovascular disease outcomes, fewer cancer screenings and deteriorating mental health — leading to greater excess mortality in years to come, with the working class and younger members of society carrying the heaviest burden. Keeping students out of school is a grave injustice.

"Keeping these measures in place … will cause irreparable damage, with the underprivileged disproportionately harmed.

"Fortunately, our understanding of the virus is growing.

---

57 Lives Versus Lives, Ramesh Thakur, *A Sense of Place Magazine*, 4 May, 2020.

"We know that vulnerability to death from COVID-19 is more than a thousand-fold higher in the old and infirm than the young. Indeed, for children, COVID-19 is less dangerous than many other harms, including influenza.

"The most compassionate approach that balances the risks and benefits of reaching herd immunity is to allow those who are at minimal risk of death to live their lives normally to build up immunity to the virus through natural infection, while better protecting those who are at highest risk.

"Those who are not vulnerable should immediately be allowed to resume life as normal.

"Simple hygiene measures, such as hand-washing and staying home when sick should be practised by everyone to reduce the herd immunity threshold. Schools and universities should be open for in-person teaching.

"Extracurricular activities, such as sports, should be resumed. Young low-risk adults should work normally, rather than from home. Restaurants and other businesses should open.

"Arts, music, sport and other cultural activities should resume. People who are more at risk may participate if they wish, while society as a whole enjoys the protection conferred upon the vulnerable by those who have built up herd immunity."

***

It was all about threat, and derangement, internal and external. Old Alex felt it all so intensely, as if a spiritual derangement mirrored through the fabric of the landscapes around him, there in that startled time; birds nesting and black swans on the lake, while every day the warnings grew stronger.

The spatial distortions cascaded as he walked, one minute a giant footprint over the suburb, the next reaching up to pull a helicopter out of the sky. The fluctuating voices and the calls from afar; the shadow calls of blessings as the familiars gathered.

Who could resist a bit of Nick Cave in that time and place:

> *And a black oily gash crawling backwards across the carpet to*
> *smash all over everything*
> *Wet, black fur against the sun going down*
> *Over the shops and the cars and the crowds in the town*
> *And this is the moment, this is exactly where she is born to be.*

That is, time is a road. The light dappled across lawns and crawled up through him, and he could feel the voices resonating up through his spine, through the channels which we would take to show you: show you.

Come hither! Listen to me! Take the embrace!

All around, in those quiet, shuttered houses where no one was venturing outside, he could hear a gathering religious fervour, spliced with snatches of COVID updates on the radio. You bet the times were riven strange.

***

"The side effects of lockdown with increased cancers, heart disease, strokes, suicides, anxiety, depression, diabetes and widespread general decrease in wellbeing and destruction of society's fabric would make it the most grossly negligent 'medication' in history."

So said one of Australia's more outspoken medical practitioners, Dr Guy Campbell, speaking from the coalface of this societal-wide experiment.

In his piece "Inhumane Lockdowns Compound Australia's COVID Fiasco", one of the most popular pieces Old Alex had ever published in his magazine, Dr Campbell wrote: "It can be strongly advocated that lockdowns have large non-COVID implications, as well as those on the economic wellbeing of our future generations.

"From a GP's perspective, I have multiple elderly patients who are distressed because they have had their basic human rights removed in not being able to see their children, grandchildren or close friends. I have multiple patients awaiting delayed surgery, including a young man requiring urgent life-saving cardiac surgery.

"I also have several younger patients living alone in apartment blocks begging me to do whatever I can to persuade my medical colleagues to advise the government to end this cruel lockdown.

"I already have experienced one COVID-related suicide and another overdose. I have never before seen so much anxiety, stress and disharmony within our community. Given the large-scale decline in our community's mental health, the only ever justification to put healthy populations into such lockdowns should be in localised areas where there is a serious risk of overwhelming the Health System. The intensity of the lockdowns has emerged from a dangerously misplaced perception of humanitarianism, when the reality is that they may do far more damage to people's lives and wellbeing than the virus itself.

"Simply, there is plenty of good evidence of the increased risk of suicide, and other health risks that are increased due to lockdown measures. This should be publicised and used to influence the COVID response/lockdown policy.

"Government needs to be more honest and open in reporting COVID deaths. For instance, the four deaths in the under-50s to date apparently all had comorbidities such as cancer, extreme obesity, heart and lung disease.

"We need a plan with an endgame to stop this present paralysis of fear, and one that both minimises lives lost and allows the majority of the population to be able to get on with their lives.

"If lockdown was a 'medication' it would never have been licensed. Worse than that, lockdowns do not stop COVID but only delays it; and the more applied, the greater the rebound."

As reported in *The Times*: "No child who was not already profoundly ill had died of COVID-19 in Britain, a large study indicated, with the researchers saying that the results should reassure parents as a new school term begins."

"In Australia to date, no healthy person has died under the age of 50 from COVID . Yet the under-50s, and especially the under-40s, are the most anxious because of the fear being whipped up by politicians and the media.

"Let's Lead by Hope, Not Fear!"

Good luck with that.

***

Around the world, including in Australia, doctors banded together to plead for rationality from their politicians.

Alex was happy to publish them; thereby adding weight to an argument which surely must have been won by now. It's called the weight of evidence, it becomes undeniable.

One such was titled: "Open Letter from Doctors and Health Professionals to All Authorities in Belgium and the Belgian Media".

The doctors argued that isolation measures had led to physical inactivity in many elderly people, with anxiety, persistent stress, and social-distancing-induced loneliness proven to have a negative impact on mental and general health.

It was an extensive and detailed document which could have easily been referring to Australia. It read in part:

"We argue that the measures to get the coronavirus under control are disproportionate, and cause more damage than they do well.

"There is no longer any medical ground to justify this policy: we therefore argue for an immediate end to all measures.

"We demand a restoration of our normal democratic governance and legal structures and an open debate, where all experts are discussed without any form of censorship.

"'A solution should not be worse than the disease' is a proposition that is more topical than ever in the current situation. However, we note in the field that the collateral damage that is now being caused to the population will have more impact in all layers of the population in the short and long term than the number of corona victims that are now being protected.

"We believe that the policy has introduced mandatory measures, which are not sufficiently scientifically founded, are unilaterally steered, and that there is insufficient room in the media for an open debate in which different views and opinions are heard. Moreover, every municipality and province is now also given the power to add its own measures, whether well-founded or not.

"Moreover, the strict repressive policy on corona is in stark contrast to the hitherto minimal policy that the government pursues when it comes to disease prevention, strengthening the own immune system through a healthy lifestyle, optimal care with attention for the individual and investment in healthcare personnel."

***

The good doctors were also spot-on when it came to behaviour of the media.

"In recent months, newspaper, radio and TV makers seemed to follow the 'panel of experts' and the government almost uncritically, where the press should be critical, and unilateral government communication should be prevented.

"This led to a public communication in our news media that was more like propaganda than objective reporting.

"In our opinion, it is the task of journalism to present news as objectively and neutrally as possible, aimed at finding the truth and critically controlling power, whereby dissenting experts are also given a forum to express themselves.

"The official story that a lockdown was necessary, that this was the only possible solution, and that everyone was behind this lockdown, made it difficult for dissenters and experts to air a different opinion.

"Alternative opinions were ignored or ridiculed. We have not seen any open debates in the media where dissenters could express their views.

"We have also been amazed by the many videos and articles by many scientific experts and authorities, which were and are being removed from social media.

"We believe that this does not fit in a free, democratic, constitutional state, especially since it leads to tunnel vision. This policy also paralyses and feeds the fear and concern in society.

"The way COVID-19 has been portrayed by politics and media has also not helped the situation."

The doctors warned that battle terminology was unhelpful.

"War terms were popular and warlike language was not lacking. There has often been talk of a 'war' with an 'invisible enemy' who must be 'defeated'.

"The use in the media of phrases like 'frontline care heroes' and 'victims of Corona' has further fuelled fear, as has the idea that we are dealing with a 'killer virus' globally.

"The relentless bombardment of numbers, unleashed on the population day after day, hour after hour, without indicating those numbers, without comparing them with flu deaths in other years, without comparing them with deaths from other causes, has induced true anxiety psychosis in the population."

***

The Australian COVID Medical Network, representing more than 500 doctors, issued the following statement.

"Many Australian doctors and other health professionals consider the lockdown measures to be disproportionate, not scientifically based, unilaterally authoritarian and the cause of widespread suffering for many Victorians.

"Thereby, we Australian Doctors and Health Professionals, in solidarity with thousands of international doctors, call for the cessation of all disproportionate measures that contravene the International Siracusa Principles.

"These Siracusa Principles are part of the International Covenant on Civil and Political Rights, to which Australia is a signatory, and are recommended by the World Health Organisation. They require all public health management policies to meet standards of legality, evidence-based necessity and proportionality, and that they recognise our basic, universal human rights.

"Of particular concern is the needless harm and suffering being experienced by the young, especially children and adolescents, by the denial of normal social interactions such as play, schooling and relationships with family and friends.

"We hold grave concerns that these effects on child and adolescent health will impact their future wellbeing for many years to come. This is occurring despite the fact that the virus poses a negligible risk to children."

The group concluded that policies such as curfews, local travel restrictions, reduced exercise and outdoor activities, imposed isolation and the quarantining of the healthy, enforced mask-wearing in open spaces, the denial of children's play, socialisation and education with friends and peers and the disruption of family relationships, as well as the arbitrary application of laws, are contrary to common sense and are seriously compromising the health of individuals and the wider society.

"Furthermore, these policies have resulted in interruptions and delays of both public and private health-care services, created unnecessary patient fear and panic, which has adversely impacted access to general health care and resulted in delayed presentations of many serious medical conditions, including cancers and heart disease.

"They have also caused a dramatic increase in mental health problems due to the imposition of isolation and loneliness on the elderly and the vulnerable, the creation of significant financial and relationship strain for many families and induced unnecessary levels of fear and anxiety among health workers and their loved ones.

"Such a disproportionate approach, coupled with a fear-based media narrative comprised of inadequate and misleading information, is a great concern and must cease as soon as possible."

***

The silencing, it sank through everyone; and must have tormented everybody's dreams in different ways. For him, then, left alone, he went to talk to the spirits of a Sistine Chapel in a forest nearby; a patch of remnant coastal woodland from whence the ancients could speak. Mostly it was simple things: "Keep Working! Finish the task at hand."

They weren't human in any way. That's how it felt to him. There were other forces at play; as they slithered through him, enthralled by the staggering beauty of a place where they too could stand up and see the world, not to be heard but to go sight unseen, to communicate only with those who would use the knowledge well. They kept repeating, we only come at turning points in history, we burn, burn to do you well; evolved in hostile climates, aware and alert, and looking, too, at a planet which had once been entirely cathedral-like in its beauty, and was now pockmarked with bad spirits and a history lurching into totalitarianism, into darker and darker times. *Spiritus Sanctus.*

***

Do No harm! So goes the most basic maxim of medical practice.

Yet their critics believed that many hundreds of Australian practitioners were doing exactly that, with senior health bureaucrats standing side by side with the nation's grandstanding politicians as they imposed draconian, highly questionable lockdowns.

One of Australia's most senior journalists, Jack Waterford, wrote at length: "Scott Morrison has repeatedly reiterated that all decisions in relation to Coronavirus public health measures have been taken in accordance with medical advice. But the advice itself has frequently been considerably less than transparent, even as he has had medical officials standing alongside him, giving every appearance of having crafted his words and drafted his decisions.

"The formal advice coming from his department and his chief medical officers has never been merely about the 'facts' and a range of medical and epidemiological opinion as to what government should do. It involves having a weather eye out for what government wants to do, and what it most definitely does not want to do. It considers what is practically feasible

— an assessment that involves an assessment of the political temperature and the personalities of relevant ministers, premiers and chief ministers.

"It involves a lot of intuition about what the government would most prefer to hear. The officials must also take into account, and be very loyal to, things that the prime minister has said in his repeated pronouncement, announcements and denouncements. The distillation of all of this might be the best the medicos can hope for, but it cannot be called the best detached judgment of what is best for the whole population."

Waterford argued that the government had the capacity to shop around for the advice it wanted to hear and was doing exactly that all of the time. It was also verballing its own officials or forcing them to verbal themselves when the government adopted a temporary or permanent position on matters such as lockdowns, state border closures, international border closures, or banning flights from particular areas.

"The Morrison system of government does not permit dissenting voices, before or after the decision. Even from the experts whose advice they claim to follow.

"Officials must toe the line. Or perhaps resign, if with certainty that the politicians and more senior bureaucrats will vilify you, and misrepresent the circumstances to make you the bad guy.

"A good deal of the advice is coming from people with no particular medical backgrounds, including people who tend to think that running a pandemic is much the same as sailing a battleship or running a fish and chip shop. Not all of their advice is good; it is rarely disinterested. Often it is not able to be tested or contested by experts."[58]

***

Humans by their nature look to national and community leaders for assurance, safety, direction, for protection from a gathering temporal storm.

Now, under the perfect cover of a public health emergency, the Australian state was omnipresent in everybody's lives.

And rather than delivering safety, they visited a nightmare upon the country. Simple old-fashioned common sense would have told you that lockdowns would not work; and would have devastating consequences on the nation's economic and social fabric.

---

58 Advice being tailored for Political, Not Medical, Purposes, Jack Waterford, *A Sense of Place Magazine*, 27 May, 2021.

All the precursors to totalitarianism were now in play; massive overlapping bureaucracies which can be moulded to purpose, ever-shifting rules and regulations, high levels of unemployment and state dependency, loneliness and social atomisation.

In that time, George Orwell was the most quoted author in the English canon.

The Origins of Totalitarianism is appositely described as a non-fiction bookend to *Nineteen Eighty-Four*: "This moment of anticipation is like the calm that settles after all hopes have died.

"We no longer hope for an eventual restoration of the old world order with all its traditions, or for the reintegration of the masses ... who have been thrown into a chaos produced by the violence of wars and revolutions and the growing decay of all that has still been spared. Under the most diverse conditions and disparate circumstances, we watch the development of the same phenomena: Homelessness on an unprecedented scale, rootlessness to an unprecedented depth.

"Never has our future been more unpredictable, never have we depended so much on political forces that cannot be trusted to follow the rules of common sense and self-interest — forces that look like sheer insanity, if judged by the standards of other centuries."

THIRTEEN
PRETERNATURAL EAGLE EYES

MEET THE hunters. Meet the scavengers. Meet the people who destroyed Australia.

In all the unfolding stories of that time, made up, as we all are, of millions of other entwining stories, some, by dint of persistence and humble courage, became emblematic.

Everything had gone deeply awry. We were all witnessing a violent abuse of administrative process, a violent breach of trust, an inexcusable fiasco.

One such story, in late October 2020, demonstrated all that had gone so terribly wrong, with the wanton destruction of the economy, the authority's abuse of the citizenry, and yet again extremely poor optics all round.

While one expects activists to be activists, it takes a lot to push small-business people into public protest.

Adam and Weave could hardly have been a better name for one of the psychic ground zeros of the debacle. The owners became national heroes when, like thousands of others, they faced the destruction of the business they had worked so hard to establish, and defiantly insisted on opening.

The previous day, co-owner Jomana Najem told Rebel News: "We just decided we are going to open because basically we know we are going to go bankrupt. If we don't work, we can't pay our rent, we can't do anything. We invested all of our money into this business.

"This is a war but an invisible war, a psychological war.

"It is about restoring dignity, we refuse to buy into this narrative. It is a lie; we refuse to buy into it any more."

Police were waiting outside Adam and Weave the next morning. Footage shows police blocking the premises.

Ms Najem said at least six customers received a haircut before police threatened her with arrest and issued her a fine for $9913, with the salon being forced to close by 11am.

Another man was violently arrested in the street outside as he waved a collection of Australian, UK and USA flags, with half a dozen police swarming him to the ground, a style of arrest that was becoming all too familiar.

Premier Daniel Andrews showed a pathological lack of sympathy.

"If you're wanting to fill your till by opening up against the rules, you're going to get a $10,000 fine," he said. "The maths of that doesn't add up."

Queue obsequious coverage.

***

The high farce enveloping the streets of Melbourne provided some of the most striking visual images and represented some of the more piquant stories in the crushing of dissent.

The heavy-handed tactics of police officers were filmed repeatedly on mobile phones and picked up and widely spread on social media.

They might have felt like they were doing the right thing at the time; but doubt was spreading like a cancer, even amongst those being asked to perpetrate some of the worst injustices in the nation's history.

There were plenty of victims, plenty of signs that Australia was no longer a functioning entity, that governments no longer saw it as their role to encourage the citizenry to live happy, productive and independent lives, that Australian democracy was dying.

COVID extended the indifferent and, often enough, destructive hand of government into everybody's life.

An inner-city bar in Sydney's Darlinghurst known as the Darlo, with which Old Alex was well familiar for its drenched alcoholic feel of comfortable daze and wasted legends, copped a $5000 fine for failing to ensure social distancing as the state's COVID cops cracked down and compliance measures ramped up.

Soul Origin cafe in the regional city of Maitland was also fined $5000 after inspectors found no COVID signage and customer tables and chairs too close together.

"Business must do their bit in this battle to keep the community COVID-safe and we have empowered more inspectors to ensure this is the case," NSW Customer Service Minister Victor Dominello told *The Daily Telegraph*. "This is about keeping people healthy and keeping businesses open."

***

This compounding fiasco, as colliding plains of crystallised circumstance washed across a freezing sky, was being written in the hearts of men, and in those old forms of communication known as newspapers.

On 5 October, a former colleague, *The Australian*'s economics editor Adam Creighton, wrote: "In the first six months of the year, there were 134 fewer deaths from respiratory diseases in Australia, which includes pneumonia and influenza, and 617 additional deaths from cancer compared with the average over 2015-19, according to the ABS's provisional mortality statistics."

"And this is just cancer.

"Does the Australian Medical Association accept any responsibility for this perverse outcome?

"How many other avoidable killer ailments have gone undetected because the AMA has given medical cover to the politicians' fixation on Coronavirus to the criminal neglect of other deadly illnesses?"

Members of the Australian Medical Association were front and centre of the disaster; and, at least publicly, head office ignored the entreaties for a serious rethink.

Australians have an unquestioning and exaggerated respect for doctors. The sight of government medical officers stepping up to the lecterns in lockstep with the nation's politicians lent credibility to the blizzard of dictates visited upon the nation.

The most prominent performances were preserved for the nation's chief medical officers, who allowed themselves to be used for the grandstanding tactics of politicians while ignoring some of the world's leading intellectuals who were questioning in the bluntest of terms the veracity of lockdowns. They really should have known better.

The AMA found itself increasingly compromised, with a significant number of its members implicated in the biggest social and financial meltdown in Australian history and the implementation of dangerously misguided policies under the guise of a public health emergency.

At the same time, increasing numbers of its members were speaking out against lockdown policies and the AMA's complicity in them.

Australians had seen the squandering of eye-watering amounts of money by the government, the quintupling the national debt, the throwing millions of people on to the dole queues and truly shocking scenes of police brutality on Melbourne's streets.

And all this destruction of the country was accompanied by a pantomime of health bureaucrats having their moment in the sun or, more precisely, the television cameras.

They had never been so important.

***

An outspoken critic of lockdowns and a member of the Australian Medical COVID Network, Dr Guy Campbell, implored the AMA to stop supporting hard lockdowns before its reputation was blighted, "which it will be".

"The AMA has opened up to the non-COVID-19 consequences of Government policies on COVID-19, so it begs the question then why the AMA still supports hard lockdowns?"

In an open letter to the AMA, Dr Campbell wrote: "More and more countries are coming round to accepting we may have to learn to live with the virus as the health and economic costs of repeat lockdowns are too high to be justified.

"As the costs start to bite widely and the pain is felt, people will look for targets to blame.

"Politicians are adept at blame shifting and the medical community may suffer high reputational damage.

"The AMA should pre-empt this by starting to distance itself by not supporting hard lockdowns and saying publicly that they provide the medical expertise and advice; it is for governments to make and implement policy with a balance of health, social and economic policy."

In a response to Dr Campbell's concerns, the association claimed: "The fact is that the credibility of the AMA is not in doubt and we are not particularly concerned at this point given the broad community support for the lockdown among Victorians, with the latest poll showing that even 57 per cent of Coalition voters support the lockdown."

That, with all due respect, was an absurd response. Much of the Australian population could be manipulated into believing almost anything, as the COVID era attested.

Professor Thakur bought in: "A clear divide is emerging between health bureaucrats and 'ivory tower' modellers, on the one hand, and clinical practitioners and GPs, on the other.

"The former are the most hawkish lockdown advocates and supporters. The latter are the ones who are seeing and having to deal with the unintended, perverse and growing health and mental health consequences of lockdowns.

"It is astonishing the extent to which the theoretical scientists and health bureaucrats remain in denial about the health damage of their policies and in violation of the Hippocratic Oath."

***

The mob is notoriously fickle.

When they realised how easily they've surrendered their freedoms for no reason at all, how even the freedom of movement had been abolished, when they understood how utterly and totally they had been misled, surely all hell would break loose. Or different kinds of leaders would rise from the debris, and another kind of human hell unleashed.

A country not just of immigrants, but of people, who, as residents of a country far from just about everywhere, were known for their love of travel, the closure of international broders and the turning of Australia into a Hermit Kingdom was a massive dislocation of normal life.

The liberty to roam your own country had never been questioned. The shutting of internal state and territory borders was an equal dislocation of the soul and spirit and freedoms of the country.

Freedom of movement, just like the freedom to protest, had been abolished.

Extremely authoritarian styles of enforcement continued throughout that October of 2020. With a population retreating into insularity, the Federation, for all intents and purposes, was being dismantled.

Western Australia, 2.46 million square kilometres of some of the most remote country anywhere in the world, introduced the most stringent border controls of all.

Australians were used to being able to travel interstate, and pretty much arranged their lives to suit.

All that came crashing to a close. With no formal fences or demarcation, you could fill volumes just detailing incidents at border controls,

Here's a sampling from the South Australian Police:

"Five people have been arrested over COVID-19 direction breaches over the past week including a man who crossed from Victoria into South Australia via a dirt road, and another man who attempted to enter the state via scrubland from Victoria after being turned back at a border checkpoint.

"At about 4.30pm on Friday, 2 October, a man was arrested for failing to comply with the emergency management directions after crossing the South Australia and Victoria border despite being refused entry and direction to travel back to Victoria on numerous occasions. The man was refused bail and has been remanded.

"At about 7.15am on Saturday, 3 October, a man was arrested for breaching directions given under the Emergency Management Act. The man was refused entry at the Dukes Highway border checkpoint and was directed to remain in Victoria. Despite turning around and travelling back into Victoria the man was later observed trying to enter South Australia through the scrub. The man was refused bail and has been remanded.

"At about 3.50pm on Saturday, 3 October, a man attempted to enter South Australia from Victoria without prior approval, exemption or essential traveller status. He then entered South Australia via a dirt road when he was arrested for breaching the emergency management directions. The man was refused bail and has been remanded.

"On Monday, 5 October, a man was arrested after failing to comply with the emergency management directions. The man had arrived in South Australia on Monday, 28 September, with an exemption but when police conducted compliance checks it was revealed that he had not completed his mandatory COVID-19 testing. He indicated that he was not going to comply and was refused bail and has appeared in court. He has since returned a negative COVID-19 test and has been bailed by the court to quarantine and reappear in court at a later date.

"At about 3.30pm on Wednesday, 7 October, police were notified that a property fence had been damaged on the South Australia and Victoria border. A registration plate was found at the location and the occupant of the vehicle was located at a hotel in northern Adelaide. The woman was arrested for breaching the emergency management directions and has been refused bail to appear in court at a later date."[59]

Bet you could make an interesting story out of every last one of those incidents.

***

These massive spiritual and social-wide derangements came at a cost.

In Australia the ruling elites who had plundered the native gifts, the drenched, irradiated spirituality of Australia's landscapes, knew nothing of what they wrought. .

There are many manifestations.

Old Alex listened to Kylie from Bunnings up at the Lakeview, complaining that she had worked two public holidays in one pay period once, and got an extra, truly measly $20 for her efforts because it had pushed her into another tax bracket.

"I would have been better off staying home with my kids," she said.

The same was true of everywhere he saw and sought. The people had been plundered. Taxed and taxed and taxed, at the petrol bowser and the beer pump, dragooned into conformity in their daily lives, so that nobility became confused with compliance; and many now lived hand to mouth. There was no aspiration. There were so many blockages on the path, not just to dignified work, but to a decent, fulfilled existence; to the ability to care for your own children.

There was for many now no hope of building a life for themselves and their families, for the young, for the old, for their partners.

The Australian Government which had placed itself front and centre of everybody's life under the cover of COVID was the same government which had bled them dry and enforced compliance as a signal of community and social responsibility, which it was not. Education standards were falling. Living standards were falling.

This bleaching of the populace by the oligarchs and plutocrats incensed Old Alex more than ever.

---

59 7News Adelaide, 10 October, 2020.

Be careful you do not destroy yourselves. Be warned; be frightened of the suffering you impose on your own people. Surely that was the sanest message to have ever leached across time.

***

Somehow most people seemed fine with it all.

As if nothing had been learnt from arresting a pregnant woman for a Facebook post, early in October of 2002, once again confronting footage of yet another pregnant woman being violently and aggressively arrested in Melbourne went viral within hours.

"We're getting used to seeing footage like this around here," said Rebekah Spelman, who has been following the lockdown demonstrations closely and was running for her local council in Melbourne on an anti-lockdown platform.

"One person in the video can be heard saying, 'She's bleeding, she's bleeding.' It looks to me, from what I can see, that this is true.

"We're seeing so much unnecessary police aggression against ordinary people living their lives. We're not criminals. None of these people are criminals

"We just want our freedoms. It is about human rights, and our human rights are being trampled and our freedoms stolen.

"To protest under these circumstances requires courage, and foolhardiness perhaps. But certainly courage."

Ms Spelman had her own experience of being aggressively arrested as a peaceful protester.

"We all know how poorly the police are acting through this, and it's a disgusting disgrace how they seem to be reveling in their 'authority'.

"As a law-abiding citizen, I should not have to be fearful of being arrested and charged for breaking no laws, or of earning myself a criminal record that will affect the rest of my life — but here we *all* are."

***

Rebekah Spelman said that at one protest in Melbourne the riot squad suddenly appeared, together with the horse squad. "They surrounded a small group of about fifteen of us. One young riot squad rookie was so gung-ho that he started shoving the man right next to me, unprovoked, and screaming at him to move. This act alone could have started a big fight that would have ended very badly if the man he pushed was aggressive.

"Thankfully, he was not; he ignored the young officer until a more senior officer next to him told him to stop.

"After being surrounded, the riot officers walked at us in groups of five and, one by one, dragged us out of the circle where regular officers cuffed us, made us stand around for awhile, then checked our ID and issued a fine for being more than five kilometres from home, and set us free.

"I was detained by an aggressive little female cop who clearly had plenty to prove. She was rude and loving it, and when she went through my backpack to find my ID, I asked her to be careful not to let the photograph that I keep in my wallet fall out and blow away. Her response was sarcastic: 'Is there anything else you'd like me to do?'

"They seemed to enjoy the show that they put on, arresting this pack of 'violent lawbreakers' for the whole nation to marvel over."

As Ms Spelman recalled of a subsequent encounter: "I just went through a police checkpoint. I told the officer that they have lost so much respect from the people and that once this is over; it's not going to just come back. I asked her if she was fine with the way things are right now, and she replied cheerily: 'Yes, I'm fine with it.'"

In Australia today there is no freedom of expression. No right to protest. No honour. No dignity of belief.

If you didn't agree with the dictates of Australia's multiple federal, state and local governments, you faced — as citizens were now facing in Victoria — arrest, handcuffing or brutally and aggressively being slammed to the ground. For doing what you sincerely believed to be right.

***

Whose dreams, in these strange times, did not grow more intense?

His were of a style. Utterly fantastical; often occurring in daylight, yet to him more real than the pallid, blinkered streets into which he had been flung. Just as he had as a child in this mortal frame, he flew over the lake and saw across the rooftops, the pale light more than enough to see their dreams. He had returned victorious, all those years before, but was never the same again. Now he saw through different eyes, and came not to pass blessing but to warn, not to explain the ancient mysteries against the backdrop of modern science and advanced computation, but to tell them all: beware. Not just of their own kind, but of gods sent crazy with their own power. How was the derangement overtaking the country, administrative, political, communal, societal-wide, not also a spiritual one? At the hands of a black-clad police officer.

***

With a breakdown in hotel quarantine in Victoria and chaos at state borders, there were many scandals in that Australian spring of 2020. In just one of them, soon to vanish in a snowstorm, there were days of revelations that Victorian Premier Daniel Andrews did not seek the advice of police or senior health officials before implementing a curfew; one of the most drastic restrictions of liberty available to a government.

He refused to release much-touted modelling he said supported his actions, while the very researchers who developed it said it did not support the extreme measures being prosecuted in Victoria, Australia's second most populous state.

You can institute a curfew on millions of people, but you won't justify it. That's pretty damned amazing in itself. How could you not fear for a future where this pathway to demolition of the individual had been so ably cleared?

Another classic case of slipperiness and abuse by process was the inquiry into Victoria's repeatedly botched hotel quarantine program, which had been the major source of a number of COVID outbreaks.

Although he was closely associated with the program, any attempt to sheet home blame to the Premier Daniel Andrews for its multiple failures was deflected under the cover of the highly politicised inquiry. After many months, and the examination of some 70,000 documents, head of the inquiry, former judge Jennifer Coate, could not find anyone to blame for the decision to hire private contractors, some of whom were alleged to have had sex with quarantined travellers. Certainly not the premier.

"The decision as to the enforcement model for people detained in quarantine was a substantial part of an important public health initiative and it cost the Victorian community many millions of dollars.

"But it remained, as multiple submissions to the Inquiry noted, an orphan, with no person or department claiming responsibility."

***

The public queued to surrender their freedoms. Politicians queued for their television spots.

Both academic and mainstream publications came out with scathing opinion pieces on lockdowns.

A columnist at Sydney's mass-circulation *The Daily Telegraph,* Joe Hildebrand, wrote: "We tell ourselves that times of crisis unite us — the Corona crisis even has its own slogan: 'We're all in this together.'

"But they don't, and we're not.

"Prime Minister Scott Morrison brought all state and territory leaders together in an effort to forge a consistent approach to tackle the pandemic. But the fig leaf almost immediately fell away from the fire hose. States executed wave after wave of shutdowns and lockdowns that went beyond the official National Cabinet advice while the Federal Government footed the bill for the masses of job losses that ensued.

"But no one could acknowledge none of it was working. The illusion, the mass delusion, had to be maintained at all cost."

***

The smaller journals were also unequivocal in their hostility to lockdowns.

James Delingpole at *Spectator Australia* asked when we turned into such a sorry bunch of cowards, snitches, collaborators, surrender monkeys and whipped curs?

"Sure, I can understand at the beginning why people might have been nervous, when information was scarce and rumours were rife. But there's really no excuse now.

"We know that COVID-19 is unlikely to kill you unless you were on your way out anyway; that there are effective treatments; that lockdowns probably cause more deaths than they save; that we're well on the way towards 'herd immunity'; that the Swedish model was the right one. So how is it that so many people remain convinced that this is our Spanish Flu and that no government measure, however draconian, is too extreme or intrusive to combat it?

"Victoria, as you know, has gone further than most by implementing curfews, roadblocks, random, warrant-free house searches. On TV, Police

Commissioner Shane Patton — in his natty all-black uniform — actually boasted that his officers had been smashing car windows and pulling out the drivers if they failed to answer questions about whether their journey was strictly necessary."

***

In a collection of essays, *Fundamental Rights in the Age of COVID-19*, published in November of 2020, editor Professor Augusto Zimmerman wrote that government measures were arbitrary and unconstitutional.

"The COVID-19 pandemic is a turning point in history. Government measures to fight COVID-19 have deeply affected fundamental rights, particularly freedom of movement, expression, privacy and association. Relying on a few appointed 'health experts', Australian governments, both federal and state, are using emergency powers to impose draconian measures that have destroyed countless private sector jobs and much of the productive sector, while leaving the bloated public sector completely intact."

There was a queue of academics behind him.

Gabriël A. Moens, Emeritus Professor of Law at the University of Queensland, critically described, in his piece 'The Role of the State in the Protection of Public Health', the manifold restrictions imposed on people to allegedly combat the virus. He characterised such restrictions as deeply paternalistic, having not only a deleterious effect on fundamental rights of the citizens but also unintended consequences for the protection of their own health.

James Allan, the Garrick Professor of Law at the University of Queensland, was another contributor. In 'Politicians, the Press and Skin in the Game', he explained how the Australian Government mishandled its response to the Coronavirus, significantly infringing civil liberties and dramatically expanding the government's role with no palatable route out of this situation.

It wasn't just academics arguing that the government had sadly over-stepped the mark, the actions of the nation's politicians were far more destructive and misguided than the public realised.

Dr Joel Kettner, Professor of Community Health Sciences and Surgery at Manitoba University and Medical Director of the International Centre for Infectious Diseases, wrote: "I've seen pandemics, one every year. It is called influenza, and other respiratory illness viruses. I've never seen this reaction, and I'm trying to understand why.

"If we had not known about a new virus out there, and had not checked individuals with PCR tests, the number of total deaths due to 'influenza-like illness' would not seem unusual this year. At most, we might have casually noted that flu this season seems to be a bit worse than average."

But, of course, we did know. It's all we ever heard about. Month after month after month, COVID led the news bulletins.

***

Director of the Centre for Infectious Disease Research and Policy at the University of Minnesota Michael T. Osterholm, published a piece in *The Washington Post* titled "Facing COVID-19 Reality: A National Lock-down Is No Cure": "Consider the effect of shutting down offices, schools, transportation systems, restaurants, hotels, stores, theatres, concert halls, sporting events and other venues indefinitely and leaving all of their workers unemployed and on the public dole.

"The likely result would be not just a depression but a complete economic breakdown, with countless permanently lost jobs, long before a vaccine is ready or natural immunity takes hold."

All these cautionary warnings, and many more, that most Australians never heard.

In other words, to hammer home the point, these views were being published widely both in Australia and around the world. This information was readily available. There was simply no excuse for ignorance. At least not from the political class. Elected to protect.

***

Adam Creighton at *The Australian*, one of the most thoughtful and hard-working journalists in the News Limited stable, wrote a series of solid stories questioning the wisdom of lockdowns.

A sampling will suffice.

Plague panic chills reason and chokes liberalism from the realm's dark angels: "Deaths are sad, but COVID-19 has taken far more than loved ones. Conventions going back centuries restraining democratic govern-ments have been dumped.

"Former British Supreme Court judge and historian Jonathan Sumption gave the most eloquent and cogent critique of the 'despotic and irrational' lockdown and mask obsessions that have 'deprived everyone of what makes life worth living' and 'thrown science out the window'.

"Sometimes the best thing you can do with despotic laws is to ignore them.

"Precedents have been set that will justify 'public health' interventions in the future on a drastic scale. The balance of power between individuals, households and private businesses, on the one hand, and the state has been up-ended by an earthquake.

"This has nothing to do with the utilitarian calculus of whether forced masks and lockdowns work, which the weight of international evidence suggests they don't. It's about whether human rights can be trampled on a governmental whim because it's popular."

***

Health Fascism Has Consumed Human Rights: "Our freedoms are under attack, not that their usual guardians have noticed. What a farce human rights have become. For years progressive politicians, academics and activists have called for stronger protection for human rights, new codes, new laws — and well-staffed commissions costing millions to oversee them. Democracies just couldn't be trusted.

"Indeed, this year has witnessed the most extraordinary attack on freedoms by democratic governments in modern history, making a mockery of such human rights acts and conventions. Yet there's been barely a peep from those in the human rights industry, who've perhaps been enjoying working from home on their large taxpayer-guaranteed salaries.

"The $10m-a-year Victorian Human Rights Commission, at ground zero for what will be seen as the most destructive overreaction in Australian history, says on its website its focus during the pandemic includes 'reducing racism' and 'improving workplace gender equality'.

"The impact of lockdowns lingers long after they have been lifted. Freedom House, a US-based think tank, recently found the pandemic had eroded civil rights in at least 80 countries, including the US, France, Belgium and Argentina. To be sure, many of these severe lockdown measures have been popular. But many stupid things have been popular. It doesn't make them right.

"The Great Lockdown of 2020 illustrates how easily we can be spooked into a kind of health fascism, where basic individual rights are sacrificed to the greater health collective, without the slightest attempt at a justification, amid fear-mongering propaganda and censorship. Anyone who wants to mind their own business and get on with life, making their own risk assessments, is vilified as selfish. Supporters of a police state and health fascism are seen as caring."

***

Those With the Most to Lose Have Suffered Dearly:

"It's been a good pandemic for the bureaucracy, banking and wealth-management, the most parasitic parts of the economy: same or more pay, work from home, and more colleagues with which to discuss the importance of lockdowns to 'save lives'.

"Since February, millions have been shunted onto JobSeeker and JobKeeper, hundreds of thousands have left the job market altogether, but public administration and financial services have increased their head-count, the Governor of the Reserve Bank pointed out.

"The hardest hit sectors have been those that produce things households and businesses actually want: construction, manufacturing, hospitality, arts and recreation, for instance.

"'All recessions are uneven but this one is especially so,' Philip Lowe said on Thursday in a speech that laid bare what he said was the 'striking' contrast in pandemic experiences of low- and high-paid workers, small and large business, the young and the old.

"'The costs of the pandemic have fallen most heavily on the first of each of those groups: those with the least resources, and with the least influence in politics and media.

"'The decline in employment has been largest for occupations with the lowest hourly earnings, while employment has actually increased for occupations with the highest hourly earnings,' Dr Lowe said."

Creighton concluded: "On the other side will be an economy more dominated by government, bureaucracy, ticket-clipping, and oligopolies, far from the free-market economy politicians spruik and many voters will believe exists."

***

On the other side of history — well, politics — the left, once largely supportive of lockdowns, was stirring in the increasingly dismal sleet. Significantly, for anyone following the detail of these eddying narratives, journalist Chris Uhlmann came out opposing lockdowns in sister papers *The Age* and *The Sydney Morning Herald.*

"The Victorian solution punishes the many for the few. It preferences the very old over the young, mortgaging the future of the entire school- and working-age population. It is hard to imagine how you could design a policy that is more profoundly unfair or damaging to a society.

"Nowhere in this often-opaque democracy has a less transparent court system, bureaucracy, police force or government than Victoria. The people there have been badly served, even as some revelled in the servitude. Its systems of power have combined to deliver the wanton destruction of its vibrant society. Its government has condemned its people to a poorer future, to higher unemployment, more poverty and less opportunity."

Uhlmann faced some difficulty from his editors getting his piece published.

On the ground there was a strange intensity to it, as if we were all destined to lie in a time of crisis. As an old journalist, it was natural for Alex to be interested in the media coverage and manipulation during the initial COVID panic, and what was essentially maintenance of heightened alarm in the populace.

Deliberately engineered bland-out of Australian media created an illusion of consensus; as exemplified by polling which showed a surge in popularity for Prime Minister Scott Morrison, despite what Old Alex and a bevy of pundits saw as his government's catastrophic mismanagement of the COVID-19 pandemic, the bureaucratic crime of the century.

Australians would be paying the price for generations to come. The mainstream media, having long ago abrogated their civic responsibilities, were having a holiday from reality. They ably prosecuted the government's scare campaigns, acting as agents for alarmism, and what looked very much like the introduction of martial law. Even when restrictions were eased and parts of Australia returned to normal, if you can do it once you can do it again.

***

The entire saga, and the media's role in it, was made worse by a narrowing of media options, important because a better-informed population would never have tolerated the trampling of their individual rights.

Australia's leading public health policy journal *Croakey* recorded: "Rarely has it been more important for communities to have trusted, reliable news sources.

"Yet the COVID-19 pandemic is threatening the viability of many media organisations, leading to closures and journalism job losses, as well as calls for government intervention. The impact is likely to be especially profound for rural, remote and regional communities, whose needs are not always well reflected by metropolitan-based media outlets."

The progressive destruction of local media outlets across the country, to which the government was an able and willing partner, ensured a flattening of the culture. According to the Public Interest Journalism Initiative's Australian Newsroom Mapping Project, more than 150 newsrooms shut down between January 2019 and May 2020. Many were in regional areas.

There was chaos and confusion at state borders. Tens of thousands of businesses faced closure. Unemployment spiralled. Many feared a 21st Century version of The Great Depression was on the way.

All of us were now stricken in time, imprisoned in our own houses.

Almost all lines of communication and dissemination of information had been corrupted.

The worst offender was the government's propaganda wing, the Australian Broadcasting Corporation, the only news many Australians listened to, and which led virtually every one of their news bulletins with COVID alarmism for months on end. Case numbers. Virulent strains. Announcement after dizzying announcement. Live crosses to press conferences. Restriction after restriction. Finding a lockdown sceptic on its solidly left channels was as unlikely as finding a climate change denier or a men's rights activist.

A runaway train had already derailed. A sledged population simply wished a return to normality, and greeted any sign of a releasing of restrictions and prohibitions with relief.

All that was left was to document the crash site.

FOURTEEN
MELTDOWN

THE ARREST of 404 people protesting outside Parliament House in Melbourne's central business district, and the issuing of 395 very punitive fines, crystallised Australia's descent into authoritarianism. Australia's police were enforcing the suspension of the democratic right to protest with pepper spray and brute force.

The demonstration on 3 November, 2020, is believed to be the largest mass arrest in Australian history. Conveniently, neither the Australian Federal Police nor the Australian Bureau of Statistics collates that particular statistic.

Certainly from the footage, the vision of hundreds of heavily equipped police coating the streets of Melbourne showed a derangement of authority. But at least some members of police forces around the country, forced to implement a version of martial law or lose their jobs, were becoming increasingly uncomfortable with their orders.

Taxpayer-funded academics barely raised a squeak. Many journalists turned a blind eye. Others were faced with a terrible decision: feed their families and stay employed, or speak out and join the dungeons of the unemployed.

Protestors carried signs including: "Tell the Truth", "Not Happy Dan", "Masks Don't Work", "Free Victoria" and "Corona Hoax 1984".

Once again protestors chanted, "Freedom, freedom."

At that point, restrictions in Melbourne allowed for groups of up to ten people within 25 kilometres of their home while wearing a mask. Police said they conducted arrests after forming a large circle to contain the protest.

Of those arrested, 395 people were fined for breaching chief health officer directions, including failing to wear a mask and breaching public gathering limits.

A police spokeswoman said protesters showed disregard for the safety of the broader community: "Victoria Police will not hesitate to fine those who clearly and blatantly breach the chief health officer's directions."

***

Following on from the violent suppression of protests in November 2020 there were a number of subsequent rallies, including an Australia Day march in January, of 2021, a nationwide Millions March Against Mandatory COVID Vaccines on 20 February, 2021, the first Worldwide Rally for Freedom on 20 March, 2021, and a second Worldwide Rally for Freedom on May 15.

"The worldwide rallies were literally a global collaboration with hundreds of cities around the world gathering on the same date and local time to protest the continuously overreaching government responses to COVID. In Melbourne, at each of the worldwide events we had attendances of several thousands of people.

"At the rally in February, police were as heavy-handed as they had been at past rallies, aggressively forcing attendees to abandon our peaceful march using pepper spray, and again rounding people up into small contained circles in order to make arrests."

Becky Spelman describes her personal experience with the police at the February rally thus: "After police had successfully interrupted the speakers and scattered the march, they spread out seemingly to ensnare as many of us as possible.

"With several others, I was told by police to leave the park, and forced to walk in a certain direction. A line of officers walked at us, shoving us and ordering us to leave.

"They funnelled us toward another line of officers who, when we approached them, told us to turn around and move the way we had come. They knowingly walked us into their trap, then formed circles around small groups of us, a tactic we now know as 'kettling'.

"Once kettled, we were aggressively and roughly hauled out of the circles one at a time by five or six armed and armoured Public Order Response Team officers, where we were cuffed, arrested and questioned, then let go without charge nor fine.

"Police seemed to relish the opportunity of finally having a chance to use their training; in a country like Australia where criminal gangs and terrorists are rare, who better to take down than ordinary citizens who have committed no crime except that of speaking out against a budding tyrannical regime?

***

Avi Yemini over at Rebel News found absolutely no shortage of material to report on during that entire period; and every confrontation he had with authorities and as he negotiated his status as a journalist made for great footage.

It was a study in aggressive, campaigning journalism.

Sometimes personalities combine with resources, floods, storms and the wildly conflicting circumstances of history. You cannot argue. You cannot truly destroy a story so intense and so human; which is written behind phalanxes of police lines, which reflects the outrage of civilians, not the genuflecting of apparatchiks.

Yemini operated at the absolute frontier of journalism and coercion; after all, to reach for a drawer full of clichés, real journalism is something someone doesn't want published.

Some people just become indestructible in the crucible of conflict. Suitable, really, for someone who once worked for the Israeli military.

And as for Monica Smit of Reignite Democracy Australia, she grew increasingly determined and sophisticated as she confronted this extraordinary — one might have hoped, once in a lifetime — story; certainly the story of her young life; and, among all the candidates, stood out as a fresher, less pretentious, more digitally enabled alternative to the moth-eaten parliamentarians with which Australia was currently cursed, a future driver of the nation's politics. For the major parties had betrayed them all.

We're a small pond, Australia.

There's a classic scene from those early November demonstrations, where Monica Smit and Avi Yemini exchange greetings in the midst of the surrounding melees, of clashes between incensed, isturbed and bewildered protestors up against walls of massed police officers.

For all the snide put-downs they received from what had become the mainstream media in Australia, itself in the midst of its greatest derogation of duty, Yemini and Smit were the only two journalists in the country consistently in this frontier space: the highly contested territory of subjugation and control.

You think you've got them classified, digitalised, compartmentalised, know exactly what they're going to say; but humans are endlessly surprising, internalised to their own flesh, mammalian; as the old-fashioned exercise of vox-popping frequently revealed, the technique Yemini had perfectly adapted to high-conflict situations.

You're on a deadline. You cannot afford to disappoint your bosses. You go rapidly, aggressively and entirely at random.

Truly, from years of having done it himself, the method produces entirely surprising results.

***

On 3 November, 2020, Yemini filed a report featuring some of the most extreme protest footage ever seen in Australia.

A five-deep wall of masked police, with mounted police behind and reserves only metres away, aggressively pepper-spray demonstrators.

To camera Yemini says: "Pepper spray has just been used. But the one question I have is, why? Why when there are zero cases, literally zero threat of these people pose of spreading the virus?

"Police are moving in on a peaceful protest of five or six hundred, I'm not sure how this protects anyone."

One apparently dignified middle-aged gentleman, wearing his compliant mask, is caught attempting to exit the ring of police: "Let me go through, please!"

"I stopped to hear a lady speaking and find myself surrounded by Victorian police. I find this very distressing," another middle-aged gent says.

Yemini to camera: "So there you have it. They are violently arresting protestors who were socially distancing until they were trapped.

"Nobody here hates you, nobody here hates you," one protestor shouts as he points at the wall of police, summoning a civility of old. Before they move in.

In another episode of serial vox-popping he approaches a woman holding a makeshift sign: "Lockdown Is Causing More Harm Than The Virus."

"What do you mean?" Yemini demands to know, already a celebrity with protestors.

"I mean exactly that. I lost my job in March. I should stay home forever. What a shitty life. I don't need a life."

One man, visibly injured, says: "Yeah, I just got tackled to the ground and kneed in the back — all that stuff. A few scratches, but I guess I'll be alright."

To camera, Yemini records, with all the visual evidence behind him: "They're lining them up to be processed."

Right at that interface.

"You're pregnant. We have a pregnant mother here."

"I live within 25 Ks. I have an exemption. And I'm being arrested?"

As to why?

"I don't know. They can't tell me."

Avi winds up the segment, winning more followers with every word, as he proves that all those millions squandered on government manipulation of the narrative was a waste of money, with the following words: "What is this truly about? Is it really about protecting us from the virus, or stopping and quashing dissent?

"Today they have set up shop behind me, a makeshift police station, to mass process all the detainees and to fine them. If you still think this is about a virus, then you are either delusional or a bloody liar."

***

The day begins peacefully enough. "It is a really nice atmosphere," Monica Smit says to camera. "People are gathering. But we are surrounded. You wonder how long it can last.

"My heart is pumping because two days ago I was arrested three times. There is an emotional response."

Make no mistake! It takes considerable resources, money, manipulation, connections, alliances, deceptions, operators with old-fashioned nous.

Monica badged her piece: "A battle against evil?"

As if trying to drive in the final nail.

A malevolence; deeply inspired, deeply filmic point in history might have gone undocumented.

You couldn't help but admire Smit for her absolute fortitude.

You bet the real narratives are laid outside government control.

Her coverage of the November mass arrests was bold, and therefore valuable.

The Reignite Democracy footage starts with another vox pop, in front of a backdrop of police and protestors. "They manipulated us into one corner," the woman says. "Didn't offer us water. There were women who wanted to go to the bathroom. This is absolutely evil."

To camera Monica says: "You know, it is really scary to see them plucking off one person at a time. Really regular-looking people. It is just scary to see my state being treated like this. I don't know if there's a word in the vocabulary which explains how sad I feel about the state of affairs in this state. You look into these people's eyes; they're sad too."

"I feel really sad that the police actually created this situation," says one protestor.

Monica also interviewed people in the queues waiting to be processed by police, which none of the mainstream media did. "I don't think I've committed a crime," says one. "I don't know why I'm being arrested," says another.

There is also footage of a scuffle with a policeman who forces her to move on. "I am a journalist, I am a journalist, don't touch me."

***

With walls of police behind her, Monica Smit describes a form of crowd policing almost never seen in Australia: "The ones in black, they're the ones that surround you and arrest you and do all that. What they do, it's like a diamond shape, they come in and they grab one person at a time. There's seven or eight of them. One's got your arm, each arm, one's got your neck. They pull your head into their chest. The others are there to literally stop the cameras from seeing what's going on. They yell 'don't resist, don't resist', and give you a little jab. Every time you get a jab, you move, and it looks like you're resisting.

"Someone's passed out here. They've probably passed out because of the emotional trauma of being surrounded by so many police."

A number of people in the long processing queues said it was their first experience with the police. "I've never been arrested, I've never broken a law, I've never been arrested in my whole life," says one young woman. "It is intimidating. I do feel like a criminal," another young woman says. "When you have two really big men standing next to you, holding you against your will, it is intimidating. It's not nice. There were cops every-where. I wasn't really going to start an argument because I was quite upset.

"When I was down there I wasn't in a group bigger than ten. We all got ushered in by the police. We got stuck. I said to them multiple times, 'Guys, are we being held against our will? Can we leave? Nobody would respond to us. 'Guys, this is deprivation of our liberty. Let us go!' Nobody would answer us."

One protestor wore a T-shirt: "Good People Disobey Bad Laws."

***

Prime Minister Scott Morrison, a man who had barely drawn breath throughout the unfolding crisis, made no public announcements during those first few days of November. He had a knack of disappearing at just the right moment. When Australia was experiencing the most violent over-the-top policing in its history, wild scenes on the streets, and one of the largest mass arrests in Australian history, the nation's leader finally fell silent.

These people didn't think of all this casting of storylines as deception. They just thought of it as politics. Their craft.

At his first media conference post the 404 arrests, on the 5th of November, the prime minister, at an event in Sydney with representatives of vaccine manufacturers Novavax and Pfizer, declared: "As we've worked through the course of what has been such a difficult year with COVID-19, one of the reasons Australia has proved to be one of the most successful countries in the world in not just handling, of course, the health impacts of the COVID-19 pandemic but the economic impacts as well, is, as a government and as governments all around the country, we have always sought to look for that next challenge and how we will solve it.

"On getting Australia at the front of the pack when it comes to vaccines, which will be game changers and as each day passes, we become more optimistic; cautious, of course, ensuring that we are going through all the necessary processes to ensure that we have both a safe vaccine and an effective vaccine.

"Now, today, we're announcing an extra $1.5 billion investment in the Novavax and Pfizer vaccines. This adds to our overall program of over $3.5 billion that we're investing to ensure that Australians will be in the leading pack of the world as we move into the next phase of dealing with COVID-19, which is the vaccine phase."

Believe what you will. Old Alex thought it was a blizzard of garbage.

Not one of the fearless journalists in attendance asked one single question about the arrest of more than 400 people in Melbourne only days before.

The representatives from those giant pharmaceutical companies Pfizer and Novavax declared themselves deeply honoured to build on their existing relationship with Australia.

Deeply honoured. And for their companies, deeply lucrative.

***

You'd swear the nation's politicians had shares in vaccine companies and were looking forward to a great dividend payout, the way government representatives so aggressively pushed their product.

Well, in a sense they did. It was their get-out-of-jail-free card for the profoundly destructive consequence of their lockdown policies. As many pundits were beginning to point out, the health consequences of Australia's lockdowns and the destruction of the economy would ultimately do a damn sight more damage than the virus would ever have.

But even the government's rollout of vaccines turned into chaos; a vision of false hope. The delays, the blood clots, the mass propagandising, the engineering and digitalisation of normal life, the rollout numbers, the vaccination hubs — all of it kept the media occupied for months; the stories spinning exactly the way the authorities wanted, with the government front and centre, allegedly saving everybody's lives. Those who had a moral objection, or were simply protesting that they were being forced to vaccinate for a disease they had almost no chance of dying from, were pilloried.

Paul Collits wrote: "Politicians the world over, not least our own prime minister, invested big-time in the vaxxer solution to their political problem — how to climb out of the ever-growing hole they dug for themselves when they abandoned forty-plus years of medical science in February 2020 in order to follow the pied piper of Beijing into lockdown purgatory.

"The vaccine emerged as the silver bullet that would get them off the hook when the punters finally woke up to the fact that the pandemic was largely a 'wag the dog' event, concocted by politicians and others invested, for a variety of reasons, in the 'convergent opportunism' that the crisis occasioned.

"When the debts were called in, when all the 'keepers' designed to buy-off the population ran out, when ordinary people finally tired of COVID Mania's large and small incursions into our private domains and of the sheer tedium of the wall of COVID — then, the vaccine would step in and save the political class from the inevitable electoral reckoning.

"We were urged to just hold on tight till the vaccine arrived, conditioned to believe all the while that the lockdowns were unavoidable. Only then we would all be then permitted to return to something at least vaguely resembling the old normal. You know: travel, seeing overseas grandchildren, interstate holidays, planning things more than a week out, getting married, hugging people, going to the pub without having to sign forms or point your phone at something, singing in church, visiting the shops without getting a lecture from a cultural mask-ist.

"Then the problems with the vaccine started to pile up."[60]

***

As pregnant mother of two Zoe Buhler put it while being arrested for a Facebook post: "What on Earth?"

Why did Australians accept the word of their government which at the same time was destroying their businesses, their independence, their dignity, their strength?

Why did they accept the loss of their freedoms?

Freedom of speech? Gone.

Freedom of movement? Gone.

Freedom of assembly? Gone.

Freedom to earn a living? For many, gone.

"2020 was a year of abject surrender, of hysteria, of derangement, of paranoia, of delusion on a grand scale," wrote Paul Collits. "A Kafkaesque year in which governments and their voters opted into the creepy new project of making the whole world a safe space.

"A year in which we gave up our cherished freedoms for a middling virus

---

60 The Contradictions of Vaccine Politics, Paul Collits, *A Sense of Place Magazine*, 6 March, 2021.

in Australia, titled "The Dirty Country", had headlines such as "Rising secrecy across Australia allows corruption to thrive", "Money for influence: the core transaction at the heart of Australian politics", and "Corruption is pervasive in Australia — it's time to stop the rot".

The second, "A Dossier of Falsehoods", carried stories headlined variously "Without truth, no democracy can stand: why we are calling out the prime minister", "A national leader with a readiness to lie and a reflex to do so when under pressure" and "The truth is precious. Let's not take it for granted."

They had better lawyers than he did.

The times create, and in their last attack before this book went to press, to adopt the arcane terminology of old technologies, Bernard Keane at *Crikey* was in flying form: "In a year in which the government's explicit highest priority — the vaccine rollout — has gone badly wrong, Prime Minister Scott Morrison's inability to effectively lead has become ever more apparent.

"Major problems in the rollout have been allowed to drift and worsen. The issue of purpose-built quarantine facilities to replace inadequate hotel quarantine has been allowed to fester. The COVIDSafe app — remember that? — is wholly useless. The consequences of mistakes made last year in the sourcing of vaccine supplies have gone unaddressed.

"But Morrison's one strength — his once-unerring feel for messaging — has also deserted him. The 'Scotty from marketing' tag always contained within it a paradox: Morrison might not be capable of getting things done, but he was outstanding at selling things to voters. Now even that skill has gone at a moment when we need a convincing national leader to drive vaccine uptake and provide reassurance as, once again, millions of Australians are locked down.

"The stakes now are enormous: the health of millions of Australians, Australia's economic recovery, our capacity to rejoin a world that is opening up much faster than we are likely to. Morrison, lacking both the capacity to deliver results and the ability to reassure Australians, is too great a risk to remain as national leader."[66]

---

66 The case for a potato-led recovery: it's time for Peter Dutton to step up, Bernard Keane, *Crikey*, 2 July, 2021.

The stories referred to in this book can all be found at the website for *A Sense of Place Magazine*.

***

For many Australians, left-leaning by instinct, it would be a very bad day when they found themselves agreeing with Sky commentator and leading conservative figure Alan Jones, often dismissed by his critics as an aging right-wing ideologue.

But on this one, it was nigh on impossible to disagree with him:

"The willingness of politicians to become followers, not leaders, from day one has damaged this country badly — and we are now paying the price.

"People are suspicious of vaccinations because they don't believe, up until now, that they have been told the truth.

"The prime minister said in a press conference last year that the coronavirus was a 'far more serious virus' for older and more vulnerable Australians, and the government's aim was to 'protect the most vulnerable' and at-risk.

"Not only were they not looked after, many died; and the vast majority still aren't vaccinated.

"But because everybody was treated as if they were about to die, money has been thrown everywhere. Our grandkids will have to pay off the debt.

"I have never witnessed such incompetence in my lifetime, nor have I seen such an abuse of the truth."

***

Despite the by now abundant evidence that lockdowns do not work, that countries which imposed harsh lockdowns and destroyed their own economies did no better than those who didn't, Melbourne snapped into a seven-day "circuit-breaker" lockdown in late May of 2021; which predictably turned into a full fortnight, and was only eased with many restrictions still remaining.

The actions were justified by a "cluster" of twenty-six in the city's northern suburbs.

"What have we learnt in fifteen months?" Alan Jones asked his viewers. "We've been led by the nose only to realise the sheer incompetence of government with almost everything associated with this coronavirus.

"The dislocation around coronavirus, lockdowns, vaccines, and the economy loom as a greater crisis than the coronavirus itself.

"Hotels, clubs and casinos closed. Can you imagine the cost of all this?

"These lunatics who make these decisions continue to be paid. The government here continues to sponsor fear and alarmism.

"Twenty-six cases in a population of 6.8 million.

"Shutting Victoria down for a fourth time is a massive failure in public policy.

"We lie to the public by saying the government is keeping you safe; what they really mean is, we hope we can keep you frightened until the next election."

***

The shooting, the shouting, the torrents of confused imagery, all came cascading into that quiet place, the refuge. And they drank and smoked another night away, in a kind of friendly, mad camaraderie which could die as easily as it was born, borne on the wind those voices now silenced. The enemies vanquished. This was conquered territory. "What are friends for?" He was still vanishing into the ether and walking down long, elegant stone verandas. The occult play was still afoot. "God is alive. Magic is afoot."

In a land which had been overrun by parasites, in the midst of a cleanup operation, they are with us, they are with you.

The blizzard of scaremongering and alarmism coming out of the radio or the television meant that many people had switched off, rather than fill their heads with senseless, in fact evil, propaganda. In regurgitating the fear-mongering of the nation's myriad governments local, state and federal, journalists were destroying the reputation of their profession. It would all wreak havoc.

My people! My people! Why have you allowed this to be done to you? Why did you not stand firm? Why have you let such evil overtake your lives?

Old Alex's housemate, who rarely drew breath on those nightly streaks of hilarity, mad but not bad, began talking of Christ in the temple sweeping aside the merchants and usurers, using force, brooking no opposition, unafraid. It was as if he, too, was being lit up in that strange swirl of other consciousnesses; because this point in history was enveloped by a swarm, not an individual, because they were powerful beyond all human wonder, because they were transforming conquered territory ready for a greater arrival, a greater embrace, when the guardians were in place and the material earth transformed.

"I've had the same images in my head," Old Alex said. "Christ sweeping into the temple. Overthrowing tables. Throwing out the cheap merchants and the grifters preying on the gullibility of the people. Except the scandal for me is Scott Morrison using the position of prime minister to make himself and his rich mates even richer, for prosperity theology done in God's name, for selling a story to the Australian people which was never a true story, for robbing the poor, for plundering the country, for destroying a sacred place which was never his to destroy.

"For his absolute and total treachery; and here we are, in Oak Flats, our lives constricted by his hypocrisy."

Yes, well he did get the odd stare. He was past caring. And every time he tried to assimilate and understand the myriad pains this government had inflicted on millions of people, his brain ran into a headwind. It was incomprehensible.

***

There were many who commented on the strange spiritualities of the time, not least the leader of the nation.

Central to understanding the prime ministership of Scott Morrison — his style, substance, policies and behaviour — was his religiosity, his fervour appearing to reach some kind of fever pitch during the COVID era.

The whole question of God and Scott Morrison once again took centre stage in not unspectacular fashion.

Remarkable footage emerged mid-2021 of the Australian Prime Minister addressing a Christian conference on the Queensland Gold Coast.

Michael Bradley at leading news site *Crikey* put the conundrum bluntly: "If Scott Morrison, like all previous prime ministers, kept his religious faith to himself and strictly separated from his public role, then there'd be no good cause to say anything about it.

"It wasn't Morrison who released the video of his speech to the Australian Christian Churches conference on the Gold Coast last week. However, he flew there and back on a government plane at taxpayers' expense and was explicit that he was speaking as prime minister, not a private citizen. The content of what he said left that unarguable anyway. It is a matter of legitimate public interest to appreciate the full meaning of his words."

Michelle Pini at *Independent Australia* was equally blunt: "Scott Morrison chose to attend a Pentecostal convention (incorrectly described as a 'church gathering" by some media) as is his personal right. However — and let's be perfectly clear — he chartered a VIP RAAF flight to take him there in style and he did so at our expense, despite this being a personal jaunt.

"We know it was personal because it was not listed in his official schedule or displayed on his website or social media channels — as the PM is prone to do with any and all official appearances, complete with suitable photo ops. Nor was a transcript of his speech made available.

"The prime minister's attendance at this event later became known through unofficial channels, which indicates that he actively concealed it."

In a statement, a spokesperson for the prime minister said the appearance was not out of the ordinary and that the prime minister was invited to address the event "the same as he attends many other stakeholder events, including for other religious groups such as the Copts, Maronites, Jewish, Hindu, Buddhist and Muslim."

To which Pini responded: "Really? Do prime ministers routinely charter RAAF jets to attend all stakeholder events, including unofficial ones? And who are the 'stakeholders' here?

"This event was a religious convention of the Pentecostal variety — that's the one to which the PM belongs. It's also where his big supporters/donors are and where, we can presume, Morrison would be counting on monetary support for his political campaign. Hardly your garden-variety prime ministerial event attendance."

The full video of Scott Morrison's address was readily available on YouTube through the Rationalists Australia channel.

The full transcript was also readily available through Eternity News under the headline: "MOCKING SCOTT MORRISON IS MAKING FUN OF CHRISTIANS IN GENERAL, NOT JUST HIM".

***

Much of the transcript was revelatory when it came to the beliefs of the nation's prime minister, the world's only Pentecostal leader. And to his handling of the COVID crisis; and his seeming indifference to the social damage he caused.

Below are a few extracts.

"You cancel out one human being and you cancel community, because community is just human beings that God loves and that is intended to connect us, one to another. Morality is about focusing not on you, but on the person next to you. It's about focusing, for me, on you. That is the essence of community. You can't pass a law for it. You can't create a building for it. It is essentially what springs from each and every one of us. Community.

"It's born of what he likes to call a covenant.

"There is relationship in covenant, which is what God sought with Israel. In covenant. Deep relationship. It's personal. It goes beyond. A covenant. More than a transaction. Family and marriage God has created in the same way. To reflect that covenant that we can have.

"It's so important that we continue to reach out and let each and every Australian know that they are important. That they are significant as we believe they are created in the image of God. That in understanding that, they can go on a journey that I'm very confident you can take them on, and I'm relying on you to do that, because that's not my job. That's yours.

"There is a fashion, these days, to not think of Australians as individuals, particularly, I think, amongst our young people, and I worry about this. People think of themselves. It's called identity politics.

"I think it's an evil thing. I think it's a very evil thing, and we've got to pray about it. We've got to call it out. We've got to raise up the spiritual weapons against this, because it is going to take our young people. It's going to take their courage. It's going to take their hope. It's going to steal them. We've got to pray about it. We've got to pray against that because it is such a corrosive thing that we're seeing take place.

"Yeah, sure, social media has its virtues and its values and enables us to connect with people in ways we've never had before. Terrific. But those weapons can also be used by the evil one, and we need to call it out.

"This is the help I need from you. I need your help. Keep doing what you're doing. I need your help to remind Australians how precious they are, how unique they are."

***

Scott Morrison wound up in full Pentecostal flight: "Can I finish with verses I just wanted to share with you? Can I do that, Brad? Have I got time to do that?

"It's not a political thing. Faith is very much an ingrained part of my life. I seek His wisdom in the same way you do, each and every day. It's important that we do that.

"I like this one. Psalm 23:5. Where he talks about preparing a banquet for you in the presence of your enemies. We've got to sit down at that banquet. I sit down at that banquet every single day. But that's where we're called.

"He didn't prepare a banquet for us in the presence of our greatest admirers and friends who would tell us wonderful and lovely things, as nice as that is. He said, 'I have prepared this banquet for you in the presence of your enemies, and I will be with you at that table.' That is a wonderful reminder to me, each and every day.

"It is a privilege. It is an absolute privilege. I've been in evacuation centres where people thought I was just giving someone a hug and I was praying and putting my hands on people, in various places, laying hands on them in praying in various situations.

"It's been quite a time, and God has, I believe, been using us in those moments to be able to provide some relief and comfort and just some reassurance. We'll keep doing this for as long as that season is. That's how we see it.

"We are called, all of us for a time and for a season. God would have us use it wisely. For each day, I get up and I move ahead, there is just one little thing that is in my head, and that is, 'Well, such a time as this.' Such a time as this. Thank you very much."

So, both a spiritual and temporal derangement.

Yes indeed, there was an occult storm. Yes indeed, the birds were flying backwards.

***

Of the incident, historian James Boyce wrote in *The Saturday Paper:* "The release of an unauthorised video of the prime minister preaching at his church's national conference last month has given Australians a glimpse of an unknown man in another world.

"Here was a leader clearly at home with his people, using mysterious metaphors to encourage fellow believers in a spiritual war in which Satan and the spirit of God are fighting it out for the souls of our nation's young people.

"No one who has heard this sermon — so starkly different from that which might be heard in a suburban congregation or even a traditional evangelical church — can continue to accept the pretence that the prime minister's Pentecostalism is so conventional it needs no further explanation or is just a private religious matter of no public relevance.

"What is required of the media is no different from the approach that would be taken with a politician proclaiming adherence to any other value system — have its teachings transparently communicated, so that people can understand what their representative believes.

"The argument that it is necessary to hide the full truth except from those who are considered ready to receive it is a slippery slope to cultism in both its religious and political dimensions. To question and critique is not, as Fogarty has argued, to be part of an inquisition; it is to participate in democracy."

***

Perhaps in that mad world of faith, God (or a god) had sent these raving lunatics, these possessed men, to bring the people to their knees.

There was, truly, a derangement of another kind in all of this.

Reputations lay in ruins, but in that surreal world of no consequence, an eternal present, rationality and common sense had fled.

It was as if the whole country was drifting down to the Antarctic, to those frozen seas, to a cliff at the end of the world. As if the Land of the Long Weekend had returned to its brutal convict origins; and all the sparks of divinity which once so braced the country had vanished once again.

Drifting algorithms, drifting distortions of history.

The entire population was now under an extreme form of monitoring and uber-surveillance that had profound impacts on their psychology, and the psychology of the nation.

All the dystopian predictions, which had seemed so fanciful a year before, came true.

Under lockdown orders, the cruelty of imprisonment, they were all sheltering in place. But against what? A virus? Government henchmen? A greater evil?

***

For Old Alex, caught in that freezing piece of coastline under the escarpment, underneath the finest temperate rainforests in the world, it felt as if the signal derangement that had overtaken the country was also overtaking him; a terrible haunting in the midst of a ghost town.

Well, ho hum. Everyone was paying a price; he wasn't the only one going absolutely stir crazy in the midst of yet another lockdown.

The government narrative was disintegrating.

Thousands of communities across the country were struggling to deal with the consequences of the government's tyrannical overreaction and abject mismanagement of the COVID threat.

If we came through to you with a begging bowl, if you threw the people on to their knees, if you destroyed their livelihoods and their independence from the state, if you controlled every last moment of their waking hours, then they might as well be robots.

Then what do you do with those superfluous men?

Thousands would be out there on the road, in those desperate times.

We would walk among them.

To look back on this period of Australian history when democracy failed is to shake your head in wonder.

***

Occam's Razor. The Best Truth is the simplest Truth. If what they were doing worked, it would have worked by now.

If you were telling the truth, there would have been no need to panic the public. If your truth was so damn compelling, there would no need for billions of dollars of propaganda and massive manipulation of public sentiment.

Instead, nobody apologised, nobody admitted fault. No compensation was paid.

The same perpetrators kept up the same noise; inflicting their taxpayer-funded derangement on a population which should have known better, but instead, impoverished, were buried inside their own homes.

Instead, sixteen months after the debacle began, sixteen long months of hysteria and disinformation from a government which had transformed the way Australians lived, which had placed itself front and centre of everybody's lives, in Melbourne, the country's second largest city, millions of people found themselves once again under virtual house arrest, unable leave their own homes without good cause.

Once again the police were being used as a politician's henchmen, as symbols of power, oppression and totalitarian discord; a living reminder to the population that they had no control over their own lives.

They could disinter us all and throw us on a funeral pyre, so frightening the moment.

A time such as this. Australia. An appalled silence crept through every strand of The Hermit Kingdom.

The story unfolded in ways none of us could ever have imagined, not in our wildest dystopian dementias.

***

Scores of Victorians responded to the announcement of a seven-day "circuit-breaker" lockdown, flocking to Melbourne's central meeting point to call for an end to "unlawful" restrictions.

Reignite Democracy Australia' protesters met at Melbourne's central Flinders Street Station to "take a stand for freedom". "Victoria is angry. Lockdowns will not be tolerated," a Facebook post from the group said. "We will not accept the constant threat of lockdowns at a cost to our businesses, our incomes and our lives."

Protesters carried placards with messages including: "We do not consent to government tyranny" and "No to the new abnormal, no to forced vaccines, no to being traced and contacted, no to unlawful lockdowns".

One news report declared: "Extraordinary photos showed the huge throng of people in the CBD, despite the entire state being just hours away from a strict fourth lockdown.

"The protesters were free to express their views on the streets until the new rules began at 11.59pm."

"Images from the demonstration showed protestors once again being violently wrestled to the ground. Eleven people were issued with penalty notices for travelling outside their ten-kilometre radius under the chief health officer's directions."

***

So let the headlines bring it on home, on that shattered ground. As history turned on a pivot, and Australia became unrecognisable, a smattering of news stories told the story:

- The psychology behind COVID lockdown panic buying, and what to do instead.
- At least three people have been arrested at a march in Melbourne protesting the tough restrictions.
- Victoria records five COVID cases on second day of coronavirus lockdown.
- You could call it many things but the kindest is probably incompetence. We have lost our marbles. We must never ever lockdown again, there is just no reason to do this to people.
- Masks may stay after Victorian lockdown ends. Facts show there is 'no need' for a lockdown in Victoria. Struggling Victorians told to go to Centrelink in live TV blunder. Diary of a Melburnian in second winter of discontent.
- The Morrison government should 'hang their heads in shame' for even considering vaccine passports for domestic travel.
- Australians see that a goodly portion of the Commonwealth-led pandemic health response has involved stuff-ups in plain sight, with bursts of incompetence accompanied by a near-disgraceful lack of remorse.
- They killed small business and REFUSE to listen to the desperate owners.
- Victoria government in 'secret' negotiations to obtain 'permanent emergency powers'."

Headlines stream a story; they can't possibly record the immense suffering the nation's political class had inflicted on so much of the population.

***

Victoria's fourth lockdown, which began in late May of 2021, had the full support of the prime minister, who commended the actions of Victorian authorities and warned that the state's struggles were a sharp reminder of the dangers of COVID.

It was utterly surreal, as if nobody had learnt anything.

Scott Morrison wasn't about to let go of the shameless fear-mongering which had characterised the entire era, nor the power it had gifted him and his ilk. An already wealthy man waited on hand and foot in his taxpayer-funded residences, he was not the one paying the price.

"The challenge and battle that we have faced many, many times, and on each occasion, together we have overcome," he told reporters. "There are no certainties, no guarantees, and a global pandemic, and against a virus, an insidious virus such as this.

"I want to commend the Victorian Government and the acting premier for their efforts over recent days, in particular, and I especially want to thank the contact tracers in Victoria for the very difficult job that they are engaged in.

"We have 218 Australian Defence Force personnel who are in Victoria, continuing to provide support under Operation COVID Assist, and I've made it very clear to the premier that any other additional support that he requires that he will receive

"With so many different points of contact that we have here, being able to work through that information and the many thousands of contacts that they're working through, I think they're doing a tremendous job and I commend them for the job that they are doing, remembering that there are many rings of containment to deal and protect Australia, deal with the virus and to protect Australians from the virus.

"There is of course our international borders, there is of course the work that is done enforcing those public health orders in the states through the quarantine system, and then there is of course the contact-tracing regime.

"So, once again, we will come through, and no matter what our success has been to date, that is no guarantee or certainty against a very challenging virus that continues to test not only here in Australia but all around the world.

"What we need to do now is what we've done on every occasion; we just need to focus on working the problem, working the issue, and working together. It's important, though, that we understand that there are many rings of containment here that need to operate.

"I want to assure Victorians that the Victorian and Federal Government are just working hand in glove."

How very reassuring!

There was more, so much more; if anybody could keep track of the deluge.

Australia has one of the highest suicide rates in the world. To midwinter of 2021, in the course of those months, thousands of more citizens had taken their own lives, many so-called "deaths of despair" which could have been avoided, than had died of COVID. There was no all-of-government effort for them. There were no logos or QR codes or warnings on every government and social media website you went near. No expenditure in the tens of billions; indeed, hundreds of billions of dollars. No rearranging of the entire society to save a few lives. No prime minister grandstanding his way through another press conference.

Few if anybody outside their immediate families cared whether those people lived or died. Yet many of those people were victims of government actions or inactions. Among those suicides were many separated fathers, like Alex himself, driven to absolute despair by the rapacious brutality of Australia's dysfunctional family law and child-support systems. Others fell into despair as a desecrated, communistic-style economy and labyrinthine bureaucracies — which increasingly characterised Australia — utterly failed to care for its own citizens or the welfare of the country at large.

With Scott Morrison as Chief Architect, the Australian Government had shamelessly scared the people into submission. And the price would be paid in lives. And yet more suicides. And in a disfigurement which would last generations.

***

Back in Oak Flats, in the midst of yet another brutal economic and soul-destroying lockdown, the same sense of dread that had enveloped those streets almost a year-and-a-half before was back. Once again, the streets were whisper-quiet, the humble housing of the area shut and bunkered, the population sheltered inside.

Once again, that roughneck pub the Lakeview, one of the only community gathering points in the entire area, was shut.

Having destroyed all normal community life, all normal social interaction, almost all life-sustaining economic activity, still the government's apparatchiks repeatedly claimed they were keeping Australians safe.

Old Alex went there one last time before it shut, perhaps forever. How could any business survive these shutdowns?

Unhappy bar staff members were forced by law to wear masks; despite all the myriad doubts about their effectiveness and negative impacts on health. Customers, that rough and ready crew, were also being forced to don a mask each time they went to the bar.

Old Alex sat in that beer garden, perhaps for the last time, and, stunned by the nonsensical nature of it all, repeated several times as he gazed down across suburban houses to the fringe of trees edging the lake: "There's an evil afoot. There's an evil afoot."

There, peering into that black sky, it was as if the Angel of Death was passing over all of them; for surely this mass derangement and destruction of all traditional Australian life could not stem from anything else.

All the research worldwide, all the evidence, showed lockdowns did not work, that they did far more harm than good. Those perpetrating this disaster on the Australian people must have known. Nothing stopped them.

Yes, if lockdowns had a face, it was demonic.

***

In Sydney, on 26 July, 2020, NSW Premier Gladys Berejiklian announced that lockdowns would be extended across Greater Sydney, the Blue Mountains, the Central Coast, Shellharbour and Wollongong.

Millions of residents, their lives savagely impacted, could now only leave home for essential reasons. Community sport would not be permitted, funerals limited, weddings outlawed.

Right across the state of NSW, including in many regional areas where there had not been a single solitary case, much less a single solitary death, masks were now compulsory.

Government orders declared: "If you are in Greater Sydney, you must comply with the stay-at-home rules. If you want to visit another person you will need a reasonable excuse to be away from your place of residence."

Once again, a shuttered, shattered place, at the behest of a governing minority who had cherry-picked their own experts to justify reshaping the entire society. Pubs and registered clubs were shut, along with theatres, cinemas, and concert halls; amusement centres, places of worship, hairdressers and beauty salons, swimming pools and public libraries; that is, all normal civilian life.

The premier told reporters: "I do not regret a single decision we have taken, because it has been based on health advice. When you are making a major decision to lock down millions and millions of people, you have to make sure it is based on health advice and not because you want to have zero cases every day,

"I have never cared about what people think about me, but I care about keeping people safe and not putting burdens on them unless we absolutely have to.

"I want to thank everybody for accepting the government decision on the two-week lockdown.

"The anecdotal evidence that we have is that people are being compliant. We are deeply grateful for that. I am absolutely convinced that if we all pull together we will start seeing the results we want to achieve over the next few weeks. We want to make sure that people have that information about testing, and their own status, and the status of their closest loved ones to make sure all of us stay safe."

According to official statistics, in Australia there had been three COVID-related deaths in the previous eight months; and not one since April. The chances of any of the current crop of a few dozen infected actually dying from the disease bordered on zero; the authorities already knew that.

The median age of death had risen to 86. Numbers of deaths due to cancer, dementia and diabetes were all above historical averages.

Self-perpetuating and self-serving political hysteria turned into societal-wide suicide, a self-generating despair which would take decades to repair.

Right across the country, rafts of restrictions were clanging into place. Restrictions were announced in Perth after a woman tested positive. South Australia closed its borders to most of the rest of the country. Queensland Premier Annastacia Palaszczuk announced new restrictions. The Northern Territory entered a snap 48-hour lockdown.

What could any of us do to stop this madness?

With their personal autonomy and their abilities to provide for their families destroyed; with the threat of fines, arrests and jail; with their lives controlled by both a conscience-free government and elements beyond their realm; a deep anger began to stir through the population, and that, too, would be impossible to stop.

***

The national derangement was complete.

A Melbourne hospital prevented a mother from seeing her son, who was suffering from a severe brain injury after a motor crash.

"We haven't been able to see our son since he woke up from a coma. We just want to hug our son."

Police were filmed arresting and pepper-spraying a bunch of ratbag kids, average age perhaps twelve, after one of them refused to wear a mask into a shop and the rest gave them a bit of lip.

The largely deserted working-class shopping mall saw yet another conflagration between police and the citizenry; every last one of the tweens involved under age.

They might have been too young to legally have sex, but they weren't too young to be pepper-sprayed and arrested in what the authorities had been assuring us was the new COVID normal.

This was the unravelling. This was one of the cascading moments in time, in that kaleidoscope of incidents, when the authorities lost control of their own behaviour, the public lost all faith in the authorities, and the official narrative lost all credibility.

A man was fined $5000 for drinking a cup of takeaway coffee in the street, in the remote central Australian town of Alice Springs. Surrounded by some of the world's most beautiful desert country, there was not, and had never been, a single solitary case of Corona in the town. Footage shows the man being wrestled to the ground and his coffee spilling onto the street.

This is the hell you created.

There is an old Jesuit saying, "Set the world alight!".

Well, so you did. But how can anyone bow down to these false, lunatic gods?

The prime minister was on his prayer knees. The result: the rest of the country was enduring an End Time delusion.

Twelve million in lockdown for the panicked fear of a disease few had any chance of catching, and those who did, an even remoter chance of dying from. How is that not the Angel of Death? How is not a national derangement? How is this not *The Origins of Totalitarianism*?

Where the darkest of Lords reap the souls of men.

The actions of the Australian authorities impugned through our every sense of self; of the familiarity and comfort of routines which humans establish by their very nature.

As many other writers had commented; there was a strange spirituality to the season, a dangerous dementia of the occult; or so it often felt.

And in all of this, this utterly lunatic time, there was the absolute immediate consequence; of lives and futures destroyed.

***

Close to home, Old Alex's local cafe, The Village Fix, was shut after the owner was arrested for not wearing a mask; the dozen or so police co-ordinating, apparently, with the local daily newspaper, *The Illawarra Mercury*, to make sure the dramatic scenes were splashed all over their front page.

The paper breathlessly reported that some people were frightened to come into town because someone wasn't wearing a mask. There might have been little or no scientific evidence that masks were effective in stopping the spread of COVID, but they were very good at instilling fear and a heightened sense of danger into a population; in manufacturing a psychic derangement.

Officers fined owner Anthony Reale, 41, $1000 for not wearing a face mask or ensuring that three of his employees wore masks.

His wife, Natalie, mother of three young children, was also arrested.

"We have been put through the wringer," she said. "Now we have to deal with all the expense of courts and lawyers. We have done nothing wrong. It was a setup. Putting us on the front page has meant we have had threats; as have other organic stores who have adopted the same stance.

"What sort of police involve themselves in activities against ordinary citizens which can lead to them being threatened, to endangering my family like this?

"None of the stories mention the struggles of small business, or that have some mask exemptions, which are very bad for some people's health.

"We have quite a bit of support across the world. Cafes from across Australia and America have messaged us; and we have also had threats; but the support outweighs the threats. We have been dragged through hell; I was treated like a dog."

NSW Deputy Police Commissioner Gary Worboys said the cafe was flagrantly disregarding COVID-19 protocols.

"There was an absolute clear resistance from the cafe owner and those people at front-of-house to actually wear a mask," Mr Worboys said. "It is clearly irresponsible."

What was clearly irresponsible policing in this derangement spreading through the entire society was the destruction of perfectly decent people's lives and livelihoods; their public shaming, exposing a family with young children to public threat.

Wherever Old Alex happened to be, he frequented the earliest opening cafe, which is how he got to know the family which ran Village Fix. You couldn't find more decent, harder-working people. And just like him, they didn't believe the government narrative either.

What was truly irresponsible was the amount of stress government functionaries were placing on ordinary citizens; a derangement of the era causing scenes of conflict between citizens and police right across the country.

***

The veneer of civilisation proved virus-thin. The consequences of lock-downs and the remaking of Australian society would spill down the generations. The derangement that took over the political class and the absolute mismanagement of the COVID crisis, beginning in early 2020, would seriously damage the welfare of hundreds of thousands of families; and mark the nation's descent into a totalitarian hell. For out of the humus of that destructive time, new kinds of leaders and forms of government would arise. A new kind of apartheid; a new kind of mass psychosis would reshape a subjugated population, the towns, the communities, families, the isolated and the much loved, transforming the way Australians interacted and cared for each other. The era would birth a new kind of cruelty.

And those who inherited this future would wonder, above all else, how anyone of conscience could have let this happen?

ACKNOWLEDGEMENTS

I would particularly like to thank the following writers, who contributed significantly to my publication *A Sense of Place Magazine* through their generous permission to republish their articles; and thereby ultimately made a significant contribution to this book.

Emeritus Professor Ramesh Thakur of the Crawford School of Public Policy at the Australian National University, author, editor or contributor of more than 50 books, and former Assistant Secretary-General of the United Nations. One of those rare academics who take their role as a public intellectual seriously, his assistance, and the highly intelligent light he has thrown on these dark times, has been invaluable.

Paul Gregoire of the Sydney Criminal Lawyers Blog, is a well known Sydney-based journalist and writer. He has a focus on human rights issues and has actively exposed social injustices perpetrated under the cover of COVID. He has written for VICE and was the news editor at the community newspaper *City Hub Sydney*. His writings on the many injustices being perpetrated under the name of keeping Australians safe have also proved invaluable.

Paul Collits, an Australian-based writer, contributes to a range of publications and collects his work at The Freedoms Project. He has worked in government, industry and the university sector. He has degrees in political science from the Australian National University and a PhD in geography and planning from the University of New England. And he enjoyed a remarkable period of creativity throughout the COVID era, from which this book has been a beneficiary.

Michael West is Australia's foremost investigative journalist. His media career began at *The Australian Financial Review* and has held senior positions at both *The Australian* and *The Sydney Morning Herald*. He is an Adjunct Professor at Sydney University. His website Michael West Media regularly exposes corporate and government rorts. His insights into the extensive corporate rorting and maladministration of government programs during COVID have been formidable.

Professor Augusto Zimmerman, is President of the Western Australian Legal Theory and former Law Reform Commissioner of Western Australia. He is editor of the book *Fundamental Rights in the Age of COVID* and has written extensively on the political incompetence characterising the COVID era.

It would also be remiss not to thank Dr Guy Campbell for his piece "Inhumane Lockdowns Compound Australia's COVID Fiasco", to this day one of the most popular pieces I've ever published in the magazine. You were great to work with.

Other writers I would like to thank include Caitlin Johnstone, Steve Waterson, Adam Creighton, Hector Drummond, Steve Waterson, Sandi Keane, Elizabeth Minter, Professor Allan Patience and Dr Sarah Russell.

Tim Flynn, founder of the facebook group End Lockdowns, deserves special mention for his contribution.

The work of Reporters Without Borders should also be acknowledged.

I would also like to thank Ethan Nash, editor of TOTT News, for the freedom to republish his uniquely prophetic take on COVID in Australia. Whatever the story, it's great copy.

And as strange as it may seem, I would also like to thank some of the invisible members of the so-called Watchers on the Watch, the Ghosts in the Machine, if you will. I know you weren't all bad.

I would also like to thank Jupuul Mari Porter, also known as Stephen Porter, for his friendship, encouragement and the hospitality he provided in Moree.

I would particularly like to thank Ashley Stapleton of Highlight Photonics and his web designer Michelle Miller for helping me rebuild *A Sense of Place Magazine*.

The staff at Hub Australia, a co-working company with offices at Circular Quay in Sydney, also deserve thanks for their friendly professionalism and support during a very long and difficult winter.

In Oak Flats, I would also like to thank Chris Rath for his company and hospitality at a difficult time, along with his invaluable computer expertise, Johnny Miller, for once again being so cheerfully annoying while helping me to understand the traditional life of Oak Flats.

Craig McCaughey, from one of the best known families in the area, deserves a special mention for his hysterical sense of humour and his determination not to let me take myself too seriously, obsessed as I was by the darkening skies all around; and the infinite perfidy of lockdowns.

And as for my previous book, the superb coffee at Anthony Reale's cafe Village Fix, in Shellharbour, helped me through the final draft. I swear Anthony's coffee is the best in Australia. Prove me wrong!

I would also like to thank the staff at Uniting Care in Gerringong, who are now taking such excellent care of my elderly parent and have helped the Stapleton family through such a difficult time.

And last but by no means least; I would like to thank "Gay Phil", a.k.a. Phillip John Matthews, who passed away on 28 May, 2021. For your waspish sense of humour, your courage, and the dignity of your passing, you will be missed — not everyone arranges for a drag queen to perform at their funeral service. My last words to him were: "You really are the Wicked Witch of the West." He just laughed.

ABOUT THE AUTHOR

Australian journalist John Stapleton was born in 1952 in the north coast town of Bangalow, NSW, on the east coast of Australia.

He began submitting stories to magazines at a young age and his determination in later years, post a successful career as a mainstream journalist, derives from those early years of rejection slips .

The first money Stapleton ever made out of writing was in 1974 when he was co-winner of a short story competition held by what was then Australia's leading cultural celebration, the Adelaide Arts Festival.

The event proved a revelation; he realised he could make money out of what he liked to do.

He graduated from Macquarie University in 1975 with a double major in philosophy and anthropology and did post-graduate work in sociology at Flinders University in South Australia.

As a freelance journalist in the 1970s and 1980s, while alternating between living in Sydney and London, his articles and fiction appeared in a wide range of magazines, newspapers and anthologies, including *The Australian Financial Review*.

John Stapleton worked on *The Sydney Morning Herald* as a staff news reporter between 1986 and 1994. The paper was then listed as one of the Top 20 newspapers in the world.

He worked for the national newspaper *The Australian* from 1994 to 2009.

As a news reporter, Stapleton encountered and wrote many hundreds of stories about everyone from street alcoholics to Australian Prime Ministers; from the staple flood, drought, fire and natural disasters of the Australian bush to scenes of urban dysfunction.

By dint of longevity.he became one of the country's most experienced general news reporters

Unfolding Catastrophe: Australia completes a quartet which began with *Terror in Australia Workers Paradise Lost*, followed by *Hideout in the Apocalypse* and *Dark Dark Policing*. All are designed as a snapshot of a particular time and place and utilise the same techniques, switching from streets scenes to internal monologues to reportage.

After leaving *The Australian*, Stapleton established *A Sense of Place Magazine* and the niche publishing company A Sense of Place Publishing.

Lightning Source UK Ltd.
Milton Keynes UK
UKHW021529150921
390625UK00009B/1790